EARLY PRAISE FOR *A CANON'S TALE*

"It has been a pleasure to read such an unusual lovely warm, humane story about this period, as so little of the personal lives of clerics, artists and people of that period in general is known. In your novel you have managed, however, to let this story of the Arles Cloister and its creators come to life and to have given the artists and clerics a voice. You draw on the knowledge of pilgrimage, the crusades, and the changes in the Liturgy at this period so well and document the sources also so thoroughly. The link to Northern Italy's Romanesque sculptors, especially Niccolo/ Nicholaus, broadens the picture of contributions by traveling sculptural workshops during the twelfth century. It makes for an immensely readable historic novel in which artist and clerics interact and play a major role... Congratulations on this major new type of publication!"

> —Christine Verzar, Professor Emerita, The Ohio State University
> Author of *Portals and Politics in the Early Italian City-State: The Sculpture of Nicolaus in Context*

"Schneider's research is simply magisterial—her accounts of the historical period, the theological disputes of the time, and the minute details about Pons, a real figure, are scrupulously rigorous. And since Pons' life was a cinematically dramatic one, it is ideally suited for novelization."

> —*Kirkus Reviews*

"*A Canon's Tale* is a compelling historical novel about a man's attempts to balance his faith with his duty to the church... a young man battles his inner demons and urges his church to follow God's message ... (he) details instances of violence and temptation in an engaging manner, using his personal faith as a lens to understand them. In such moments, he comes across as flawed but captivating. And as the novel follows him through the years, from his service as a canon until his death, it incorporates some intriguing views of the real historical events that may have impacted him."

> —Foreword Clarion Review

D1003288

A Canon's Tale

 FriesenPress

Suite 300 - 990 Fort St
Victoria, BC, V8V 3K2
Canada

www.friesenpress.com

Copyright © 2021 by Marilyn A. Schneider, PhD
First Edition — 2021

www.MarilynASchneider.com

Quotation credits appear on page 383.

Illustration credits appear on page 387.

ISBN
978-1-5255-8247-9 (Hardcover)
978-1-5255-8248-6 (Paperback)
978-1-5255-8249-3 (eBook)

1. FICTION, HISTORICAL, MEDIEVAL

Distributed to the trade by The Ingram Book Company

A Canon's Tale

MARILYN A. SCHNEIDER

In memory of Professor Meyer Schapiro,
celebrated art historian, famed intellectual and scholar,
who first started me on this exciting journey
into the provenance of the beautiful sculpture
at Saint-Gilles and Saint-Trophime at Arles.

With thanks to my family for their support.

Preface
Discovering Canon Poncius de Baucio

This is the tale of a remarkable young canon, Poncius de Baucio, who lived in the twelfth century and served at the Cathedral of Saint-Trophîme at Arles, where he was responsible for building the beautiful cloister that still stands today. Many, if not most, of the people in this tale are documented and actually lived in the twelfth century. All of the background historical events included in this tale actually occurred and are part of the historical record. Yet this tale has never been told. It has remained hidden within dusty church manuscripts for over 800 years.

When I was reading these original documents handwritten in medieval Latin, looking for firm evidence to date the cloister and its sculptures for my PhD thesis in art history, I began noticing small discrepancies between what I was seeing in the manuscripts and what appeared in their published transcriptions, their purportedly accurate and complete published transcriptions. These are mostly legalistic documents, records of donations, or events such as resolutions of disputes, and the principal individuals and issues are usually detailed. Quite understandably, however, the publishers had edited and deleted seemingly unimportant or repetitive bits. But how were they to know that such deleted bits might actually be real gems in some other context?

The dusty manuscripts do contain hidden treasures, little clues, often in casual references, such as where a donation or agreement was signed, or who witnessed an event. I carefully recorded the locations cited and because communal structures are built around the cloister, as each communal structure appeared, so too the cloister gallery built against it might possibly exist. For example, if the dormitory is cited as the site of an agreement in January 1166, then the east gallery might also have existed by then. When the framework suggested by the hidden clues was linked with a thorough architectural analysis, the chronology of construction of the cloister and its surrounding communal buildings slowly fell into place, along with the dating of the sculptures.

As I was carefully exploring these newly found clues, the individual named Poncius de Baucio also emerged and his career could be followed through 1165, clarifying the somewhat enigmatic date on his epitaph that was long embedded in the cloister. This epitaph names him a *canon regular*, the first use of this term there, so the canons were *canons regular* by 1165, living communally under the strict Rule of St. Augustine, living in communal buildings around a cloister.

It was the canons' decision to become *canons regular,* to adopt the strict Rule of St. Augustine, that required the construction of communal buildings around a cloister. But that decision could not have been made easily. The canons were very well-established at Arles; they lived very comfortable lives; they enjoyed wives and children, they lived in private dwellings; they were doing God's work. Why would they choose to give up their wives and children, their mistresses, and all their possessions? Why would they decide to adopt the Rule? Why would they bring such upheaval into the chapter? How could that decision have come about? Who or what could bring them to opt for such a dramatic change?

Such questions require leaps of imagination that are precluded by the rigorous standards of scholarly research, but that are possible in the historical novel. Poncius de Baucio was the first to be called a *canon regular*. A leader in the chapter, he must have been well respected by his peers, and because he was well-connected through his powerful family, he could help ensure the necessary financing for a building project. But for him to get his chapter to adopt the Rule, he must have been fervently, passionately committed to the issue, zealously committed to the change. What would so inspire him? What events could have so fired him up?

We have taken what we know of Poncius, what we know of his career, what we know of contemporary events, and what we know of inspiring individuals he may well have met, and given our imagination free rein. And by imagining what could have happened, we may well get a better picture of what did happen. Here is his tale.

HISTORICAL FIGURES WHO HAVE ROLES IN THE NOVEL

Poncius de Baucio, or Pons, was a young canon at the Cathedral of Saint-Trophîme at Arles who came from the House of Baux.[1] It was most likely he who managed to convince his chapter to adopt the Rule of St. Augustine, thereby renouncing their wives, families, and mistresses, giving up their own wealth, and embracing a strict communal life. This required the construction of enclosed communal buildings around a cloister. The beautiful cloister that still stands there is the result.

The career of Poncius de Baucio can be readily documented in twelfth-century manuscripts.[2] He is first mentioned in 1131, when he was called a *presbiter*. In 1139, he accompanied the archbishop to Barcelona because a document written there named him *subdiachonus*, or assistant, to the archbishop.[3] In 1141 he was identified as *Balcherio capellano meo* by the archbishop.[4] By 1142 he was elected *capud scole*.[5] Subsequently, he was identified as *capud scole* in 1142 and 1147. He is frequently named as *precentor* at Arles from 1152 through 1158. In 1165 he was called both *capud scole* and *precentor*. He

1   For the genealogy of the House of Baux, see "Del Balzo (de Baux)," *Libro d'Oro della Nobilità Mediterranea,*
     http://www.genmarenostrum.com/pagine-lettere/letterab/del%20Balzo/DEL%20 BALZO.htm. Pons is included here as "C.4 (Naturale) Pons (+post 1143)."

2   See for instance the *Authentique du Chapitre,* also called the *Liber Sancti Stephani vel Sancti Trophimi Arelatesis Aecclesiae de Rebus Ibidem Pertinentibus,* Arles, Bibliothèque Municipale, MS 1242. For modern transcriptions of the documents in these manuscripts, see Joseph Hyacinthe Albanes and Ulysse Chevalier, eds., *Gallia christiana novissima: Histoire des archevêchés, évêchés, et abbayes de France,* vol. III, *Arles* (Valence: Imprimerie valentinoise, 1901). See also Marilyn Armstrong Schneider, "The Sculptures of the North Gallery of St.-Trophîme at Arles," PhD diss., (Columbia University, 1983), 73–80.

3   On Poncius de Baucio's accompanying of Archbishop Willelmus Monachus to Catalonia, see Schneider, "Sculptures," 73, and Albanes and Chevalier, *Arles,* nos. 3228, 535, 538. For the document drafted by *Poncius subdiachonus,* see Albanes and Chevalier, *Arles,* no. 535. See also Schneider, "Sculptures," 73.

4   Albanes and Chevalier, *Arles,* no. 538.

5   See the *Authentique,* Arles MS 1242, fol. 125, no. 70. See also Schneider, "Sculptures," 74.

died in October 1165, and on his epitaph, which long appeared in the cloister at Arles, he was identified as *capud scole* and *canon regular*, the first such reference to the canons having adopted the Rule, or becoming *regular.*

Heretics:

Peter of Bruys was a known twelfth-century heretic whose Petrobrusian heresies spread throughout Provence. Not much is known about his early life other than that he may have been born at Bruis in southeast France, and he began preaching his heresies in the dioceses of Embrun, Die, and Gap. He was a priest who was deprived of his charge. He was burned to death sometime in the 1130s in front of the abbey church of Saint-Gilles.[6] His teachings and doctrine are well-known to us through a treatise written by Peter the Venerable, *Contra Petrobrusianos.*[7]

Henry of Lausanne was also a known heretic. A former Cluniac monk, he was a follower of Peter of Bruys. After Peter's death, he continued to promote and spread these heresies and was particularly effective in Toulouse among the cloth weavers and merchants, as well as in Narbonne and Gascony. When Bernard of Clairvaux was asked to travel through southern France to preach against this heretic, he did so, and challenged him.

Church Leaders:

Peter the Venerable, or Peter of Montboissier, was a Black Monk of the Benedictine Order. Highly respected, he was the head, or general, of the Order of Cluny, after having begun his career at Vézelay. He journeyed both to Catalonia, as documented in his *Contra Petrobrusianos,* and through Spain,[8] where he became interested in Islam and had scribes translate many

6   See "Petrobrusians" in *The Catholic Encyclopedia.*
7   Jacques-Paul Migne, ed., "Petri Venerabilis Contra Petrobrusianos hereticos" in *Patrologia Cursus Completus, Series Latina*, 1854, vol. 189, cols 719–850.
8   Peter's journey to Catalonia has almost always been dated early, before 1142, largely because he describes his personal visit to Sant Pere de Casserres, where he saw the Rock Salt Mountain, in his *Contra Petrobrusianos,* which is now usually dated at the end of the 1130s, either 1137/38 or 1139/40. His journey through Spain, where he became interested in Muslim culture and commissioned a Latin translation of the Qur'an, is sometimes dated around 1139. See "Blessed Peter of Montboissier" in *The Catholic Encyclopedia.*

Arabic documents. Only the dates of his journeys to Catalonia and Spain are uncertain.

Bernard of Clairvaux was a Cistercian, a White Monk. An influential leader in the Order of Cîteaux, he was highly respected. Bernard of Clairvaux was invited by Cardinal Alberic of Ostia to travel to Provence to preach throughout the region to combat the Petrobrusian heresy, and so he traveled through southern France in June 1145. Pope Eugenius II asked Bernard to lead the call for the Second Crusade at Vézelay, and then to promote it widely.

Abbot Suger was abbot at the monastery of Saint-Denis from 1122 to 1151. He was a counselor to both King Louis VI and King Louis VII of France. In 1137 he began rebuilding first the west and then the east ends of the abbey church of Saint-Denis, inaugurating what would become known as Gothic style. The church was dedicated in June 1144. He also built a cloister decorated with column figures at the abbey.

Nicolaus, Canon of Saint-Ruf, was in the company of Archbishop William Monachus in Spain in 1140, where Nicolaus penned and witnessed a charter.[9] Scholars[10] suggest that he was the Nicolaus, Canon of Saint-Ruf, who in 1154 became Pope Adrian IV, and who was born Nicholaus Breakspear at Abbot's Langley, near St. Albans.[11]

Royalty:

Louis VII, King of France, convened an assembly at Vézelay on Easter 1146 to call for the Second Crusade, after having been urged by Pope Eugenius II

For evidence that Peter's trip to Spain took place in 1142–1143, see Charles Julian Bishko, "Peter the Venerable's Journey to Spain" in *Spanish and Portuguese Monastic History 600–1300* (London: Variorum, 1984).

For the suggestion that Peter began his journey through Spain with his trip to Catalonia and Sant Pere de Casserres, so that both trips took place 1142–1143, see Charles Julian Bishko, "Peter the Venerable's Traverse of Spain: Some Further Observations" in *Spanish and Portuguese Monastic History, 600–1300*, (London: Variorum, 1984).

9   See the charter in Albanes and Chevalier, *Arles,* no. 537.

10   See R. L. Poole, "The Early Lives of Robert Pullen and Nicholas Breakspear," in *Essays in Medieval History, presented to Thomas Frederick Tout,* ed. A.G. Little and F.M. Powicke (Manchester: 1925), 67–68.

11   See Schneider, "Sculptures," 64–66.

to lead the expedition for it. King Louis and Eleanor of Aquitaine participated in the Second Crusade.

Following the Crusade, they stayed in the Holy Land, where King Louis celebrated Easter before returning to France by the land route in 1149.[12] On their return journey, the sovereigns passed through Provence and visited Saint-Gilles, where in October 1149 King Louis wrote to Abbot Suger, so they are known to have visited Saint-Gilles[13] on their return to Paris and the French domain.

Eleanor of Aquitaine, Queen of France, participated in the call for the Second Crusade and accompanied her husband, Louis VII, on the Crusade.

Known Sculptors:

Master Brunus of Saint-Gilles was a sculptor, known to us because he signed two of the large stone pier figures on the façade of the church at Saint-Gilles. The figure of St. Matthew still bears the inscription *"Brunus me fecit,"* but the signature on the figure of St. Bartholomew has been lost. Because of the inscriptions, it has always been assumed that he directed the workshop that was responsible for the sculptural program at Saint- Gilles.

....

12   Amy Kelly, *Eleanor of Aquitaine and the Four Kings* (Cambridge: Harvard University Press, 1950), 71, and Alison Weir, *Eleanor of Aquitaine: By the Wrath of God, Queen of England* (New York: Vintage, 1999), 75, both suggest that the sovereigns travelled north on the land route via Aqua Pendente, crossing by the Jural Alpine Pass into France, where they rode through Burgundy to Auxerre. This proposed route through the Jural Pass would have taken their crossing into Provence much too far north to account for their known and documented visit to Saint-Gilles, however. It is much more likely, therefore, that the sovereigns followed the alternate routing of the *Via Francigena*, which turned westward near Piacenza and Pavia, continuing on through the pass near Torino and Suse, which would join them with the pilgrimage route to Santiago de Compostela, taking them through Arles to Saint-Gilles.

13   Louis VII's passing through Provence and visiting Saint-Gilles is well documented. See Francois M. Guizot, *The History of France from the Earliest Times to the Year 1789* (London: 1882), I: 429. Guizot dates the visit of Louis VII to Saint-Gilles October 1149. Whitney Stoddard, *The Façade of Saint-Gilles-du-Gard, Its Influence on French Sculpture* (Middletown: Wesleyan University Press, 1973), 130, dates the visit 1148, but Hindley's timeline states that Louis left the Holy Land in June 1149, so the visit to Saint-Gilles could not have been before 1149. See Geoffrey Hindley, *A Brief History of the Crusades: Islam and Christianity in the Struggle for World Supremacy* (London: Robinson Publishing, 2004), 83–84.

The names of other sculptors who worked at Saint-Gilles are unknown. Art historians have tried to identify other individual masters who worked on the façade by their style and then have assigned names to them, based on either the piece carved or the style of their work. For example, many identify one of them as the Angoulême or Thomas Master, because work assigned to him at Saint-Gilles shows stylistic similarities to sculpture at Angoulême in western France, and the pier figure of Thomas is usually attributed to him. (I have arbitrarily assigned him the name **Master Gilius**.) The pier figure of James the Less is also usually attributed to him, and some have attributed the pier figure of Peter to him too. Thomas, James the Less, and Peter certainly all share large, decorated halos, as well as other stylistic traits.[14] Most scholars attribute or link to this sculptor some of the relief sculpture on the bases and socles, usually at least the Cain and Abel scenes.[15] None of the sculpture on the superstructure is ever linked to him, however. No one sees his style or his handiwork on the superstructure, which suggests the Angoulême Master was no longer there at Saint-Gilles when the superstructure sculpture was carved.

Master Gilabertus of Toulouse was a sculptor, known to us because of inscriptions once visible on the bases of pier figures representing St. Thomas and St. Andrew, "*Gilabertus me fecit*" and "*Vir non incertus me celavit Gilabertus*" ("Gilabertus, no ordinary man, made me"). Together with six other reliefs, they were rescued after the destruction of the cloister of Saint-Étienne, Toulouse, and have been shown to have supported the transverse arches of the barrel vault of the chapter house there.[16] It is assumed that Gilabertus directed the workshop that produced the pier figures and a series of capitals there. This sculpture has never been securely dated, with estimates ranging from 1120 to the 1150s. It is usually now dated 1120–1140 or in the late 1130s or 1140s.[17]

....

14   Stoddard, *Façade*, 28–29 and 19–24, confirmed this stylistic relationship of the St. Peter pier figure to the pier figures of Thomas and James the Less, which he attributed to the "Thomas Master," whom he, as well as others previously, suggested showed a stylistic relationship to sculptural work at Angoulême in western France. See Stoddard, 41–44, for an overview.

15   See Stoddard, *Façade*, 45–53, 59–62.

16   Linda Seidel, "A Romantic Forgery: The Romanesque 'Portal' of Saint-Étienne in Toulouse," *The Art Bulletin* 50, no. 1 (1968), 33–42.

17   For a succinct review of the various datings, see Stoddard, *Façade*, 149–150 and footnote 46, where he seems to settle on a date in the 1130s.

It has long been postulated that Master Niccolo traveled to France and saw Master Gilabertus's apostle figures at the Chapter House of Saint-Étienne, Toulouse. This contentious issue is still debated.

Master Gislebertus of Autun has long been known as the sculptor who worked at the Cathedral of Autun from 1120–1135, carving figures, many of which are elongated and distorted. His identity as the sculptor has been assumed because of an inscription, *"Gislebertus hoc fecit,"*[18] on the Last Judgment tympanum, which is usually dated 1130–1135 or before 1135. Many of Master Gislebertus's carved capitals show the elongated distortion of the figures on the tympanum, but some, including those originally in the transept of the cathedral but now preserved in the Chapter House, show a gentle charm comparable to that of the Cluny capitals.[19] This master also carved the lintel depicting the nude Eve, which originally appeared on the north portal but is now displayed in the Musée Rolin at Autun. Only this relief sculpture of Eve survives from the original north portal sculptures.[20]

Master Niccolo of Lombardy was a sculptor and architect, known to us because he signed some of his work naming himself as the sculptor at the Sagra di San Michele, at the Cathedral of Ferrara and at San Zeno in Verona, where two of the inscriptions on the reliefs identify him. At the Cathedral of Piacenza is another inscription not naming him but so closely resembling the one at the Sagra that it has been attributed to him.

He was active in north Italy from 1120 to 1150. Sculpture securely attributed to him appears:[21]

....

18   Linda Seidel has more recently proposed that this inscription refers not to the sculptor at Autun, but to an historical patron, the distant ancestor of a local ducal family, who was being remembered and honored here for his role in originally acquiring the relics of Lazarus. See Linda Seidel, *Legends in Limestone. Lazarus, Gislebertus, and the Cathedral of Autun* (University of Chicago Press, 1999) Chapter 1, 6 ff.

19   See John Beckwith, *Early Medieval Art: Carolingian, Ottonian, Romanesque* (New York: Praeger, 1964), 212–215, and fig. 202.

20   See Denis Grivot and George Zarnecki, *Gislebertus: Sculptor of Autun* (New York: Orion Press, 1961).

21   Dating of the sculpture at the Sagra and at Piacenza are taken from Christine Verzár Bornstein, "The Capitals of the Porch of Sant'Eufemia in Piacenza: Interacting Schools of Romanesque Sculpture in Northern Italy," *Gesta* 13, no. 1 (1974), 5–26.

- on the Zodiac Portal of the Sagra di San Michele, which should probably be dated 1120;

- on the porch at Sant'Eufemia in Piacenza, which should probably be dated between 1107 and 1125;

- at the Cathedral of Piacenza, which should probably be dated between 1122–1130, and particularly on the south portal there, which should probably be dated ca. 1130;

- on the Cathedral of Ferrara, ca. 1135;

- at San Zeno in Verona, ca. 1138;

- and at the Cathedral of Verona, 1139–1145.

Another sculpture less securely attributed directly to Niccolo appears at the church of Sts. Peter and Paul in Königslutter, in Lower Saxony. There a carved corbel table that is also now sometimes attributed to him or to a member of his workshop, primarily because the hunting scenes depicted with animals (e.g., a rabbit hunter) virtually replicate what appears at the Cathedral of Verona. The style of the carving resembles work at Piacenza, but the inscription, which does not name Niccolo, is written backward, like a mirror image.[22] Both the virtually duplicated scenes and the backward inscription suggest this work was copied by someone in Niccolo's workshop.

It has long been postulated that Master Niccolo traveled to France and must have seen the apostle figures from the chapter house of Saint-Étienne, Toulouse. John Beckwith,[23] for example, argues that although his work is based on that of Wiligelmo, Niccolo must have visited Toulouse once, or even twice, and that he must have studied the sculpture in Saint-Sernin and in the chapter house of Saint-Étienne, Toulouse, as shown by the bulk of his figures. The lines and postures of his figures are comparable to the pier figures at Saint-Étienne, Toulouse.

Yet many doubt the connection. Evelyn Kain,[24] for example, argues that the similarities are all superficial and that there is a fundamental difference

....

22   See Evelyn Kain, *The Sculpture of Nicholaus and the Development of a North Italian Romanesque Workshop* (1986), 159ff.

23   Beckwith, *Early*, 189–190.

24   See Kain, *Sculpture*, 107–114. Kain notes that the Toulouse apostle figure is in an architectural niche defined by colonettes with capitals, much like the low relief figures

in plasticity in the relationship between figure and architectural background. She further argues that Niccolo's incorporating sculpture into a tympanum can be the result of a general French influence.

This contentious issue is still debated, yet it simply inconceivable to most that Niccolo could not have known and studied the work of Gilabertus at Toulouse.

Master Benedetto Antelami is a known Italian sculptor and architect, who in 1178 carved and signed a relief sculpture of the Deposition from the Cross, which is in the right transept at the Cathedral of Parma. By 1196 Antelami was beginning work at the Baptistry of Parma, where he decorated the portals with carved figural lunette tympana and lintels.

Because of close stylistic similarities between his work and some of the capitals in the east gallery at Arles, Geza De Francovich has suggested that Antelami may have worked or apprenticed at Saint Trophîme at Arles, where he may have carved the capital of the Dream of the Magi and Flight into Egypt in the east gallery.[25]

However, few other scholars have accepted this connection, and none have directly linked the other sculptures in the Arles cloister to north Italy. Whitney Stoddard concluded that Antelami must have known both the east gallery of the cloister at Arles and the façade at Saint-Gilles but that Antelami could not have carved the Flight into Egypt capital at Arles, because it lacks the sensitivity of the Italian sculptor.[26]

De Francovich's suggestion that Antelami apprenticed at Arles in Provence would certainly explain the close stylistic similarities. Moreover, when Antelami later decorated the portals at the Baptistry of Parma, his lunette depicting the Adoration of the Magi almost identically reflects the disposition of the same scene on the tympanum at Saint-Gilles, with a central seated Virgin Mary, the Three Magi to the left—one kneeling, one pointing

....

in the Moissac cloister, but at Toulouse it has been adapted to the angle of the stone, while Niccolo's prophet figure at Ferrara, on the other hand, is carved directly into the substance of the block and becomes the block.

25   See Geza De Francovich, *Benedetto Antelami Architetto e scultore e l'arte del suo tempo* (Milan, Italy: Milano, 1952), 136–137.

26   See Stoddard, *Façade*, 270–271. But see Stoddard, *Façade*, 151–153 and 180–196, for a discussion of the possible relationship between the sculpture at Saint-Gilles and the sculpture of North Italy.

to the heavens, one standing while clutching his gift to his chest—and to the right, a seated Joseph being warned by an angel, swooping down out of the background in front of him. This similarity suggests Antelami had been in Provence.

In conclusion . . .

Only the characters of Beatrice, Isabel, and Gilbert are not to be found named in any documents and are totally imaginative fabrication. At that time, everyone believed in God, in heaven, and in hell, and these three characters were created to test the strength of Pons's faith, to push the limits of his convictions, and to challenge his commitment to his mission.

The two named sculptors at Arles, Guillelmo and Pietro, are also not named in any document as artists working at Arles, nor have they inscribed their names on the sculpture there. But there can be absolutely no doubt that these two sculptors—whatever their real names might have been—lived, that they worked in the north gallery of the cloister at Arles and on the façade at Saint-Gilles, and that we are forever indebted to them for carving some of the magnificently beautiful sculptures still visible for us to enjoy there today.

*"Audiam quid loquatur in me; Dominus Deus quoniam loquetur pacem in plebem
suam et super sanctos suos et in eos qui convertuntur ad cor."*
The Vulgate Bible. Psalmus 84:9[27]

*"I will hear what the Lord God will speak in me: for he will speak peace unto his
people: And unto his saints: and unto them that are converted to the heart."*
Douay-Rheims Bible. Psalm 84:9[28]

....

27   *The Vulgate Bible* is the late fourth-century Latin translation of the Bible, mostly the work
of St. Jerome. It became the commonly used translation, or the *versio vulgata*, from which
its name derives. It is not written in a vulgar form of Latin. It became the Latin version of
the Bible officially used by the Roman Catholic Church for prayer and liturgy. Although
St. Jerome produced three translations of the *Psalms*, it was the second, based on the
Septuagint, that became popular in Gaul and was incorporated into the *Vulgate*. This is the
version used in this book.

28   The *Douay-Rheims Bible* is a translation of *The Vulgate Bible* into English. It was first
translated by the English College, Douai, with the New Testament published in 1582 in
Rheims and the Old Testament published in 1609/10 at the University of Douai. It was
subsequently revised, first by Bishop Richard Challoner and then in Dublin by Bernard
MacMahon. Although other modern editions of the Bible are much more commonly
used, these modern editions typically go to the original Hebrew, Aramaic, and Greek texts
for their translations. Because the *Douay-Rheims Bible* is a more direct English translation
of St. Jerome's *Vulgate Bible,* which is what would have been used by the canons at Arles in
the twelfth century, it has been used here for the English translations.

Matins

Vigils during the Night—no bells

On the road to Saint-Gilles

---

*I*t was a time of faith. Men believed. To the chosen few, of whom there were many, the Christian God spoke directly and laid out His wishes and orders. But He sometimes changed His mind, or perhaps His messages were not understood.

God had spoken clearly to each of the two passionate young men, both now on their way to Saint-Gilles, when they were but young boys, telling each of them to devote their lives to Him. Both had always listened to God's message.

One of the two, Pons, had always been certain of his calling as a canon after God had spoken to him as a young boy, telling him he was to devote his life to the Church. The pious young man had never once doubted his calling, even if he was now somewhat unsure about the pathway to it.

The young canon was now walking steadily and rather briskly in the heat of the mid-morning sun along the road in southern Provence from Arles to the town of Saint-Gilles. Pons still remembered fondly how excited he had been when, as a very young boy, his much older brother would take him with him from time to time, from their fortress home to the exciting port town of Arles.

Arles was only a short, leisurely horse ride away, a ride much shorter than the time between the ringing of the bells marking the hours for prayer, but Arles was the most exciting place he had ever seen. It was full of ancient Roman ruins from long ago when it was the provincial capital of Rome, bustling with merchants selling anything you could want or imagine, and it sheltered mysterious travelers from every corner of the earth, who spoke strange languages that only the merchants seemed to understand.

But most thrilling of all was when Pons could sometimes manage to get away from his brother and slip unaccompanied into the cathedral during Mass. Whenever possible, he would get in and push his way discretely through the crowd, through the stench of so many men and women standing so closely together there, and squirm and wiggle to get up close toward the front where he could hear, see, and even smell God. Well, if not God himself, at least the aura of God around those clerics who were closest to God.

Even as a very young child, Pons had understood that God lived at the cathedral. Listening to the beautiful chanting of the canons was like hearing the singing of the angels, who had sung when the baby Jesus was born. The wondrous scent of the incense and the beautiful garments and drapery transformed this place, made it unlike anywhere else he knew on earth. This was where God lived. This was God's house.

Seeing the Mass always filled the young lad with wonder and awe. He would hear the celestial singing and chanting of the canons and the pealing of the bells in response. He would smell the unusual, otherworldly scent of incense and see the altar draped in magnificently embroidered, shiny fabrics, transforming this place into God's house. And then the archbishop, dressed in wondrously rich garments, would perform the miracles, turning bread into flesh, wine into blood. Little Pons would see the rituals of the liturgy performed—rituals everyone believed in, rituals everyone watched in awe, rituals everyone followed obediently and respectfully. During Mass, the pealing of the bells no longer simply marked the hours for prayer; they called to God and marked the spot where He would come and be present.

Listening and watching ever so attentively, young Pons would be transported into another world by the haunting mysteries of the liturgy, by its hypnotic musical chant, by the numbing scent of the incense. The little hairs on his head and neck and arms and back would stand up, and he knew God was passing over him. God was touching him. God was embracing him. Yes, at those times he had experienced and known God.

By the age of ten, Pons had been given to the canons and to God. Now at twenty-five years of age, he had already professed his solemn perpetual vows, after becoming a young canon—one of the ecclesiastics who formed the council of the archbishop and assisted him in ruling and governing his diocese—several years before. He had entered the priesthood, received his tonsure, and become a member of the chapter of canons of the cathedral at Arles.

As he walked steadily and briskly, the young man pushed back the ends of his crown of thick black hair under his peaked cloth cap, wiped his forehead again, and realized he must slow his pace just a bit. It was extremely hot, no hotter than usual, but hot enough to make one lightheaded and nauseous if one overexerted oneself under the blazing Provençal sun. So he began controlling his movement by planting each footstep more carefully, a bit more slowly, to slow his progress just a bit, but not so much that he would not reach his destination in time. He had resolved to get there. He must get there in time.

He was walking westward from Arles, following the beginning of the *Via Tolosana*, one of the four main pilgrimage routes to Santiago de Compostela, but that blessed town was certainly not his goal, at least not this time. He knew that throughout this century, as well as the last, thousands of the faithful had preceded him on this part of the path, just as many more would undoubtedly follow later, while making the pilgrimage westward but continuing on through Montpellier and Toulouse, well beyond where he was headed, and crossing the Pyrenees into the Iberian Peninsula through Castile and on past northwest Léon.[29] Their goal was to touch and worship the blessed relics of the Apostle James, the first apostle to be martyred, who had been beheaded in Jerusalem, but whose tomb had miraculously later been discovered at Santiago de Compostela. And, of course, other pilgrims had also walked this path toward his own destination, Saint-Gilles, which was the other port of embarkation for Jerusalem and the Holy Land.

....

29   See Jean Vielliard, ed., *Le Guide du Pèlerin de Saint-Jacques de Compostelle* (Mâcon, France: Imprimerie Protat Frères, 1963), 34.

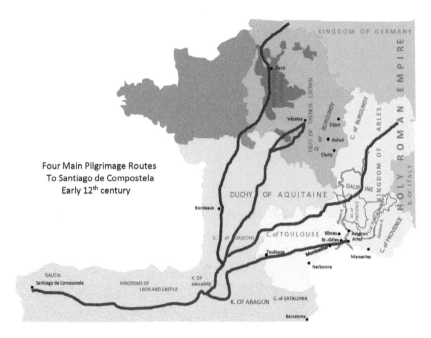

Map. Four main pilgrimage routes to Santiago de Compostela. Early twelfth century.[30]

One day he, too, would try to make the pilgrimage to Santiago de Compostela, as would any good Christian. But not today. No, not today. Pons's goal was much nearer today, and, as he now admitted privately to himself with just a bit of chagrin, acknowledging he would probably have to purge this at confession, this journey today was more compelling for him than making the full pilgrimages . . . at least today. His goal was not very far, only twelve *milles*[31] or so, much less than half a day's walk from Arles, and since he had left early, just after *Prime*, or first hour, he could certainly expect to arrive before midday. His goal today was to reach the abbey church of Saint-Gilles, in the town of the same name, the first town on the route, the town that was the other embarkation point for Jerusalem.

Today was Good Friday, and normally he would have been occupied with his duties at the cathedral, but when he had learned the news during his frequent strolls around Arles that Peter of Bruys was expected to arrive

. . . .

30   At that time the area we now know as Provence was not southern France, but was a
      semi-independent fiefdom of the Holy Roman Empire controlled by local counts,
      notably the Count of Barcelona and the Count of Toulouse.

31   "Mille passus," the Roman measurement of 1,000 paces.

at Saint-Gilles today to preach his terrible blasphemies, Pons had asked for permission in chapter to be relieved of his normal duties for the day so he could go to Saint-Gilles to hear him. Pons had argued convincingly that he considered it his duty to hear this heretic Peter, his duty as someone called to lead the faithful. He wanted to hear the heretic. He needed to hear him. Not, of course, because there might be any merit in the heresies, but rather to be able to better understand why so many now seemed to be taken in by these frightful heresies, why they were so enticing even to the faithful, why these ideas were spreading so easily and widely.

To his surprise, the *decanus*, or dean, and the chapter had agreed and had given him permission, but only if he could find someone else to fill in for him and fulfill his duties. Like most of their fellow Christian churchmen, his chapter wanted to suppress this virulent and threatening heresy. They certainly believed it would not hurt the pious young canon. Moreover, it was Good Friday, which was a day of fasting, and Mass would not be celebrated at the cathedral until Easter Sunday, so duties were light. So why not let him go?

It was only last night that his friend William Garnerius finally had agreed to fill in for him, after Pons had pulled him aside as they were walking back from the church in the middle of the night, just after celebrating *Matins*, which long ago was called the night *Vigils* or *Nocturns*. This Divine Office of Readings, a lengthy service of recitations during the night, was one of the canonical hours, the prescribed set of prayers and psalms, the devotions that marked daily divisions of time.

Pons had now been walking too quickly in his determination to arrive in time. Although he was probably about halfway there, the twenty-five-year-old was now feeling somewhat lightheaded and nauseous from the heat, and knew he needed to stop for a short but necessary break. The tall, lanky but muscular young man was in good physical condition, but he had been walking too briskly for too long, stopping only briefly to celebrate *Terce,* the third hour, in private. His journey had taken him first under the relieving shade of cypress trees, but now mostly under the baking and blisteringly hot Provençal sun.

After spotting a small cove sheltered by cypress trees not far off, he left the path and approached it, entering cautiously. Why, he wondered fleetingly to himself, were cypress trees so often associated with death and mourning, and always placed in cemeteries? Certainly here, along this path, they were anything but, instead offering a bit of shade and respite against the blistering sun.

Vincent Van Gogh painting. A Wheat Field with Cypresses.
Metropolitan Museum of Art, New York, NY.[32]

Finding himself to be all alone and quite safe, he removed his chaperon, or hooded cape, sat down on a rock under the shade, and held his head in his hands for a few minutes before taking a drink of water from his wineskin pouch. He would never, of course, be so foolish as to remove his traveler's leather pocketbook pouch, richly and beautifully decorated in the motif so favored by pilgrims, the scallop shell imprint of St. James, because the risk of bandits was always present.

Feeling more comfortable, he loosened the ankle ties of his leather sandals briefly and visibly relaxed as he looked up at the trees arching above him. Even under the trees, rays of the brilliant sun pierced through in spots, and the cooler green shade flickered with hypnotically dancing yellow-green lights.

Suddenly he was startled by an ugly old woman, trailed by two bedraggled and filthy children, a lithe and somewhat taller girl and a pouting young boy,

----

32   This is the first of three very similar, almost identical oil paintings by Vincent Van Gogh, all done in 1889 and based on his view from his room at the Saint-Paul-de-Mausolé mental asylum at Saint-Rémy-de-Provence, not far from Arles.

who all appeared soundlessly in the grove and seemed to have emerged from nowhere. The woman was a stooped old hag with big warts and long, matted, filthy gray hair, but wearing a fine and obviously expensive elegant cape, held at her shoulder by an elaborately ornate bejeweled clasp in the shape of a many-spoked wheel.[33]

"A coin for a poor old woman?" said the old hag with a croaking voice, extending her hand. Startled, Pons jumped up, almost tripping over the ties of his sandals.

"I am but a poor cleric and have no coins to give you," Pons lied defensively. "I travel with nothing of value at all except my blessing, if you be a good Christian."

Pointing to the leather pocketbook, the little boy sneered, "But he doesn't know hunger," as the young girl put one hand on her still undeveloped hip, thrusting it forward in an attempt to be provocative while adding, "And he is a pretty one for us girls, for sure!"

"Keep it to yourselves, my pets," the hag hissed, chastising them gently.

"Have no fear, dearie," announced the hag to Pons with a slight smile in a more level voice. "I'm but a lone Gyptian, a lone Luri,[34] with only two young ones, and on my own journey far from home. I have no band of ruffians with me and will do you no harm." She stood motionless, looking directly at him for several moments before frowning quizzically and adding, "But I would like to see the hand that would bless me."

Nervously and cautiously, but thinking she was asking for his blessing, Pons took a couple of steps forward, slightly extending and raising his right hand as if to bless her, but to his surprise, the old hag quickly grabbed his wrist instead. Taking his hand, she turned it over and began gently caressing the palm, tracing forms on it with her index finger.

"I see it is you who needs the blessing, my young friend," she declared in what was now a gentle, kind voice. "Before the cock crows thrice, you will renounce your own and lose what you would hold most dear."

. . . .

33   The wheel suggests the sixteen-spoken chakra, which, as the Romani symbol derived from the Indian twenty-four-spoked Ashok chakra, links the Romani to their East Indian ancestry.

34   Luri was one of the early tribal names of the Roma, or gypsies, who were also called Gyptians in the Middle Ages when it was mistakenly believed they were wandering Egyptians.

"What are you talking about, old woman?" Pons laughed nervously. "I think you are confused and are now mixing me up with St. Peter in the story of our Lord's Passion."[35]

"No, it is only your future that is written clear here for my eyes, not any Peter," she responded calmly, while continuing to look at his palm. "But have no worry, dearie. I also see twin numerals, 5 and 5.[36] Hah! So you'll live quite a while before we hear that old cock crow." She laughed wholeheartedly. Then, after recognizing a look of puzzled incomprehension on Pons's face, she spoke again with a kind and gentle smile. "So sorry," she apologized. "That would be an L and a V for you who still use the old Roman system," she added mischievously with a grin. "That's 'quinquaginta et quinque' for you, or 'fifty and five' for me, so you will live to see your LV years."

Then, after a moment, her face darkened and her voice thickened ominously as she quietly murmured, "But I also see a blade here, a sword blade, and a pool of hot blood spreading out on cold stone."

"Now, that is truly absurd, you foolish old woman!" Pons interjected, withdrawing his hand in indignation at this last folly. "I am a cleric, a priest. I'm not a knight. I do not engage in warfare!"

"So you say! So you say! Be that as it may, it is written clear," concluded the old hag, who turned and slipped out of the cove behind the two children, as soundlessly as they had entered.

Pons leaped forward, trying to see where she had gone, and whether a band of ruffian bandits would be waiting for him, but this time he did trip on his sandal laces, and by the time he could stumble out of the cove of cypress, the old hag had disappeared, as if she had melted away into the heat of the Camargue, the river delta between the two arms of the Rhône.

Unnerved more by their sudden appearance than by the hag's silly, absurd, so-called prophecy, Pons returned to the cove to gather his wits, to calm down,

. . . .

35   The Bible relates that at the Last Supper Christ predicted that Peter would deny knowing him three times before the cock crowed, to which Peter protested. Christ was then arrested, and Peter did deny knowing him three times, before the cock crowed. See Matthew 26:33–35 and 69–75, Mark 14:29–31 and 66–72, Luke 22:33–34 and 56–61, and John 13:36–38 and 18:15–27 for the biblical accounts.

36   Gypsies or Romani people are now usually believed to have originated in India. Studies of their language found that they shared basic words, including numbers, with the eastern Indian languages, so their own numbering system would probably have been the Arabic system.

and to take stock of what had happened. The old hag had seemed to mean him no harm. Although she was obviously a foolish and crazy old woman, she had done nothing untoward other than to utter her bizarre prophecies. And most importantly, there was no indication of a band of bandits for as far as he could see.

He took another sip of water from his wineskin. He knew he had to continue on soon if he was to make it in time, so after a very brief rest, he emerged cautiously again from the sheltered cove to continue his day's journey under the relentlessly piercing sun of the luminous blue Provençal sky.

As he began walking again in the blistering sunlight of the open plain, he could now see wild horses off in the distance, and his heart quickened.

"There they are! My magnificent wild horses!"

As always, the fully-grown mature horses were almost white, while the younger ones were darker gray and the youngest brown in color. Two hawks soared above, looking for prey in the dry grasses, then dived quickly to disappear from view and to claim their quarry.

Of course, he knew the horses were not really his, but that did not sway his feeling of kinship with these magnificent wild beasts. As a young boy he had several times been permitted by his brother, Raymond of Baux, to accompany him along this route through the Camargue, and Pons had always looked forward to seeing the horses that Raymond had taught him about. Because Pons was so much younger and had never known their father, he looked to his elder brother almost as a father, and Raymond had always treated him rather kindly. His brother Raymond was the Lord of Baux, eldest son of the now-deceased William Hugh of Baux, the powerful local feudal lord based near Arles. It was Raymond who about a year before the death of their mother, Viernes, had "donated" Pons as a ten-year-old lad to the chapter of canons at the cathedral at Arles, along with a small endowment of land that would provide income, and the *carta canonicaturae* had clarified that Pons would hold this until his death, after which the donation would go to the chapter of canons.

The two brothers were not at all alike, as different as could be. As members of the family of the lords of Baux, both brothers believed the family legend that they were descended from Balthazar, one of the three Magi cited in the biblical story of the Nativity. While the arrogant warlord Raymond of Baux always viewed his noble predecessor as a wise and powerful, conquering ruler who had succeeded brilliantly in tracking the star from the east in pursuit of the impressive goal of discovering the infant Christ, the pious Pons always envisioned their predecessor as humbly kneeling in obedience before the holy babe and reverently prostrating himself to offer gifts.

As he walked, Pons had been thinking about his past and his brother, but he now returned again to his current dilemma. He now seemed to struggle almost daily with what God wanted of him in his calling. Did every young canon go through this? Did every young canon question the direction he was taking? When would he be sure of the path God wanted him to take as a canon?

"Please, Blessed Father, please, God," he began begging aloud. "I beg You. I ask You once again—with all humility, from the depths of my soul—please, please show me what it is You want of me. I know You want something special of me . . . but what is it? Please, please give me a sign. Show me the way You want me to take. I humbly beg of You to please show me the path You want me to take."

Although once again he received no response, of one thing Pons was certain: he knew without hesitation that his being given to the chapter so long ago had started him on the right path, on the right course, and for this he was truly grateful to Raymond, his brother. Whatever Raymond's full motivations had been in donating the ten-year-old boy,[37] Pons had been given to the canons and to God. He could devote his life to God at the cathedral at Arles.

As he continued walking, once again Pons began reminiscing, thinking back to when he had first arrived at the chapter. He remembered how formal the event had been, how his brother had led him and several of his men through the Portal of St. Stephen and the city of Arles into the cathedral enclosure,

---

37   Undoubtedly Raymond's motivation in this was at least partly laudable. After all, their family had long had a strong relationship with the church at Arles. In 1088 their father, William Hugh of Baux, along with their mother Viernes, and their older brother Hugues had donated property to the church of Arles. In 1091 their father had donated more property to the Arles church, this time with the consent of their mother, their brother, and Raymond himself. See http://fmg.ac/Projects/MedLands//provaixmar. htm#_Toc28604186 (*Foundation for Medieval Genealogy / Medieval Lands* / Provence-Aix, Marseille / Chapter 4. Marseille :.B. Seigneurs de Baux, Vicomtes de Baux / / Guillaume-Hugues de Baux, Raymond de Baux," which cites the manuscripts the *Livre Noir de l'archevêché d'Arles,* Marseille, Archives Départementales des Bouches-du-Rhône, MS 3 G 16, fol 44, and the *Livre Rouge de l'archevêché d'Arles,* Marseille, Archives Départementales des Bouches-du-Rhône, MS 3 G 19, fol. 363.

and just beyond into the nearby archbishop's palace, where several others had joined them. After a long discussion between his brother Raymond, the archbishop, and several canons, one of whom Pons later came to understand was the *prepositus*, or provost, who was in charge of administering chapter property, Raymond of Baux finally presented Pons first to the Archbishop Atto, who welcomed him, and then to the *caput scole*, or chancellor, who was in charge of the school and who would draft an official document formally recording this transaction with a list of the witnesses to it.

Finally, after what had seemed like forever to the rather frightened young boy, and certainly was a very long time, the *capud scole* turned Pons over to one of the canons, Peter Villelmus, who gently took the now teary-eyed lad by the hand and instructed him to say goodbye to his brother. After a quick embrace and a few words of encouragement from Raymond, Peter Villelmus led Pons away to his own house nearby.

For several years and through his adolescence, young Pons had lived with Canon Peter Villelmus and the priest's wife and family. Although a few of the clerics who were still single lived together somewhat communally, sharing common residences, many of them were married and had wives and families, while others had mistresses. Almost all lived separately in their own houses. The domestic arrangements in Peter Villelmus's house had been quite comfortable, comparable, in fact, to those of Pons's early life as a child.

Pons had been born the third and very late son of the Lord of Baux, who had died just before the time of his birth. With two older brothers, Raymond and Hugh, as the heir and a spare, and with an older sister, Poncia, it was not clear how the late-born, sweet little Pons might be useful in the family's ambitious struggles for territorial control. Nevertheless, he had been taught to read and write, and had received some rudimentary education before being given as an oblate, or donated child, to the church at Arles. At Arles he was tutored along with other children of the canons.

As a young lad, Pons had early shown himself to be not only a clever boy and a reasonably quick learner, but also confident and rather personable. He would always try quickly to complete his duties and studies at the chapter so he could quietly slip out of the portal to make his way to one of the many antique Roman monuments in the town, all of which were the legacy of its being an important Roman political center long ago, and the young boy loved exploring them. For the Romans, Arles had been an important port on

Mare Nostrum, the Mediterranean Sea, located near the mouth of the eastern branch of the Rhône River that split upstream to fork into two branches.

Usually for short escapes, young Pons would follow the short path up the hill from the cathedral to go to the remains of the huge Roman theater that had long ago been built up with houses and religious buildings[38] and where he would have great fun trying to follow and walk along some of the remaining rows of seats. Whenever he had a bit more time to spare, he would go over the little hill to the ancient Roman arena. Occasionally, especially when it was really hot, he would head out in the other direction and work his way toward the Rhône River, sometimes stopping briefly nearby to explore the cool barrel-vaulted underground passages with huge supporting pillars[39] that opened onto the city's forum.

If he was feeling really adventurous, occasionally he would attempt a real excursion and continue on to seek out and try to sneak into the underground portion of the *Château de la Trouille* that was claimed by the foreign usurper, the Count of Barcelona, who was rarely there. The château was composed of curious remnants of old Roman palace buildings that were oddly built with alternating rows of stone and brick, with hollow tile tubes making openings within some of the walls.[40] It had many rooms or chambers, and remnants of even more rooms and chambers, dug into the earth, all great fun to explore. And if its inhabitants were not in residence, and he could manage to sneak in, the underground rooms offered a wonderfully cool respite from the merciless sun.

His real favorite site, however, at least certainly by the time he had entered adolescence, was the old Roman arena.[41] The arena now looked more like a fortress town than an arena because it had been built up, filled up, with houses and shops, like a little town itself. Oh, how he loved exploring the old arena, where he would often encounter pilgrims or travelers who were passing through Arles.

The town of Arles was an exciting, busy, bustling place, full of strange and exotic sights, sounds and smells, teeming with strangers, many in unusual

38   The Roman theater from the end of the first century BCE could originally hold 8,000 people on its thirty-three rows of seats.
39   The Cryptoporticus from 30 BCE that was the foundation for the Roman Forum.
40   This was the Palace or Baths of Constantine, built in the fourth century AD.
41   The Roman amphitheater, from 90 AD, originally held 20,000 spectators.

dress, often speaking in unknown languages. Located then at a mouth of the Rhône River, Arles was a seaport, a regular port of call for ships coming from or bound for each of the two maritime giants, Pisa and Genoa. Travelers here would always seek out the ancient arena, looking for shops for commerce or food and lodging at one of the inns there, for both were nestled among the myriad dwellings set within the cooling, ancient, thick stone walls of the arena. There the cordwainer made shoes, the cobbler repaired them, and the blacksmith shod horses and forged tools. One could find anything there, from horse tack to woolen cloth, from horses to armor, from a bed to sleep for the night to a pallet behind a curtain on which to spend several moments with a prostitute in a local stew.[42] One could buy not only fresh bread, meat, sweet olive oil, or earthy red wine, but all kinds of exotic fruits and spices—even conical loaves of that new crystallized "sugar" brought over from the crusading kingdom.[43]

The Arles arena was a boisterous, noisy market, with eager vendors noisily hawking their wares, each vying with the others, each trying to draw the attention and the pocketbooks of the travelers. "Touch this wool! Feel the solid weave of this cloth!" "Taste my sweet, rich olive oil!" "Taste this beautiful honey." "Smell this exotic saffron." "Look at this strange thing—it's called a 'fork.' It's what people eat with now in Byzantium and in the Italian states."[44] Everything and anything was on offer for sale at the Arles arena.

One vendor had even mistakenly tried, long ago, to lure a youthful Pons onto the pallet in his stew, where his whore was displaying her goods. "Come in," he had said. "She'll teach you what you want to know!" And although the youth had declined, a new rigidity on his newly developing adolescent body had forced him to walk rather awkwardly back to Peter Villelmus's home, where that night, Pons entered puberty with his first emission. Followed, of course, by confession, light penance, and, in due course, forgiveness. Yes, Pons had learned that anything could be found at the Arles arena, and after that first emission, from time to time, as a curious adolescent, he could not

---

42   "Stew" was the village brothel.

43   On the introduction of the new refined sugar by Italian merchants to the west, see Hindley, *Brief*, 65.

44   See Hindley, *Brief*, 67, where he notes that the "new-fangled eating fork," often first encountered in Byzantium, was introduced more widely by Italian merchants living in the Crusader settlements.

refrain from returning to that vendor or to another, simply to sneak a forbidden peek at the forbidden female wares. But even as an adolescent, he did understand that these were forbidden to him, that they were sinful, and he struggled hard to try to contain his urges.

In fact, Pons's faith was strengthened as a result of his explorations at the arena. Many of the travelers he met there were pilgrims en route to or from Santiago de Compostela, but Pons also encountered some travelers who were going to or returning from Jerusalem across the sea or to or from Rome, both holy pilgrimage sites. As the pilgrims talked about these holy places and holy relics, the bright youth's curiosity and excitement about such wonderful places grew, and as his vision of the world expanded, so, too, his faith had strengthened.

As his faith grew ever stronger, the youth had applied himself ever more diligently with the canons and progressed fairly quickly as an oblate, eventually becoming a postulant, or candidate, and continuing through his novitiate, or period of training to become qualified and eligible for admission to the order of canons. He had eventually taken his solemn vows, received his *tonsure,* or shaving of the top of the head, was given a *surplice,* or large-sleeved tunic to be used for liturgical dress, and he was ordained a *presbyter,* a priest or *sacerdos,* entitled to perform liturgical duties and priestly functions, subject to the authority of the bishop. At twenty-five years of age, he was now a young canon, one of the ecclesiastics in the council of the archbishop, helping run the diocese.

The young man now continued walking along the road, so deep in thought he did not notice the sun-bleached sandy earth was giving way first to sporadic bushes, then to small trees, and as the road eventually narrowed into a wide lane, he barely noticed the towering cypress trees forming a prolonged arch above, along the length of this section of the route, offering temporary respite and shade from the brilliant yellow sun blazing above.

Reminiscing about his past long ago had helped pass the time as he continued walking, but now he was again becoming disquieted and somewhat anxious.

"Blessed Father, God, I know You must have a plan for me," he cried aloud. "I know that is why I was given to the chapter, and I know You want me to do Your work. But what is that work? I have become a canon at Arles. I carry out choir duties at the cathedral, and I assist with the administration of church business.

"Our chapter is successful, very successful, in fact. Our business is thriving. Almost every day we receive pledges of trade goods, volumes of goods—and valuable ones, too, like olive oil. And when the penitents have been granted their indulgences, we record and document these gifts. Is that what You want of me, God? To help carry on the chapter's business? To be Your business-man? I seem to be very good at that, but is this what You want of me?"

After once again, as usual, receiving no immediate answer, Pons turned his thoughts to what lay ahead at Saint-Gilles, where the heretic Peter of Bruys was expected to speak. Pons had learned that Peter of Bruys had, in fact, once been an ordained priest, yet this former priest now profaned God with his notions.

Pons now recalled what Archbishop Bernard had warned him about this morning just as he was about to leave Arles.

"We recognize the sincerity of your devotion to your faith, and we know that you want to help in fighting these heresies," the archbishop had said. "They are now being spread not only by Peter of Bruys, that accursed former priest, but now also by his follower, Henry of Lausanne. Beware these her-esies! They are so treacherous! So evil! And they are spreading like a plague throughout the County of Provence, throughout the County of Toulouse, throughout our entire region! We must suppress this threat to our Church, and we pray to God that you may, somehow, be able to help."

Canon Pons had understood full well the archbishop's particular vehe-mence in wanting to suppress this heresy, especially because of the arch-bishop's own personal involvement. Not long ago, Archbishop Bernard had apprehended Henry of Lausanne, the follower who was perhaps even more charismatic than his mentor. The archbishop had turned Henry over for trial by Pope Innocent at the Council of Pisa held in 1134, and Henry had been imprisoned, but somehow he had managed to escape.[45] It was Peter of Bruys himself who was expected to speak at Saint-Gilles, but both of these heretics had to be stopped.

As he thought about the priest turned heretic, Pons braced himself once more, with a bit of dread, for the evil heresies he might hear. This did not

---

45   See Andrew Miller, "Henricians" in *Short Papers on Church History* (London: 1874) vol. II. chap. 25, and "Henry of Lausanne" in *Encyclopedia Britannica* (1911), vol. 13.

dissuade him from continuing on his venture, of course. No. Armed with the blind confidence and certainty of youth, his vague anxiety was simply transformed into excitement and anticipation. By nature, he was normally a fairly confident and sanguine fellow, yet somewhat excitable and prone to zealous pursuit, with blood usually governing his humors,[46] but his spleen now began pumping forth its yellow bile as his excitement was growing. He began walking faster and ever faster.

"I must get there in time, but what will I find there? What blasphemies will I hear? I know You will help me understand and deal with whatever I hear, dear God, but what will I hear? If I can get there in time . . ."

Young Pons grew ever more excited, his yellow bile now surging through his limbs, his youthful vigor rising in anticipation of the heretical spectacle, which his soul may have dreaded but which his young mind and heart eagerly wanted to learn about.

Off in the distance to his right, past the hillocks of lavender and bees' nests, he saw another small herd of wild horses of the Camargue, but these were nervously prancing about, skittishly darting to and fro as if they, too, sensed that something exciting and somehow threatening was going to happen.

*　*　*

As Pons was making his way westward, another solitary figure had also been traveling along the *Via Tolosana*, but eastward from Montpelier, and was now making his way to the same destination, the town of Saint-Gilles. It was Peter of Bruys.

Peter of Bruys was walking slowly but steadily, his head bent in deep contemplation, his face partially concealed by the hood of a cape, worn to ensure anonymity despite the heat of the Camargue. After having decided it was worth the risk of traveling alone, Peter had sent his four companions ahead

---

46　Medieval medicine followed the ancient Greek and Roman belief that in the human body there were four humors, or fluids, produced by organs: blood, phlegm, yellow bile, and black bile. The four humors had to be in balance for good health, and the dominant humor governed personality. Too much blood, produced by the liver, made one sanguine; excessive phlegm, produced by the lungs and brain, made one phlegmatic and sluggish; too much yellow bile, produced by the spleen, made one choleric; excessive black bile, produced by the gallbladder, made one melancholic.

to prepare the site and to ensure he would be able to effectively preach his message when he arrived at the abbey church in the town.

He had been fervently undertaking his mission for almost twenty years now, and today he admitted to himself that he was indeed becoming rather weary.

"Dear God, please speak to me again. Tell me, do You really want me to continue my mission? Are the people listening? Could it perhaps be time for me to give the mission over to another" he asked aloud, rather forlornly.

Peter was from Bruis,[47] a town midway between Avignon and Grenoble. Orphaned at a young age, the miserably destitute young boy could easily have been doomed but instead had been taken in and raised by the good-hearted and simple-minded local parish priest. A bright young lad, Peter easily took to learning to read and to write, and when it became obvious that he had surpassed what his rather limited mentor could offer, he was finally sent off to study for the priesthood.

Once ordained as a priest, he was sent home again and given a small parish in the Dauphiné. At first, he had tried faithfully to uphold all the tenets of his faith, but doubts had early begun to creep in, doubts born mostly from his early education, but also in some small part from his painful awareness of the total destitution from which he had been rescued.

Peter had first learned to read from the Bible, of course, one of the very few manuscripts or written works in the parish, but he had read and re-read it many times as a child, and then many times again later as an aspiring priest. Slowly but surely, Peter eventually came to believe that God had led him and opened his eyes to the real truth of the Bible.

He knew God first led him to question whether the entire Bible had come directly from God Himself. God helped him to recognize that the only books in it that had been written by men who had actually walked with Jesus Christ and known Him were the four Gospel books written by Matthew, Mark, Luke, and John, so it was only those four Gospel books that could, without a doubt, have been directly inspired by the Son of God. Soon God helped Peter deduce that if only the four Gospels had been directly inspired by the Son of God, then therefore, only these four Gospels could be acknowledged with certainty to be the absolute and true word of God.

47   Not much is known about Peter of Bruys's early life, other than that he may have been born at Bruis in southeast France, so his early life as described here is conjecture.

Peter knew it was God who led him to question the validity of the rest of the New Testament as well as the Old. Peter came to recognize that all the other New Testament writings and epistles, and the entire Old Testament, as well as all the vast collections of expository patristic writings of the venerable church fathers, were merely the writings of mortal men. Mortal men like himself. And if all those writings were nothing but the works of mere mortal men—fallible men, fallible men like himself—and if they had not been directly inspired by Jesus Christ himself, how could anyone know whether they were directly inspired by God? Peter feared they were not the true word of God!

Within a year or two of his being ordained, God led him to conclude that it was only the four Gospels that should be accepted literally, without question. Only the four Gospels were certain to reveal the true doctrine. If the Old Testament and the rest of the New Testament as well as all the patristic writings were not the true word of God, they could not be accepted literally and without question. Eventually Peter came to recognize that these other writings should instead be rejected! He believed God was commanding him to reject them!

Once God had shown Peter that only the four Gospels were certain to reveal God's truth and thus have true doctrinal authority, Peter came to recognize that many of the rites and rituals of the Church were not derived directly from the four Gospels. Church rites, such as infant baptism, the Veneration of the Cross, and the mystery of the Eucharist went beyond what was written in the four Gospels, and did not literally follow the writings of the four Gospels. Even the sacred Mass itself, as performed in front of the altar within a church structure, did not take place in the Gospels. None of these rites and rituals as performed by the priests took place in the Gospels; none derived directly and literally from what was described in the four Gospels. So Peter concluded these rites and rituals did not come directly from God. He finally understood that God had shown him that these rites and rituals were only fabrications of men, of mortal, fallible men. They were useless. They were false. They were wrong! Peter believed God was commanding him to reject them! They were anathema!

Using Peter's own life circumstances, God had also shown Peter how terribly awry the entire social order had gone. Some prospered, while most others lived continually on the brink of starvation and death. The wealthy, the feudal lords, the urban merchant class, even most members of the Church all prospered, while everyone else, the urban poor, the rural masses, including Peter's own birth family, lived in total, abject poverty. How could God want this? Peter believed that God could not want this. God *must* not want it! Otherwise, why would God have rescued him from destitution and death, rescued him through the hand of his simple-minded and beloved yet poor parish priest?

Peter saw that the Church itself held tremendous wealth and power and that most of the clergy belonging to it came from the prosperous wealthy class. The Church built magnificent huge monuments for its rituals, draped itself in beautiful adornments, indulged itself with lavish golden and silver implements for its rituals. The Church prospered while the poor masses starved. Peter concluded this must be wrong! God must want the Church to return to the poverty and simplicity of its beginnings—its beginnings at the time of the apostles in the four Gospels. God must want the clergy to return to the poverty of the apostles!

As his doubts emerged and began to grow, Peter had tried at first to discuss his convictions with his fellow priests and with his bishop, but they refused to listen and simply told him to keep quiet about it all. His doubts continued to grow, becoming ever stronger until he eventually began preaching his views. As his views became more and more radical and unorthodox, ever more unacceptable to the clergy, he was first scolded, and then reprimanded and disciplined by the bishop.

Finally, he became too outspoken, too radical, too unorthodox for his bishop and for his church. Traditional punishments had proved ineffective at keeping him quiet, so finally he was removed from his parish. He was deprived of his charge. He was removed from his calling. He was defrocked. He was no longer an ordained priest.

As Peter now walked slowly toward Saint-Gilles, he thought about the events that had brought him to where he was today: embittered, branded as a heretic by the Church. He knew he could never have simply kept quiet about his doubts. It was God Himself who had revealed to him how misguided the Church had become. It was God Himself who had shown him that many of its rites and rituals were anathema. Yet he, Peter of Bruys, had been branded a heretic, that most vile of sinners. He had been defrocked, forbidden to minister to his faithful, forbidden to administer those rites which he did believe to be true, such as baptism for those old enough to make the personal decision to become Christian. He had been deprived of his charge—all because he had been trying to proclaim God's true message, what God Himself had revealed to him as truth!

No, he could never have kept quiet, and so had begun his mission. Almost two decades ago he had begun preaching his "heretical" views, starting in the local dioceses of Embrun, Die, and Gap, and then spreading out more widely. By now he knew he had gained many, many believers, many followers, throughout the counties of Provence, Toulouse, and Gascony, but especially in the towns of Narbonne and Toulouse.

But the task God had set before him seemed never-ending. The message God had given him to proclaim was still deemed "heretical" by the Church. He was despised by his fellow clerics, even by his beloved simple-minded mentor.

"I have worked so hard to preach what You have revealed as truth to me, dear God," Peter cried aloud but softly and rather dejectedly. "Dear God, Father, I know You want Your Church to be cleansed of its corruption. You want the Church to rid itself of its misguided rites and rituals. You want the clergy to be cleansed of its vices. It is You who wants this.

"So many have heard me preach Your true message. But no matter how many hear Your message, no matter how much headway I gain in spreading Your truth, the Church seems to become ever stronger and more powerful and more corrupt.

"Do You perhaps want me now to turn my mission over to another—to someone else, perhaps to Henry of Lausanne—to someone who can more effectively spread Your word?" he asked quietly. "Is it time to do so? Please, dear God, if so, give me a sign if that is Your will. But if not, please give me the strength and wisdom today to speak Your truth once again, to bring Your message to those gathering at Saint-Gilles," he ended his prayer.

Recognizing in the distance the town of Saint-Gilles, Peter found a small copse of cypress trees. Remarking to himself that cypress trees are associated with death and mourning, he rebuked himself for submitting to such dark, ill humors. But then he stepped off the path and entered into the small copse where he knelt in prayer, asking for God's blessing and asking for divine guidance. Finally he began to prepare himself, to organize his thoughts, because he knew he must once again, as always, give a stirring presentation if he was going to win more converts to God's real truth.

*   *   *

For young Canon Pons who was approaching from the other direction, the journey had seemed to take forever, but after quite some time, he finally approached the town, and his pace quickened further. His journey had been solitary so far, except for the unnerving old hag with her two young ones, but he now began encountering other travelers, first a few, then a few more.

Pons soon joined several more people who were on their way to hear the heretic, and following them, he walked along the ramparts of the town, entering at a portal where they joined a small group of people who were gathering there. Moving eastward with them along the street, he could see one castle fortress fairly nearby, and another at the far other side of town. Soon he was at the center of the town, standing at the ghastly maw of a construction site that marked where the new basilica was now, once again, under way, to be built for the abbey of Saint-Gilles.

It was because the lucrative abbey drew so many visitors that the bishops of Nîmes had long tried to claim it for their own diocese. Nevertheless, the abbey and its monks had long suffered miserably. In fact, for many decades the abbey had struggled with difficulties arising from its troubled relationships not only with the local counts of the house of Toulouse, but also with the Order of Cluny and the papacy, all of which claimed special rights over the abbey.[48] Saint-Gilles had been made a possession of the Order of Cluny in 1066 by Raymond of Saint-Gilles, who was then Count of Toulouse, but the count had also kept some rights to the abbey for himself. At the same time, it was also still deemed to be a papal possession as well, and this gave the abbey some special privileges and independence. So when Pope Gregory tried to force the monks to accept an outsider from Cluny as their abbot, to head the abbey, the monks resisted and openly opposed governance by Cluny.

Meanwhile, the local counts continued to exercise what they believed were their own rights, tyrannizing the town and abusing the abbey as if it

---

48   On the abbey's troubled relationships with Cluny, the papacy, and the local counts, see Amy G. Remensnyder, *Remembering Kings Past: Monastic Foundation Legends in Medieval Southern France.* (Ithaca: Cornell University Press, 1995), 236–239. See also Stoddard, *Façade,* 128ff and especially 157ff, for a summary of the history of predation by the local counts. See also M. l'Abbé Goiffon, *Bullaire de l'Abbaye de Saint-Gilles* (Nîmes: P. Jouve, 1882) for the papal bulls and papal communications about the abbey in this period.

was their own personal property. In 1105 Count Bernard took the abbey for himself and fortified it while plundering it for his own gain. In 1117 Viscount Bertrand again took the abbey for himself and built his own castle up against it, after expelling the abbot. In 1121 Bertrand's brother, Alphonse Jourdain, Count of Toulouse, again exerted proprietary rights, took over the town, built another castle, and plundered the abbey, but he also imprisoned the Cluniac abbot and shipped him back to Cluny, thereby enabling the monks finally to elect their own non-Cluniac abbot.

In 1125 the new pope, Honorius, restored the abbey of Saint-Gilles to the powerful and wealthy Order of Cluny for reform, at the request of Peter the Venerable, but the monks hardened in their resistance and continued to refuse to submit to governance by Cluny. By 1132 the issue of their obedience to Cluny was taken to Pope Innocent II, who decided in favor of Saint-Gilles: the abbey would retain its "special privileges" and "ancient liberty" as a papal possession and free abbey, so all future abbots could be elected from within the abbey. Only if an outsider was elected abbot must that individual come from Cluny, so Cluny would have only limited influence over the abbey.

Pons knew only a little of this history of turmoil, but he also recognized the result of this new clarification of their rights: the monks and abbey were now finally beginning at last to pull themselves together and focus on rebuilding their church, after having floundered for decades. Although Pope Urban II had first consecrated the altar of a new basilica in 1096, it was not until 1116 that Abbot Hugh was able to begin work again, starting with the crypt, and even now, almost two decades later, only parts of the crypt had been vaulted. It was only two or three years ago that the abbey's relationship to Cluny had finally been satisfactorily resolved, and progress on the rebuilding could really begin again.

The construction site was a frightening, huge, ghastly mess. Gigantic piles of stones and timber were piled somewhat haphazardly around the cavernous maw in the earth that opened into the crypt. Pons saw that Peter of Bruys had not yet arrived, and he realized that if he were quick about it, he probably had time to satisfy his curiosity and find the inscription he wanted to see to confirm some of what he had learned about the history. Carefully slipping away from the gathering crowd, he picked his way through piles of stone and rubble and climbed onto the west wall of the crypt, toward the south end. The crypt was open here, but the west wall of the crypt was completed, as was the crypt projection that would one day hold the central portal above it.

Lowering himself carefully from the wall onto the wooden scaffolding that the workmen had left, he slipped, badly scraping his shin, but was thankfully able to jump onto some rubble, stopping his fall. He was a bit shaken because he was a fairly agile young man and usually was not so clumsy, but he now gave out a hearty loud chuckle. He not only knew some of the troubled history of the basilica, but he had also read the *Liber Miraculorum*,[49] written just over a decade ago by the librarian of Saint-Gilles, who had dedicated the book to Abbot Hugh. The *Liber Miraculorum* described the demolition of the earlier church to make way for Abbot Hugh's new one, and it gave several accounts of the miraculous intercessions of the blessed St. Gilles himself, who had saved several men who had fallen from these same walls.

"I wonder if St. Gilles had a hand in stopping my fall today, as well," Pons thought with a chuckle.

Dusting himself off, he realized his shin was bleeding, but after spitting on it to clean off the dirt, he could easily see the injury was really only a minor scrape. Continuing his quest, he worked his way along the exterior of the crypt wall. He found several epitaphs of monks at the abbey who had died during the period the west wall was being constructed and who had been laid to rest with their epitaphs carved into the west wall: Brother Frotardus,

+HICIACETFROTA RDVS QVI OBIIT ...

(Here lies Frotardus who died ...)

Saint-Gilles. Exterior west wall of abbey crypt. Epitaph of Frotardus.

and a little further south, Brother Hubilotus,

....

49   For the *Liber Miraculorum*, see Stoddard, *Façade*, 132.

+HIC IACET HVBI
LOTVS QVI Ob ...

(Here lies Hubilotus
who died ...)

Saint-Gilles. Exterior west wall of abbey crypt. Epitaph of Hubilotus.

and then on the projecting south face of the wall, Brother Petrus de Brozet.

+ HICIACET
PETR'DBROZET

(Here lies Petrus
De Brozet)

Saint-Gilles. Exterior south wall of abbey crypt. Epitaph of Petrus de Brozet.

Pons continued his quest, working his way along the exterior south flank of the crypt, and near the bottom of a wall buttress not far from the west end, he found it. There it was. The dated inscription documenting Abbot Hugh's beginning the construction of the new basilica two decades ago in 1116.

ANNO DOMINI M° C° XVI° HOC SEPULTVM
EGIDII AEDIFICARI CEPIT ...

(In the year of Our Lord 1116 was begun the
construction of this crypt ...)

Saint-Gilles. Abbey church. Dedication inscription of 1116.

It was there, just as his good friend Canon Jordan had told him it would be.

Pons now listened carefully for a just moment, noting with relief that he could hear no rise in the commotion of the people gathering near the construction site. Apparently, Peter of Bruys was not yet approaching, so Pons would undoubtedly have a bit of time. He knew he would hear no bells to mark the hours because it was Good Friday, but it did seem to be midday, so he decided to quietly celebrate the short office of *Sext* alone here.

But as he was singing quietly, his eyes kept focusing involuntarily on the inscription. He forced himself first to complete the office before leaping to the stone wall.

"What on earth are these?" he asked himself as he fingered the carving. "What is this? What's going on . . . ? What are these little circles above the Roman numerals?"

Standing back a bit, he carefully read out the Latin inscription, *"ANNO DOMINI M° C° XVI° HOC SEPULTUM EGIDI AEDIIFICARI CEPIT . . .*

"I'm absolutely certain I know all the little abbreviations we use in our medieval Latin epigraphy,"[50] he said to himself. But what are these little circles above the Roman numerals and only above the numerals? They are like little Os, and only above the Roman numerals. Very, very strange . . . Wait a minute! Oh. Oh! I wonder . . ." he suddenly gasped aloud, with a flash of imperfect, vague recognition.

....

50   Such practices include putting horizontal lines above letters to indicate omitted letters, often UM or ORUM, and using standard abbreviations such as DNI with a horizontal line above it to indicate DOMINI, or writing a fancy Q with an I inside to indicate QVI, etc.

"Could these little circles be the letter Os that Arabs use somehow with their numbers?" he wondered. "But what would they mean? Could they perhaps, somehow, make these Roman letters into the new numbering system I have heard about that the Arabs use? How very curious . . ."

Years earlier, during his childhood expeditions to the Roman arena at Arles, several of the more learned pilgrims returning from Arab-held lands in Iberia had begun telling him about a new numbering system that the Arabs use. They didn't really understand the Arab number system, but they were certain it used an O somehow to mean something.

"Maybe the stone carver here, or whoever commissioned the stone carver, knew how to write numbers in the new Arab way? I wonder . . ."

A cold shiver went down his spine, as he remembered the old hag telling him that what she foresaw for him was twin numerals that for him meant L and V years. He quickly shook off his foreboding, however, and continued inspecting the inscription.

"Maybe someday I will learn about this Arabic number system," Pons vowed to himself.

His inspection of the inscriptions was then rudely cut short, interrupted by some loud shouting from the raucous crowd now gathering out in the open courtyard in front of the abbey construction. Moving quickly, Pons returned to the scaffolding and climbed—more carefully this time—out of the crypt's cavernous hole and onto the firm ground above. Easily dodging the small, controlled fire that was kept lit for use in the construction, he pulled his hood over his head to be able to blend in with the crowd more easily, and quickly slipped through several dozen onlookers to approach the center of the group, which was already rather large.

The loud shouting must have been for something else because Peter of Bruys still had not appeared. The crowd continued growing ever larger and was becoming rather unruly. After some time, Pons noticed that an attractive young woman had pushed near him, moving discretely up toward him, and was now standing next to him. She was dressed quite respectably yet rather modestly in a long, light gray woolen mantle, fastened in the front near her throat with an unexpectedly large silver brooch to loosely cover a long, plain bliaud and had covered her head with a headdress of a long veil fastened to a simple metal circlet. For her part, she was very surreptitiously sizing him up, seeing a strong, physically attractive young man, dressed as if making a religious pilgrimage, and judging him to be respectable and probably trustworthy.

Recognizing her to be a proper young woman, probably of the prosperous merchant class, Pons was surprised and rather taken aback when she addressed him.

"Please, sir, do not think me improper or forward, but may I stand here next to you?" she said. "I am from this town, and I came out today so I could later attend the mid-afternoon Good Friday service at *Nones*—you know, the Veneration of the Cross.

"But I just learned that this crowd has gathered here to hear a new prophet named Peter, who is coming here to speak. I do so want to hear what the new prophet has to say, but I am becoming a bit uneasy and rather nervous about the crowd, even somewhat frightened. Everyone appears so excited and anxious. And I see you are wearing a cross yet carrying a traveler's pouch with the pilgrim's scallop shell. Are you on a pilgrimage to Santiago de Compostela?"

"Mistress," responded Pons politely but rather coolly, "you are most welcome to stand near me for safety while listening to the heretic, Peter of Bruys, if it would make you more comfortable to do so. But I am not a pilgrim on his way to Santiago; I am a priest. I have taken solemn vows as a canon at the cathedral church at Arles.

"I must caution you that Peter of Bruys is branded a vile heretic! I, too, want to hear Peter of Bruys speak, but only to help me combat his teachings. As good Christians, our chapter and the Archbishop at Arles know that Peter's views are heresy, pure heresy, but I want to hear what he is saying and to understand the heresy to be able to combat it. I beg you to remember that whatever Peter of Bruys says is heresy."

Before the young woman could respond, this private conversation was effectively cut off with the arrival of a small group of men, some of whom seemed known to others in the gathered crowd, who called out, "There he is! There he is!" Peter of Bruys and four of his followers approached the edge of the crowd, where Peter mounted a pile of stone blocks, apparently intending to address the gathered crowd that now began to quiet down so as to be able to hear this new prophet.

Peter waited in silence for several minutes with his hands raised to heaven, as if summoning truth from above, and as he waited, the crowd began nervously fidgeting and anxiously looking around. Peter finally began.[51]

"You faithful gather here on this ground because this is where a huge new abbey church is being built, built on the blood and sweat of good Christian men," Peter began calmly, slowly, but with a slightly raised voice, turning briefly to point toward the construction. "But the true Church knows nothing of such stones and walls. The true Church does not consist of stones and walls. The early apostles knew that it is not beautiful walls and buildings that make a 'church.' The apostles knew that the true Church is the community of the faithful who gather together to pray to God. The true Church consists of you and me," he continued, first gesturing widely to the crowd, then folding his arms on his chest, "the community of the faithful, who gather together to pray, who believe. I call on you to follow in the footsteps of the early apostles, to follow their example."

Peter had immediately gained the crowd's full attention, and they now were listening, having quieted down. Peter was preaching in earnest, preaching to the crowd what he believed, what he knew to be true, what God had revealed to him. He was a good speaker, a fairly effective orator, and he paused for a moment before continuing in a lower voice, now that he had their attention.

"What I say to you is what the early apostles believed and lived, what the apostles who knew our Lord and Savior believed. The true Church does not consist of glorious buildings, nor of rich golden and silver altars. The true Church does not need such riches. It does not need such structures. It does not need such buildings.

"Did the early apostles have glorious church buildings? No!" he continued, slowly shaking his head. "We do not need a special holy place to pray. The apostles did not have a special holy place to pray. We may pray to God as effectively in a barn as in a special church building. We may pray to God as effectively in a stable as in a special church building. A stable! Was our Lord Jesus Christ not born in a stable? Did the Magi not worship Him in a stable? We, too, may worship Him in a stable. We do not need special church buildings. Church buildings are useless.

....

51   We cannot know for certain what Peter of Bruys said when preaching, but we do know
      the main tenets of his heresies from Peter the Venerable's treatise, *Contra Petrobrusianos*.

"Did the early apostles have special consecrated altars of gold and silver?" he asked, again slowly shaking his head. "No! We should do as the apostles did. We may commune with God in a stable as well as before an altar. We will be heard by God in a lowly stable just as surely as if we were standing before a golden and silver altar. Consecrated altars are useless.

"Our Lord God hears us in a barn; our Lord God hears us in a stable. We do not need church buildings like this," he insisted, again turning and gesturing toward the construction. "Buildings like this are unnecessary. They are erected solely for the glory of the clergy."

The crowd now began whispering softly to each other while shifting quietly in contemplation, and Peter, sensing their attention, raised his voice. This man of conviction would earnestly tell the crowd what he knew in his soul to be absolutely true.

"The true Church does not need the chants and ceremonies of the clergy," he continued. "Let the monks and priests sing their songs in a tavern if they must. Let the monks and priests sing their songs in a field if they must. God is worshiped with the heart, not with special music and chants.

"Why is this new building being built? Why are these altars, these walls, these buildings being built? Who are these altars, these walls, these buildings being built for? These altars, these walls, these buildings are not needed for us to worship God! The early apostles did not need altars such as these, or walls such as these, or buildings like these to worship God. God does not want these altars, these walls, these buildings!

"These altars, these walls, these buildings are not built for God! These altars, these walls, and these buildings are being built for the clergy, for the priests, for the monks here!" he declared. "For the benefit of the monks! For the benefit of the clergy! For the glory of the monks and clergy! For the glory of the greedy, wealthy clergy!"

Now beginning to move and shift more nervously around, the crowd continued murmuring, now a bit more noisily, a few barely nodding their heads in agreement, many shaking their heads ever so slightly. Peter raised his voice further to thunder out over them.

"These walls, this building is an abomination to God!" he stridently proclaimed, thrusting his arms out as if in disgust. "Church buildings like this one should be destroyed, not built. Those who are building it should be stopped! We who are gathered together here are the true Church, and we condemn this structure. We, the true Church, condemn this monument! We condemn this damnable structure!"

The crowd now began simmering much more noisily, becoming a bit more boisterous as everyone seemed to begin speaking softly with someone, perhaps his or her neighbor. Everyone was now talking, some to themselves, some speaking as if to Peter. Some men and women were nodding their heads as if in partial agreement, as if understanding the thrust of Peter's argument, while some were shaking their heads as if in disbelief or more vigorously in outright objection.

"God will condemn you for saying this," shouted out one cowled and rather stout man, apparently one of the local monks. Others in the crowd then shouted or nodded their agreement. "Yes, yes, He will condemn you!"

"Please, just let him speak," pleaded one of Peter's followers.

Three cowled monks from the abbey now pushed aggressively forward and jumped onto the stone blocks, trying to wrest the crowd's attention away from Peter, but two of the speaker's followers also jumped up and flanked him, acting as sturdy buttresses against any interference with him. The crowd grew ever more restless, each one pushing forward, trying to better see what would happen.

Peter continued in a thundering voice, shouting to be heard above the general din now arising from the crowd.

"And what would the clerics do for you to save your soul in these church buildings? What would they do for you? They would baptize you, the faithful—but for a price! Ah, yes, only for a price. They would baptize anyone for a price! They would baptize you at any age—even babies, infants. Infants, who cannot reason, who are incapable of rational thought, who are incapable of believing in God, who are incapable of truly understanding or believing in anything.

"Yes, the Gospels tell us that a person must be baptized to hope for salvation, as Jesus Christ, Himself, as an adult, was baptized in the Jordan River by John the Baptist. But for baptism to bring salvation, the person must believe, must have personal faith! How can an infant, who has no reason, who has no faculty for believing, have any personal faith in Jesus Christ?" he asked, raising his hands and shoulders in a questioning gesture. "And if an infant does not have personal faith in Jesus Christ, how can pouring some water over its head bring salvation? Baptism of infants is worthless!"

"Baptism can bring hope of salvation only to those who are old enough to understand, to reason, to believe, and who then accept and have faith in Jesus Christ! Baptism of infants has no value—except to the priest who collects your payment before he splashes the holy water! Baptism of infants has no value at all—except to pay for the priest's dinner! Baptism of infants is worthless!" he shouted.

Driven and now desperate to convince more followers of his own convictions, Peter now began ranting at the crowd, screaming what he knew to be true and what he knew to be false, because God had revealed the truths and falsehoods to him.

"Baptism of infants is useless!" he screamed again.

"You should burn in hell!" cried out one of the cowled monks.

Audible collective gasps punctuating full cries now burst forth from some in the crowd. Some men and women began shaking their heads, and then a few began vigorously shaking their hands and arms at Peter. Two young men leaped onto the stone pile, attempting to grab Peter, but they were rebuffed by his followers, and in the ensuing scuffle fell backward onto the ground. As one of the monks lunged to grab Peter by the shoulder, Peter fell momentarily but managed to jump onto another stone higher in the pile, barely escaping the attack with only a bloodied forearm and the loss of his cloak, as the monk fell forward onto several members of the crowd, who shouted derisively.

A man of conviction, Peter persevered, continuing on unabatedly, earnestly trying to save souls by stirring up doubt and repugnance for the teachings he knew to be false. His face now became strangely calm as he pointed dramatically toward the crypt of the church under construction, and thundered, "Those same priests would celebrate Mass at the altar in the crypt there, and they would tell you they will give you Eucharist, the flesh and blood of Christ, that will save your souls.

"Our Lord Jesus Christ gave His flesh and blood but once to his disciples, by dying on the cross. Priests now try to tell you they can repeat this with the Eucharist. Priests tell you that they can change bread and wine into Christ's body and blood, that the bread and wine of Eucharist are His body and blood.

"Hah! Are priests magicians? Are they wizards? Can they change bread into flesh or wine into blood? Can they perform Satan's evil magic? Or are they just tricksters?

"What the priests offer in the Mass is bread and wine. Bread and wine in remembrance of our Lord's Last Supper. Bread and wine in remembrance of our Lord. But only bread and wine! Nothing but bread and wine! The bread they give is nothing but unleavened bread! The wine nothing but wine!

"Priests and monks cannot repeat what Christ did but once. Christ's body and blood are remembered through the Eucharist; they are not present in the Eucharist. How can a priest or monk change the bread and wine into Jesus Christ's flesh and blood? They cannot do it! Their ceremonies and chants cannot do it! They are charlatans! They are deceivers!

"I denounce their chants! I denounce the charlatans! I denounce their ceremonies! These trickster ceremonies did not come from Christ Himself. The Eucharist bread is nothing but bread! The Eucharist wine is nothing but wine!"

Pons gasped at Peter's words. Many in the crowd were now vehemently shaking their heads, stunned at these words, thunderstruck at the fierce intensity of Peter's denial and denigration of that most holy Christian sacrament.

"May you burn in hellfire," screamed one of the cowled monks again, "and we will gladly send you there!"

Three men jumped up after Peter, but he leaped quickly away, crossing along the stone pile to reach a carpenter's cache where one of his followers waited and pulled up a large wooden crucifix that had been laid there.

Grabbing the cross, Peter screamed out, "And finally, this! This! The cross that the clergy would put at the altar. The cross that some of you came here today to venerate. This instrument of Christ's death that the clergy would have you venerate. Venerate on the day of His death! Venerate! Kiss and pray to!

"This is what killed our Lord! Would you kiss and pray to what killed our Lord? The cross is no more worthy of veneration than a scabbard or sword or knife. It is an instrument of death! It is an abomination! An instrument of death! It is the unholy instrument of our Lord's death!

"The clergy would have you kiss and pray to the shameful instrument that killed our Lord! Kiss and pray to this instrument of death! We abhor this unholy instrument of death. We abhor this cross! We abhor this abomination!"

Pulling the cross to the nearby ongoing fire at the corner of the construction site, Peter thundered, "The cross should be destroyed—not venerated. It should be destroyed! All crosses should be destroyed! All crosses should be broken up and burnt! I condemn these unholy crosses! I call upon you to cut down the crosses in this foolish, shameful building and cast them into the fire. Burn them to erase the shameful memory of Christ's crucifixion!"

Pushing the cross into the fire, he shrieked, "I will destroy this cross just as I will destroy this church building!"

Erupting with rage, leaders in the crowd now burst forth in fury, shouting with uncontrollable anger. Until now they had been heating up but confused, thunderstruck at the fierce intensity of Peter's attack on those things held most sacred, but they had been paralyzed, in shock, just as Pons had been rendered speechless.

But the anger and fury of the riled crowd now boiled over. Peter was maligning and blaspheming those mysteries and institutions that the Church had revealed to them as truth, that they had been taught were truth. Things they knew were truth. Truths that the true Church had taught them, that the priests and clerics defended.

"You will burn in eternal flames," screamed a cowled young man, "and we will put you there! Now! Now! Get him!"

Following the lead of three cowled young men, the crowd immediately surged forward, swelling up into a raging throng, transformed into a murderous mob. Pushing violently forward, it trampled whoever was stationary and in its way. Pons, though a sturdy young man, was brutally jostled, then pushed aside as if he were nothing and thrust tight up against several others where he was locked tight, unable to move.

Seizing Peter, the mob wrenched the flaming wooden cross from his hands and then grabbed his arms, then his legs, twisting and pulling them as if he were a condemned man and they were the rack, pulling his vile arms and legs. They cried for blood—Peter's blood.

"Seize him! Kill him! Kill him!!"

Several older men, led by two of the cowled men and following their example, had already thrown more dry wood on the small fire, as if they somehow had foreseen or planned its purpose. Several swarthy young men now grabbed more wood from the construction site and skillfully heaved it onto the fire, stoking it even further. The fire blazed up, now a horrific bonfire, with huge ravenous tongues of flame licking through the air.

Heaving Peter into the fire, the crowd now screamed with furious hatred, with venom, yelling profanities, screeching shrill warnings of eternal damnation. Three swarthy young men pushed up the end of one burning crossbeam to overturn the flaming cross on top of Peter, pinning him with it, imprisoning him, locking his body in the heart of the bonfire.

"We'll send you straight to hell now, you damned heretic!" one yelled.

Peter now writhed in agony, screaming as the fingers of fire quickly began destroying his clothing and hair, sizzling and hissing as it leaped from his hair to his tunic. Peter screeched in horror as it started charring his skin.

"Burn to death on your own damned cross!" shrieked a young man in the crowd.

The mob's faces were ablaze with anger as the people shouted profanities and violently waved their arms. In the hellish cacophony, little could be singled out and comprehended, except for the executioners condemning the burning figure.

"Go to hell, you God-damned heathen! You wanted to destroy the sacred cross. Well, burn under it! Burn under the cross! Go to hell under the cross! Burn in hellfire forever!"

The stench of burning flesh and hair began searing through everyone's nostrils, ripping at their throats, but no one turned away from the spectacle. Near the fire, an old woman's shrill, high voice could now be made out, screeching, "Serves you right, you heathen bastard! Telling us not to have our babies baptized . . . You would send our babies to hell! Our precious little babies. Now it is you who goes to the flames of hell!"

As the crowd now eagerly watched the spectacle, they covered their noses and mouths against the not unfamiliar yet horribly acrid smell of burning hair and flesh that pierced their throats, so the thunderous cacophony began dying down a bit, and more individual cries could now be heard.

"Who needs the holy sacrament now?" roared one man with a cackle.

"Who needs some holy water now?" chuckled another. "Look at him. Ho! Who needs holy water now?"

Several young boys near the front began laughing.

"Hah, hah! Look! Look! He's peed and shat all over his pants, and the pants are still burning! Peed and shat himself! Peed and shat! Peed and shat! Peed and shat!" they chanted.

Captivated by the horror unfolding before them, no one could turn away. For some, the spectacle was exciting action entertainment. For others, it offered a vicarious thrill. Torture as entertainment. Torture as a thrill. Some seemed not to believe this was really happening. Some seemed to find it satisfying, viciously satisfying. The satisfaction of inflicting pain on something you hate. The pleasure of hurting what you cannot understand, what you cannot accept . . . What you do not want to accept. Torture as vindictiveness. Torture as pure nastiness. Torture as pleasure.

From one of the very young boys clinging to his father while laughing, "Look, look! Hah, hah! Now his prick is on fire! Now his prick is on fire!"

From his father standing next to him, with a chuckle, "Yeah, that's good roasted heretic cock."

From another, "We'll see who's in hellfire now."

Uncontrollable now, the mob surged ever forward, each pressing to see the burning flesh, each spewing forth his own venom. Even as a few in the crowd began recoiling from the horror before them, the horror they had wrought, they could not avert their eyes, could not turn away, did not want to look away, but instead pressed forward to witness fully the horrific yet spellbinding event, mesmerized by the sight of the charring flesh, hypnotized by the sight of another man's pure pain, thrilled by the sight of a blasphemer being punished. They watched it all, seduced by the self-righteous satisfaction of seeing a condemned man, a heretic, a devil, suffering excruciating pain, burning slowly and painfully to death.

As Peter howled in agony, the putrid smell of burning flesh seared through any coverings of nostrils, fouling mouths, choking throats. Fetid, sick smoke was everywhere, burning eyes, seizing stomachs. Yet no one turned away, even as the smoke could not hide the clear image of the painful agony of a heretic being roasted to death, a man being punished by burning to death in excruciating pain. A man being put to death by a mob.

Overcome with nausea, Pons doubled up and vomited, again and again and again. But having eaten little that day, what came up was mostly soured water. Pons was reeling, sickened, not so much by the stench as by the murderousness of the crowd, not by the putrid stench of burning human flesh but by the uncontrolled violence and venomous hatred.

What had he expected here? Certainly not this. But what?

Lauds

Dawn—bells at daybreak

Anno Domini MCXXXV

1135

Still in the town of Saint-Gilles

Pons was beside himself, overcome with horror and revulsion. He could not think. Everything he knew, everything he believed seemed to be burning in his head, searing through his heart, and the acrid but horribly familiar smell of burning flesh only exacerbated the overwhelming feeling of rottenness and wanton destruction.

Though young and strong, he was being crushed by the violent crowd trying to get a closer view of the horror. Turning violently away to brace himself against the onslaught, he knocked directly into a young woman, the same woman who had sought comfort and safety next to him.

"Oh, oh . . . Ugh." Without thinking, he grabbed her roughly by her shoulders and held her as he braced himself against the physical thrust of the mob.

At a brief lull in the onslaught, and again without thinking, he pivoted around, this time grabbing her wrists roughly with one hand, and pulled her indelicately yet protectively behind him through the screaming crowd toward the corner of the yard. There he pinned her against a building, covering her with his own body to protect both her and himself from the violence.

Doubling over suddenly, he heaved again and again, but there was no more soured water left to come up. He straightened up. He was now angry—very, very angry. He felt betrayed somehow. His loins throbbed with a need to fight. He didn't know who or what to fight. As the yellow bile surged from his spleen, coursing through him, overwhelming any equilibrium he had maintained, his young body pulsed with anger and rage.

He looked again at the young woman and saw she was now crying, sobbing uncontrollably. Then she, too, doubled over, vomiting. Standing up, she began wildly flailing her arms. She, too, was distraught, beside herself. He pinned her arms more securely and held her tight. They were both now shaking uncontrollably. Neither of them seemed able to breathe. Shaking, they still held each other closely as their hearts pounded thunderously, almost in unison. When Pons finally loosened his grip, the young woman reached up and pulled him close to her. They continued holding each other tightly, simply as an escape from the obscene horror surrounding them.

Stench. Putrid burning human flesh. Burning excrement. Burnt bowels. Sour vomit. Screaming. Cries of anguish. Crying. But what was ever so much worse was the hideous laughter, piercing jeers, murderous curses, righteous rage, brutal cruelty, enjoyment of inflicting pain, excruciating pain, foul condemnations . . . This was hell.

Some time passed, and the mob finally began to lose interest and to disperse. Although surrounded by stench and chaos, cruelty and brutality, the young pair had found an escape together and now seemed enclosed in a protected space, in a protective cocoon spun by their bodies clinging to each other. As the horror began receding, Pons finally realized he was still holding the young woman. She had been shaking uncontrollably from what she had witnessed, but the shaking now slowly subsided, to be replaced by gentle sobbing. He lifted the woman's face to look at her. He saw she was probably almost his own age, or maybe a bit younger. She was beautiful, very beautiful. He wanted at that moment to protect her. Without understanding his gesture, with no intent whatsoever, without knowing why, he naïvely kissed her gently, protectively, on the forehead.

She continued sobbing quietly as they stood together a while longer, but finally took several deep breaths to regain her composure. She looked long and deeply into his eyes. Then, quietly taking his hand in hers, without a word, she now pulled him and led him into a lane leading away from the abbey, and he followed, again without a word. After several turns in what seemed to be a maze—left, right, right, left—she opened a door and entered, quickly pulling him in. They entered a small room, crowded with a small table with a candle, two rude chairs, a pallet for sleeping, a chamber pot, and two small wooden chests, one of which was heaping with bits of fabric, threads and yarn. There was a fireplace and chimney in the corner, an iron pot, a small bucket of water, and a small window that could be opened for air.

Still without a word, she turned to face him, gently taking his hands in hers and holding them for several moments while carefully studying his face, as if arriving at a decision. Releasing his hands, she then slowly removed the circlet from her head, placed it carefully on the table, and then, even more slowly, she removed her head veil, turning momentarily to hang it on a wooden peg on the wall. She then pulled Pons's hands to her head as she gently shook her head, freeing her hair, allowing it to fall, loosely, softly, lusciously—oh, so lusciously and oh, so temptingly—onto his fingers. With this touch of her hair, he lost his will to resist and began running his fingers through the luscious locks.

He and this lovely creature had fled the horror together. They had escaped the reality that was hell and found this relief, this moment of respite. Together they had fled what was evil. Together they . . . Again, without understanding why, he kissed her once more, this time on the cheek.

"Ah . . . Such luscious hair!" he thought. "I have never before touched such like this. And such soft skin! So beguiling. To touch it . . . ! Oh, how lovely it feels!"

He kissed her again on the cheek, this time less innocently, and found he could not remove his lips, which ventured along her cheek to her ear. She gasped slightly. She now undid her brooch, removed her cloak, then deftly removed his cape. Still without a word, they quickly unlaced their sandals, then each pulled off their bliauds. When she removed her long linen chainse, Pons began hesitantly touching her body, wordlessly moving his naïve and inexperienced hands along the curve of her hips to explore the mysterious hollow of her waist. Then he quickly moved his hands to her head again, to run his fingers through her hair—her magnificent, luscious hair that now seemed less forbidden and fell so temptingly.

"I should not do this. Oh, I know I should not do this," he whispered desperately to himself. "But oh! Yes! It is so good . . . So right . . . So . . ."

And then he stopped thinking.

Still standing, she pushed his short chainse off over his head, running her open hands slowly over his chest, then lightly kissing his breastbone, before pushing his braies down his legs. In response, he gently kissed her eyes, her neck. He kissed her mouth, at first gently touching her lips with his own, then eagerly, hungrily exploring hers.

Very hesitantly, he bent down to kiss each of her breasts, first barely touching them, then gently caressing them, but he soon found himself eagerly exploring them, then massaging, gently kneading the exquisitely soft and tender white flesh. His hand moved slowly down her taut belly toward her blessed mound, venturing to touch it only briefly. His own member had long been ready, erect, straining hard for release, and by now commanding his every action.

Now grabbing and cradling her buttocks, he instinctively pulled her to him to mount her, but she recoiled, becoming first hesitant, then seemingly fearful, agitated, and unresponsive. Shaking her head, she jerkily pushed him away. She began to cry, to sob, ever so softly. He was taken aback, at first confused, then truly embarrassed.

"I'm sorry. I am truly sorry. I didn't know what I was doing. I really didn't realize . . ." he whispered as he pulled away.

He now was ashamed, mortified, that because of the urgency that had been surging, pulsing, through his own youthful loins, he might have forced her. He had simply been doing what he had imagined himself doing too many times in his youth while looking at the whores on the pallets in the stews at the Roman arena. Though he had never done this before, he knew he wanted her body. He wanted this beautiful creature. He really wanted this, but he understood he could not have it, because . . . because she did not want it so.

Embarrassed, and acknowledging her reluctance, he held her tenderly, motionlessly, for several minutes, until she was quiet. Penitently, he then meekly took both of her hands and softly, innocently, kissed each finger before gently placing her hands on his chest. He was genuinely trying to comfort her—sincerely trying only to comfort her. He stroked her throat, then moved aside the hair falling on her neck and gently kissed the back of her neck. He tenderly kissed each of her closed eyes before stopping to look at her.

Fully intending now to pull away, Pons hesitated for a few moments, and then once again could not help himself. He kissed her lips once, but ever so gently. To his abject surprise, she now kissed him back, and the kiss became ever more aggressive, more intense, then stronger, then more impassioned. This time she slid her tongue into his mouth, gently exploring, gently caressing his tongue, then rhythmically stroking it. Again, he stopped thinking.

They slid down to the sleeping pallet and lay facing each other. He gently explored each breast ever so tenderly, first with his fingers, then with his lips. Reaching behind his head, she kneaded his neck, then his shoulders. Their torsos began to sway back and forth together until she finally leaned back, took his hand, and moved it between her legs. Hesitantly, he inserted his fingers to explore the unfamiliar opening, so warm, moist, and inviting. As he began stroking her with his hand, her hips began swaying rhythmically in unison.

Reaching down, she now gently touched him, encircling him with her hand, before gently stroking, caressing, massaging, encouraging him. Both of them were now breathing very heavily as she gently guided his engorged, swollen member to its new welcoming home, her warm, moist, now ready-to-receive opening. An initial awkward thrust, then a more certain slow thrust, then another, then again and more rhythmically again and again. Deeper, surer, again and again, again and again . . . Oh. Oh . . . Oh, heavenly host! Fount of goodness and blessings! Fountain of paradise!

At last, the pair held each other as they lay there, spent, unthinking. Pons felt so full, so good, so wonderfully good. It had been so powerful, so almost uncontrollable, yet so natural. He was now so stunned at how good he felt, at how powerfully pleasurable it had been, that he still did not think. He now knew the wondrous pleasure of sexual union. He and this lovely creature had come together as one. Though both naïve, they had somehow joined together in perfect synchrony, in beautiful intimacy, in absolutely wondrous carnal pleasure.

As they now lay next to each other, Pons gently raised his hand to this lovely creature's face, tracing the edge of her hairline along her forehead, the curve and hollow of her cheek, the slight ridges above her lips. Pulling the soft curve of her chin toward him, he gently kissed her lips. Burying his head in her neck, he softly stroked her hair.

"This softness . . . Her hair, her skin, oh, it is all just as I imagined it would be. So good, so very pleasurable, so natural," he told himself silently, still not thinking.

But as they lay together, Pons finally did begin to question himself with some confusion. "How did this happen? How could this have happened?" he now asked himself. "Oh, she is a lovely creature! Such a lovely creature. And she is, after all, only a woman, a lesser creature, a weak creature with base, physical urges. But I am a man, a higher order of being, who should have been able to control such urges. How did I fall into this? How did this happen?

"I was feeling protective of her! That's it! I was protecting this weak creature, this lovely weak creature," he convinced himself defensively. "Yes, that was it! I am certain of it. I was doing my duty and protecting her. It was our shared fear and revulsion at that obscenely hellish horror of Peter of Bruys's execution by fire. That's what drew me to her. That's what somehow joined me with her. That's what somehow bound me to her. That's what pulled me down onto her! Yes, it was our shared horror as good Christians that somehow bound us together. We were two innocents! Two innocents frightened together."

Still a bit stunned and confused at what had transpired, Pons now realized he still felt very protective of the woman. He did not feel any real shame or remorse, because he had not yet confronted the full reality of what he had done; he was not yet able to face up to the import of his having succumbed to the temptations of the flesh.

A few moments later, he was both surprised and chagrined when the young woman began shaking slightly again and sobbing ever so quietly.

"It was so horrible," he heard her murmur. "The fire, the smell . . . It was murder. They wanted to kill him. They enjoyed seeing him burn. They were laughing . . . It was so awful, so ugly. I was so frightened. So very, very frightened. I am still so frightened."

"You were not alone. I was there. I am here, now."

Pons continued holding her tightly until she eventually stopped shaking, stopped sobbing, and finally was calm. He realized, once again with some surprise, that he was still feeling strongly protective of her. Sitting up, he took her hand and kissed it gently.

"What is your name?"

Now calm, she first smiled, then lowered her head, a bit embarrassed at the absurdity of the timing of the question.

"I'm sorry. It's just . . . My name is Beatrice. And yours?"

"Pons. Pons de Baucio. And you said you live here in this town?"

"Yes, my mother and Alphonse Jourdain, the Count of Toulouse, were lovers when they were both young, and she was his consort for a few years."

"She was. . . So you are. . .?" Pons began, rather startled.

"Yes, I was born here sixteen years ago, and by the time I was walking the count was occupying the town and building his castle, despite threats from the pope. Then the count began losing interest in my mother. He needed to marry to get an heir, you see. So he threw us out of the castle. But my mother had managed to keep hidden some of the gifts he had given her—treasures really—and she sold them to set herself up respectably here. She was able to remain on good terms with some members of his court, so she was able to support herself as a seamstress. She and I worked together here until she died earlier this year.

"What about you? What's your story?" she continued.

"I am a priest, as you know, a canon at the Cathedral of Arles. But I am of the House of Baux, and I am the youngest brother of Raymond, Lord of Baux." Pons began slowly, before continuing more animatedly with a wry smile.

"Curiously enough, your story and mine intersect in a rather convoluted way through this town. So perhaps the stars[52] preordained our meeting and . . . coming together. Fourteen years ago, my brother Raymond was one of the local feudal lords working with Alphonse Jourdain, the man who fathered you, when they were all was threatened with excommunication by Pope Callixtus if the count wasn't stopped from attacking and sacking the monastery of Saint-Gilles. Well, the Count of Toulouse was not to be stopped, and the threat was carried out the next year.[53] It was just before those events that I was given to the chapter of canons at Arles.

"I really wanted to join the chapter, though, because I know I was called to it by God. So whatever my brother's full reasons were for donating me to the cathedral chapter at that time, I am grateful that he did so," he continued,

52   In twelfth-century thought and belief, the stars governed everything, all events.

53   Pope Calixtus II threatened Alphonse Jourdain, Count of Toulouse, as well as Raymond and his men with excommunication in June 1121, if Jourdain did not stop attacking the monastery of Saint-Gilles, and a papal bull of April 1122 confirms that they were subsequently excommunicated. For the Count of Toulouse, see Stoddard, *Façade*, 158, and Goiffon, *Bullaire*, 61, 65. For Raymond of Baux, see http://fmg.ac/ Projects/MedLands//provaixmar.htm#_Toc28604186 (*Foundation for Medieval Genealogy / Medieval Lands /* Provence-Aix, Marseille / Chapter 4. Marseille :.B. Seigneurs de Baux, Vicomtes de Baux /, Raymond de Baux)

telling her about his family, about his father dying before he was born, and about his being given over to the chapter at Arles.

Pons did not want to clarify further, but being no fool, he had come to more fully understand his brother's motivations in donating him as a lad to the chapter at Arles. Within the political turmoil in Provence, the Archbishop of Arles not only held great spiritual authority but had come to wield substantial political power as well. Raymond was very ambitious. By endowing and donating one of his two brothers, the pious younger one, to the chapter to become a canon assisting the archbishop, the Lord of Baux was building an asset from which he could certainly expect eventually to reap rewards, rewards of religious or political intercession, or both. When the excommunications were carried out shortly thereafter in 1122, both Raymond and the count could benefit from Raymond of Baux's connection to the archbishop, which could help gain their reinstatement into the good graces of the Church so they could be assured of salvation when they died. Raymond had played his game of *échecs*[54] well, parlaying his naïve, pious, and otherwise useless younger *pedes*, or pawn, of a brother into a more valuable "bishop."

"Do you have a woman?" Beatrice asked quietly and rather hesitantly. "Will you take a wife and have a family, like most other priests?"

"I . . . Um . . . Uh . . . Well, I haven't thought about all that. I just don't know," Pons stammered. "At Arles I live communally with two other young canons. When I was younger, I lived with the family of one of the canons, Peter Villelmus. I, um . . . I . . . I have a great deal to think about. I'm just not sure I know what God wants of me. And now I am really confused about so many things."

"But most of the canons do take wives, don't they?" she asked persistently.

"Yes. Of course," he responded quickly. "But I'm not. . . I have not yet made such a decision."

The two young people lay there in each other's arms, each of them now thinking as they were falling asleep.

Beatrice immediately began to feel a bit of remorse for what she had done, not for having fornicated with such a virile young man, but for having done it with someone whom she now feared she might have misjudged.

....

54   The game of chess was certainly well-known and popular in southern Europe by the twelfth century. It was called *échecs* in French, *escacs* in Catalan, and *scacchi* in Italian.

When she had begun showing interest in boys a couple of years ago—or, rather, when young men had begun showing interest in her—her mother had been brutally frank with her to scare her with the real facts of life. Her mother had certainly told her all about her own history and liaisons, and about how to give and receive pleasure, and Beatrice had even discretely peeked in and watched at times when her mother was involved with a gift-giving "court friend." No, what had frightened the young girl was her mother's frankness about how narrowly she and Beatrice had escaped total destitution and starvation after the count had thrown them out. Her mother had successfully frightened the girl into recognizing that she would have to choose her partners carefully if she wanted not to end up being tossed into the street as a used whore once her mother could no longer support her.

"I was really so overwrought by the violence of the crowd burning that heretic that I may not have been thinking clearly enough," Beatrice thought to herself. "But no. No! He does seem nice, strong, and gentle. And so protective. I really do like him! And he's so respectable—and he's a priest. As my mother always said, the wife or mistress of a priest never starves! So why is he so stupidly innocent and confused and not yet ready even to think about taking a woman, wife, or mistress?" she wondered.

As for Pons, he was thinking about the man who had fathered Beatrice, the powerful Count of Toulouse, feudal overlord of that region who had long claimed control of the town of Saint-Gilles. The Count of Toulouse and his brothers had a long history of harassing the abbey of Saint-Gilles, and robbing the abbey of its treasury, all in defiance of the pope. Rolling his eyes, Pons noted with a sigh that in these struggles between the feudal lords and the papacy, excommunication was not an effective control when the feudal lords could buy relief from the punishment and sentence.

As they lay together, Pons returned to thinking about what had transpired, his reverie first focusing only on the pleasure before soon taking a more critical turn.

"Beatrice. This lovely creature is named Beatrice," he thought to himself. "Should I begin thinking about taking a wife? After all, we canons do marry. Peter Villelmus had a wife, a family. Must I deny myself such pleasure? It was just so. . . so good. And right . . .

"Perhaps I should marry. Should I marry her? She is asking about marriage," he thought. "After all, I certainly know what St. Paul wrote in Corinthians,

"... Bonum est hominia mulierem non tangere

"It is good for a man not to touch a woman.

"Propter fornicationes autem unusquisque suam uxorem habeat et unaquaeque suum virum habeat ...

"But for fear of fornication, let every man have his own wife: and let every woman have her own husband ...

"Volo autem omnes homines esse sicut me ipsum ...

"For I would that all men were even as myself ...

"Dico autem non nuptis et vidius bonum est illis si sic maneant sicut et ego.

"But I say to the unmarried and to the widows: It is good for them if they so continue, even as I.

Quod si non se contient nubant melius est enim nubere quam uri." (I *Ad Corinthios* 7:1–2; 7–9.)

"But if they do not contain themselves, let them marry. For it is better to marry than to be burnt." (I Corinthians 7:1–2; 7–9.)

Then he was not only stunned, but dumbstruck as another realization finally hit.

"Beatrice. My lovely, lovely Beatrice. Such a lovely creature. But ... it was outside the sanctity of marriage! It was fornication! I will 'burn' in hell, as St. Paul warned! I will burn! *Mea culpa!* I must confess it ... I must confess it as soon as possible," he now realized with his first painful throes of real discomfort in his conscience.

"She is a lovely creature, but a creature of temptation. A woman! A woman who is but a vessel of temptation! A woman with vile, base, physical urges who tempts man! A woman who arouses urgings of the flesh! Urgings of the flesh that I was not able to control.

"Was I tricked? Was this the devil's work? Was I tricked into the temptations of the flesh? How could all this have happened? I am a canon, a priest. Until now I have always refused to succumb to such base urgings of the flesh. Was I lured into temptation by this beautiful creature? Was I tricked?

"She led me into it! I had thought this beautiful young woman, this creature, was so pure. But how could a pure creature have led me into it? And how could we have joined together so easily, so well? There was no awkwardness at all, despite my own sexual inexperience.

"But what about this young woman? She seemed so respectable, but was she innocent? Was she pure? She's the daughter of a consort!" he thought to himself. "A consort who raised her and probably taught her everything she knew.

"No! I do believe she was innocent!" he tried to argue with himself. "After all, she and her mother seem to have run a respectable shop as seamstresses. Even if her mother was formerly a consort, a whore, she used the gifts to set up shop as . . . the gifts . . . . The gifts were treasures looted from the abbey of Saint-Gilles! Beatrice's appearance of respectability was undoubtedly financed by treasures stolen from the abbey!"

"Oh, no! No! Oh, dear God! Forgive me, Father. Oh, please forgive me! *Mea culpa, mea culpa, mea culpa!* Please, forgive me! Father, forgive me! Forgive me! It's so much worse.

"Beatrice, this woman, is the unwanted bastard offspring of the Count of Toulouse. The Count of Toulouse, who sacked the abbey and . . . stole from God's house! Her appearance of respectability paid for by treasures stolen from God! Oh! Oh, no! Dear God, please forgive me! Please forgive me, St. Gilles. Please, Blessed Virgin, forgive me."

Despite this realization, his body was so physically relaxed that he was ready for sleep. Both young people fell asleep, but Pons slept fitfully. He dreamed of angels fighting violent sword battles with evil human land barons. They fought on an open plain full of churches that were crumbling in the turmoil, and through the battleground rode a beautiful young woman with flowing hair mounted on a white horse. But as the horse slowly changed color, darkening to become black, the young woman slowly changed into an ugly old hag, a demonic figure.

Later in the night, long, long before dawn, Pons awoke with a start. He now knew God had spoken to him in his dream, showing him the truth about Beatrice. He now knew how grievously he had sinned. Filled with shame, he knew he must confess his sin.

"Oh, dear God!" he whimpered aloud. *"Mea culpa. Mea culpa."*

He was not only full of shame, but nervous and anxious. He was far from the chapter house, his religious home at Arles—far both physically and emotionally—but as a devout young canon, he knew his duty was to celebrate the canonical hours, also known as the Divine Office or *officium divinum*.[55] This

---

55   The canonical hours, the Liturgy of the Hours, is also known as the Divine Office or *officium divinum,* "divine service" or "divine duty."

official set series of prescribed prayers and devotions was to be performed at set times of the day. These eight set prayer rituals ordered each and every day, bringing order to his life. Every day at these eight fixed times, his life would refocus on his faith through the recitation and chanting of the psalms, prayers, and liturgy appropriate for that hour.

Yesterday, for the first time in several years, he had simply forgotten to celebrate the hours, not only *Nones* at mid-afternoon, but even *Vespers*, the early evening prayer at sunset, and *Compline* later in the evening just before retiring. At *Nones* he had been overcome with the horrific events of the day, with witnessing the brutality of the burning of the heretic. At *Vespers* there had been no ringing of the bells to mark the end of day because it was Good Friday. But so what? He had forgotten! Forgotten! Because he was too busy . . . in sinful fornication.

Pons now recognized that he had been so involved in what now seemed an unreal, sinful encounter with Beatrice that he had neglected his duty. What had come over him? No matter what sins or thrills or horrors he would come to experience in his life, the pious Pons knew it was inexcusable for him to neglect his canonical duty. He had to celebrate the hours. He desperately needed to celebrate the hours.

No bell had now rung to mark *Matins*—also known by its older name, *Vigils*—of the night, but this hour in the middle of the night was never marked by bells. Yet he had awakened, as usual. It was his soul that had awakened him.

Highly agitated, filled with shame and chagrin, almost as much for having omitted his duty as for the memory of the previous night's carnal transgressions, Pons dressed quickly and lit the candle on the small table to celebrate the predawn night vigil, the Divine Office of the Night, the Office of Readings. He took his little copies of the necessary manuscripts from his pouch. Beatrice stirred in her sleep.

Making the sign of the cross, Pons invoked the Holy Trinity, Father, Son, and Holy Spirit, before opening his *Breviary* for the daily office and his Psalter. Kneeling down at the window, he first recited the prescribed antiphon:[56]

....

56   For the various historical traditions on the structure of *Matins*, see Abbot Charles Egger (trans. Fr. Lawrence Byrne), "The Liturgy of the Hours according to the Tradition of the Spiritual Authors of the Canonical Order," *The Liturgy of the Hours*, Canons Regular of Saint Augustine, http://newsite.augustiniancanons.org/. Retrieved April 25, 2011. See web archive: https://web.archive.org/web/20111220222621/http://newsite.augustiniancanons.org/liturgy/liturgy-of-the-hours/.

"Domine labia mea aperies et os meum adnuntiabit laudem tuam."

"O Lord, thou wilt open my lips: and my mouth shall declare thy praise."

(*Psalmus* 50:17)

(Psalm 50:17)

He then began softly reciting the prescribed psalm.

"Deus in adiutorium meum intende Domine ad adiuvandum me festina . . ."

"O God, come to my assistance: O Lord, make haste to help me . . ."

(Psalm 69:2)

(*Psalmus* 69:2)

After reciting the Lord's prayer,

"Paster noster, qui es in caelis . . ."

"Our Father, who art in heaven . . ."

he began reciting the next prescribed psalm.

"Ad te Domine levavi animam meam Deus meus in te confido non erubescam . . ."

"To thee, O Lord, have I lifted up my soul. In thee, O my God, I put my trust, let me not be ashamed . . ."

(*Psalmus* 24:1 ff)

(Psalm 24:1ff)

Beatrice awakened only momentarily and, recognizing that Pons was praying, she turned over in disinterest and quickly fell back once again into a deep sleep.

Pons now began softly chanting the prescribed psalm, the Invitatory, in its entirety.

"Venite exultemus Domino iubilemus Deo salutari nostro

"Come let us praise the Lord with joy; let us joyfully sing to God our savior.

Praeoccupemus faciem eius in confessione et in psalmis iubilemus ei

Let us come before his presence with thanksgiving and make a joyful noise to him with psalms.

Quoniam Deus magnus Dominus et rex magnus super omnes deos . . ."

For the Lord is a great God, and a great King above all gods . . ."

(*Psalmus* 94:1ff)

(Psalm 94:1ff)

Pons continued by singing softly the prescribed hymn.[57]

| "Quo corda adhuc torpentia ad laudes Dei excitantur . . ." | ". . . with which hearts inert by sleep become awakened to praise God . . ." |

As he continued, the familiarity of the incantations, the predictability of the well-known series of psalms, and the comfort of the known repetitions all began to calm his troubled spirit. As he continued further, some real peace began to descend into the depths of his being. By the time he had completed celebrating his *Vigils*, he had succeeded in disciplining the flesh so that his soul had gained the upper hand.

Recognizing his re-found peace, he was truly grateful, and he thanked God, pledging to make a full confession immediately upon his return. Finally he rose from his devotions, broke off a dry end of bread from a loaf on the table and put it in his pouch, poured a bit of water with a jug from the water bucket into his wineskin, and walked quietly to the bed. Lowering his head, he joined his hands in prayer, asking mutely for the young woman's pardon, before making the sign of the cross near her head. Without waking her, he finally bid her an unspoken goodbye before extinguishing the candle and walking out the door into the darkness to begin his return walk to Arles, where he would make his full confession.

Walking very quickly in the darkness, on the path now illuminated by an almost full moon and a million stars, Pons was so deep in thought that he had no fear of bandits, no fear of losing his way. He walked very quickly and purposefully in the dark, knowing that his soul needed to return to Arles. Before going very far, he stopped, remaining right at the side of the road to rest briefly and to sip some water and eat a bite of his bread before setting out again quickly.

After a couple of *milles*, appreciating the benefit of traveling at night under the coolness of the stars, Pons began jogging, then running, moving very quickly with very few stops for rest. Moving quickly, he could not move silently.

Eventually he heard the rustling of his beloved wild horses that he had disturbed in passing. After recalling for a brief moment his dream with the horse turning from white to dark, he now could not stop thinking about the

....

57   Both the Latin and English pieces of this prescribed hymn, as described by Hugh of St. Victor, are taken directly from Egger, "Liturgy."

wild horses' transformation in color: from brown or dark gray when young to almost white when mature.

He now admitted to himself that perhaps he envied them in some way. Maybe that was, in part, why he was so drawn to them, because he did envy them a bit.

"These horses are wild and free, yet God has ordered their future so clearly," he mused. "As they mature, they transform from dark to light. Theirs is a natural progression from darkness to light, from darkness to purity.

"If only life could be as simple for us men. God speaks and gives us the direction, but he does not always identify the path clearly enough. God gives us choice, and sometimes then seems to leave it to us to find the correct path, even though it can be so difficult to know which path to take.

"And it's so very difficult to stay on the correct path, to reach purity and light."

For so long he had struggled almost daily with what direction God wanted him to take. And now this. What had happened with Beatrice had seemed so right and so natural at the time, but it now weighed heavily on his soul, and he knew he had to confess it. Did every young priest experience such powerful urges, urges that seemed so right and natural but should not be given into? Urges that seemed to conflict with his duty and calling? Did every young canon get tugged in these opposite directions?

He knew he had to return as quickly as possible to the chapter. He knew he needed to confess. He knew he needed to return to his duties. He needed twice each day to attend the meeting of the canons called chapter, where they would listen to a reading of a chapter of guidance. He needed the routine of publicly chanting the Divine Office at choir service. He needed the routine of obediently following behind the archbishop in choir processions, of escorting him in the celebration of Mass. He needed to busy himself assisting the archbishop in the governance of his diocese, helping him administer the cathedral's lands, revenues, and wealth.

He needed the routine. He had to return to those duties. He needed them because they brought structure and order—and meaning—to his life.

Just as day was about to break, he arrived back at Arles and immediately entered the church, making the sign of the cross on his breast. Prostrating himself in front of the cross, he silently confessed and renewed his determination to maintain mastery over the flesh. That would have to suffice until he could make a formal confession. His soul would make its peace with God.

Other canons began entering the church to celebrate *Lauds*, to offer praises to God at daybreak and to recall with the dawn the memory of Christ's resurrection. As Pons joined them, he again made the sign of the cross on his chest.

After the prescribed Invitatory, they began chanting the several Psalms of *Lauds*, beginning with Psalm 92.[58]

". . . Dominus regnavit decore indutus est indutus est Dominus fortitudine et praecinxit se etenim firmavit orbem terrae qui non commovebitur.

"The Lord reigneth, he is clothed with majesty; the Lord is clothed with strength, wherewith he hath girded himself: the world also is stablished, that it cannot be moved.

Parata sedis tua ex tunc a saeculo tu es

Thy throne is established of old: thou art from everlasting

Elevaverunt flumina Domine elevaverunt flumina vocem suam elavabunt flumina fluctus suos

The floods have lifted up, O Lord: the floods have lifted up their voice; the floods lift up their waves

A vocibus aquarum multarum mirabiles elationes maris mirabilis in altis Dominus

The Lord on high is mightier than the noise of many waters, yea, than the mighty waves of the sea.

Testimonia tua credibilia facta sunt nimis domum tuam decet sanctitudo Domine in longitudine dierum."

Thy testimonies are very sure: holiness becometh thine house, O Lord, for ever."

(Psalm 92:1-5)

(*Psalmus* 92:1-5)

---

58   Although there was considerable variation in choice of psalms for the various hours in early Christian practice, the earliest sources note Psalm 62/63 as the morning psalm and associate the three "lauds" psalms, 148, 149, 150 with cathedral morning prayers. See Michael G. Powell, "Introduction to Medieval Christian Liturgy, II.3 The Liturgy of the Hours," *An Introduction to the History of Christian Liturgy in the West,* Ad Hoc: Resources for Teaching and Research relating to the History of Christianity, Divinity School of Yale University, http://www.yale.edu/adhoc/research_resources/liturgy/hours.html. Retrieved April 25, 2011. See web archive: https://web.archive.org/web/20150316190200/http://www.yale.edu/adhoc/research_resources/liturgy/hours.html.

    Abbot Egger, "Liturgy," cites the twelfth-century Hugh of St. Victor as describing Psalms 92, 97, 62, 66, and 148, 149, 150 for the celebration of *Lauds*.

They continued by singing Psalm 97.

"Cantate Domino canticum novum quoniam mirabilia fecit salvavit sibi dextera eius et brachium sanctum eius . . .

Iubilate Domino omnis terra cantate et exultate et psallite . . ."

(*Psalmus* 97:1, 4)

"Sing ye to the Lord a new canticle: because he hath done wonderful things. His right hand had wrought for him salvation, and his arm is holy . . .

Sing joyfully to God, all the earth; make melody, rejoice and sing . . ."

(Psalm 97:1, 4)

Eventually they began singing the gloriously beautiful "morning psalm," Psalm 62:[59]

"Deus Deus meus ad te luce vigilo sitivit in te anima mea quam multipliciter tibi caro mea

In terra deserta et invia et inaquosa sic in sancto apparui tibi ut viderem virtutem tuam et gloriam tuam . . .

Sicut adipe et pinguidine repleatur anima mea et labia exultationis laudabit os meum

Si memor fui tui super stratum meum in matutinis meditabar in te

Quia fuisti adiutor meus et in velamento alarum tuarum exultabo . . ."

(*Psalmus* 62:2ff)

"O God, my God, to thee do I watch at break of day. For thee my soul hath thirsted; for thee my flesh, O how many ways!

In a desert land, and where there is no way, and no water: so in the sanctuary have I come before thee, to see thy power and thy glory . . .

Let my soul be filled as with marrow and fatness: and my mouth shall praise thee with joyful lips.

If I have remembered thee upon my bed, I will meditate on thee in the morning:

Because thou hast been my helper. And I will rejoice under the covert of thy wings: . . ."

(Psalm 62:2ff)

....

59   The earliest sources for matins or morning prayers call this psalm 62 the "morning psalm." See Powell, "Introduction."

Continuing ever on, they first sang the canticle of praise from the Hebrew Bible in Daniel 3 before lifting their voices for the buoyant three *laudate psalms*.[60]

Pons especially loved *Lauds*, a major canonical hour. Its music was so glorious, including not only psalms specially selected because they referred to the break of day or resurrection of Christ, but also the spectacular three *laudate psalms* with psalm and antiphon, or response sung in Gregorian chant, that stirred both heart and soul.

First, Psalm 148.

"Laudate Dominum de caelis laudate eum in excelsis . . ."	"Praise ye the Lord from the heavens: praise ye him in the high places . . .
(*Psalmus* 148:1ff)	(Psalm 148:1ff)

Then, Psalm 149.

"Cantate Domino canticum novum laus eius in ecclesia sanctorum . . ."	"Sing ye to the Lord a new canticle: let his praise be in the church of the saints . . ."
(*Psalmus* 149:1ff)	(Psalm 149:1ff)

And finally, Psalm 150.

"Laudate Dominum in sanctis eius laudate eum in firmamento virtutis eius	"Praise ye the Lord in his Holy places; praise ye him in the firmament of his power.
Laudate eum in virtutibus eius laudate eum secundum multitudinem magnitudinis eius	Praise ye him for his mighty acts: praise ye him according to the multitude of his greatness
Laudate eum insono tubae laudate eum in psalterio et cithara	Praise him with the sound of trumpet; praise him with psaltery and harp.

....

60   On the inclusion of the Canticle from Daniel 3 in *Lauds,* and on the three *"laudate psalms,"* see Powell, "Introduction," and Abbot Egger, "Liturgy."

Laudate eum in tympano et choro laudate eum in cordis et organo	Praise him with timbrel and choir: praise him with strings and organs.
Laudate eum in cymbalis bene sonantibus laudate eum in cymbalis iubilationis"	Praise him on high sounding cymbals: praise him on cymbals of joy:
Omnis spiritus laudet Dominum."	Let every spirit praise the Lord. Alleluia."
(*Psalmus* 150)	(Psalm 150)

As the canons raised their collective voices to the heavens, singing praise to God, Pons again found his perfect peace. He had once again found his way. For the moment, at least, he again recognized his own path, the path God had laid out for him.

Prime

Sunrise—first-hour bells

Anno Domini MCXXXIX

Four years later. Arles, early 1139

For months and months after his two "encounters" at Saint-Gilles, Pons sought answers, seeking guidance from God, reading what he could find, and exploring the depths of his naïve young soul. The burning of the heretic was very troubling to him because Peter had not been given the chance to recant, to receive God's forgiveness for his sins and so be welcomed into heaven.

What the young canon had heard from Peter of Bruys had also somehow unnerved him, however, and had somehow made him uncomfortable. What he had heard had raised some vaguely disturbing questions for Pons, compelling questions involving his faith: questions about the Church and its property, about the conduct and work of the chapter of canons.

Of course, Pons was absolutely certain, from the depths of his being, that what Peter of Bruys taught was wrong. How could Peter be right when Pons knew beyond a doubt that God was present in the church? From the time he was a young boy, Pons had known that God lived in the church. How many times had Pons himself experienced God in the cathedral, felt God "touch" him, felt God pass through him? How many times had God revealed His presence to Pons through the wondrous sights and sounds and smells of the rites and rituals in the cathedral? It was those church rituals that put Pons in touch with God. It was through those church rituals that Pons had come to know God. How could those rites and rituals be fraudulent if they brought man closer to God? How could they be wrong? No, God was present in the church, and He revealed Himself to man through the mysteries of church rituals.

Heresies! Yes, of course Pons knew what Peter had preached were heresies. Nevertheless, those heresies had made him uncomfortable. They had raised vague questions about the conduct and work of the canons as well as about the church property they administered, and these issues continued to dig their way into his thoughts, to gnaw at the edges of his mind. And, of course, because of Beatrice, Pons recognized that buried at the root of his disquiet were the very primal issues of women and the urgings of the flesh—especially that most compellingly demanding issue of *those* urgings of the flesh.

Although Pons was confident that his faith was secure and that with God's help he would eventually resolve these questions, intellectually he now seemed to be floundering. He often explored the issues with Canon Jordan, his closest friend, and he continued seeking guidance and advice from other fellow canons. He read not only the Bible, but whatever writings or treatises they could recommend that were close at hand and available to him, and whatever he could find regarding his relationship as a canon to God.

He engaged in heartfelt discussions with Peter Villelmus, who had been like a stepfather to him after receiving him into his family at Arles. At first Peter Villelmus was very tolerant of the young man whom he liked so well, but as Pons became ever more outspoken, challenging, and strident in his views, the discussions began taking an ugly turn, and started turning into heated, nasty arguments.

"How can a canon dedicate his life to God if he enjoys a home and family, if he keeps a wife and family?" Pons would challenge Peter Villelmus, completely ignoring the fact that as a child he had been generously and lovingly taken in as a member of such a family. "You know as well as I what St. Paul wrote:

"Volo autem vos sine sollicitudine esse qui sine uxore est sollicitus est quae Domini sunt quomodo placeat Deo

Qui autem cum uxore est sollicitus est quae sunt mundi quomodo placeat uxori et divisus est"

(*I ad Corinthios* 7:32–33)

"But I would have you to be without solicitude. He that is without a wife is solicitous for the things that belong to the Lord: how he may please God

But he that is with a wife is solicitous for the things of the world: how he may please his wife. And he is divided."

(I Corinthians 7:32–33)

"Can a priest truly love God and only God, can he keep focused on his primary duty to God if he gives in to the demands of the flesh and turns to his woman every night?" Pons would rail with the passionately arrogant, naïve certainty of youth.

Angry and feeling betrayed, almost as if by his own son, Peter Villelmus would counter, "How can you be such an insufferable fool, such a naïve, stupid young fool? How can you believe yourself to be good and pious when you attack someone who has loved you, who has cared for you? I raised you. I treated you like a son. I welcomed you into my own family. And this is what you say to me in return?"

Undeterred, Pons continued to challenge, to question. Armed with the blind confidence of youth, Pons came to view his spiritual turmoil as evidence of responding to God's calling, so that despite his vague spiritual unrest, he wholeheartedly threw himself into his duties as a canon in the cathedral at Arles. Now it was just after the canonical hour of *Prime* that he was walking in the clear light of early morning toward the entrance to the chapter house to begin some work.

There on the small colonnette to the left of the open window arch immediately left of the portal was the carved figured capital on which he had come to gaze so many times. Here was the mythological siren, a sea nymph, here partly fish rather than bird, but partly a voluptuous woman, with full lips, long hair, and a nude torso with invitingly rounded breasts. Softly fleshy breasts and softly rounded abdomen. Seductive. Beguiling. The woman seductress who lures men to their destruction.

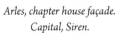

Arles, chapter house façade.   *Arles, chapter house façade.*
Capital, Siren.   *Capital, Luxuria (lust).*

Breathing slowly and now a bit heavily, Pons immediately walked slowly westward a few steps along the porch, forcing himself to stop at the third and last open arch of the chapter house façade, near the western end of the porch. Shaded from the sun by the wooden roof of the porch, he forced himself to look intently for some time at the small carved figured capital on the colonnette at the left, just as he had invariably done so many times before.

Here was another female figure, a counterpart to the siren, perched similarly on the corner of an identical round capital drum covered by long vertically fluted petals, crowned by a single floret on each capital face. This female figure had the face and hair and lips and breasts, nominally similar to those of her seductive sister, but here the female was revolting and disgusting. This disturbing image was *Luxuria*, a wanton, wicked woman whose invitingly rounded breasts were being sucked on by horrid, repulsive serpents. The seductive young woman here had been transformed into the disgusting, horribly revolting figure of lust, in degradation, with abominable creatures from hell.

If the seductive siren capital had been placed in the arcade outside the main portal to the chapter house as a caution to the canons, this figured capital had been placed here as a much sterner admonition, one that was usually helpful in quelling Pons's urgings of the flesh. Shaking his head ever so slightly, Pons remembered when he had seen these two capitals being installed on the decorative façade of the chapter house. When was it? Certainly several years ago, probably almost a decade, and not too long after he had been so intrigued by the stews at the Roman arena. But even then, he would never have guessed how much he himself would one day need these poignant reminders.

Entering the chapter house at Arles, he now quickly sat down to work at his desk. The chapter house was the center of activities for the canons, and it was already quite noisy, not with the resounding chant of echoing praise, but with the mundane daily sounds of business and work. Located to the southeast of the cathedral church, the chapter house had been constructed with its broken barrel vault only a decade or two ago.

The cathedral at Arles was prospering and thriving because the Archbishop of Arles exercised great feudal and secular power in addition to his religious authority, but it was the chapter of canons that assisted him. The canons were businessmen, capable and very successful businessmen. Maintaining the holdings of the cathedral and administering the cathedral's land, revenue, and wealth were important duties.

Because they were good businessmen, the canons carefully documented all donations and exchanges; that is, all transactions involving transferred ownership of goods. The canons understood that for a transaction to be truly binding, it was necessary to document the transaction, to document where and when it took place, along with a list of witnesses to the event. They understood that in any transaction where a donation was given by an individual to obtain some heavenly dispensation, God could certainly be counted on to remember the dispensation, but mortals often tended to need reminding about their part of the arrangement. So the canons drafted and maintained clear, legally binding records of all business transactions enacted on behalf of the chapter and the church.

Pons was one of those to whom such documentation work was now delegated and entrusted. Pons began busily documenting another donation of olive oil to the chapter in the record book of the chapter's business, the *Liber Sancti Stephani vel Sancti Trophimi Arelatensis Aecclesiae de Rebus Ibidem Pertinentibus*.[61] As he was finishing this record, he was surprised, chagrined, to

....

61   This manuscript is the *Authentique du Chapitre*, Arles, Bibliothèque Municipale, MS 1242, in the library at Arles.

find his mind had wandered, once again, to Beatrice. But at least it was for the first time in quite a while.

After returning to the chapter from Saint-Gilles that fateful day, he had confessed his sin, done his assigned penance, and had seen her but once since their encounter. A couple of months after that day at Saint-Gilles, she had come to Arles to purchase cloth and had called at the gate of the chapter's enclosure to the town, asking to speak with Pons. He was now remembering how lovely, how beautiful, how even more voluptuous she had appeared to him that day and how just the sight of her had sent waves coursing through his loins. Refusing to succumb to those urgings, he had met with her only briefly, for a few minutes, and had immediately renounced her firmly, formally, and very coldly.

"You should not have come here. You should not seek me out again. Our encounter was a mistake, a terrible mistake. What happened was wrong. What we did was a sin, a grave sin that put both my soul and yours in peril of hell. I have repented, and God in his great mercy has forgiven me.

"If you have not already repented, I invite you, I beg you for the sake of your immortal soul, to enter the cathedral and make your own confession with one of my brethren."

And with that admonition, he had abruptly turned away and closed the gate on her.

If only he could close his mind on her as easily. At first, she had entered his thoughts almost daily, or rather nightly, but after many, many months he did not think of her so frequently. He had worked very hard to free himself from thoughts of her. When he was unable to contain his thoughts, he would confess and get assigned a penance to do, but as time passed, he knew he was gaining the upper hand. He was more than relieved, and rather proud, to realize that he was finally winning his battle against the urgings of the flesh and was usually successful in restraining both his thoughts and his loins.

Looking up from his work, he saw old Bernard, an elderly and highly respected canon, with Jordan in the chapter house, rifling gently through a loosely tied stack of unbound documents they were pulling from a dusty container they had apparently removed from long-term document storage. Pons flashed them a friendly smile, and Jordan beamed back a huge grin before untying the stack, removing a battered old document from it, and walking quickly over to Pons.

Greeting him warmly, he proudly handed Pons the document, exclaiming, "Here it is at last! It's the partial copy of the old *Institutio Canonicorum*, or Rule of Aachen, that was originally drawn up long, long ago.[62] I told you I had once been told that there was a partial copy of it somewhere around here, and with help from Canon Bernard, who has been around here much longer than the all the rest of us, I finally found it." Bernard was considered by both young men, and by the rest of the chapter, to be a respected scholar and a local expert on church history.

"As we already know," Jordan continued, "each and every chapter of canons devises its own rules of conduct, normally basing them on an established model, often the *Institutio Canonicorum*, and as I mentioned earlier, my mentor once told me he thought our chapter had discussed revising their rules of conduct quite some time ago."

"Yes," Bernard confirmed, joining them. "Some decades ago the archbishop announced that he intended to endow the chapter generously, but he wanted the chapter to reform, so the chapter considered revising their rules of conduct to accord with the proposed reforms, and to do so, they undoubtedly secured this copy to consult as a model."

"Let's look at it together," Jordan offered.

The young pair gently opened what remained of the document on a desk. As they examined it carefully together, old Bernard shuffled away to fetch another volume.

"The Rule of Aachen certainly encourages communal life," observed Pons, "and it also permits canons to own and to hold their own private property and to live in private residences."

"Yes," retorted Jordan, "and this is what our chapter finally agreed upon, as we well know: to adopt a communal life, but to permit the canons to hold private income and private property. They decided to build a refectory, so they could eat communally if they wanted, but they still each kept their own private incomes and residences."

"But can you live communally if you have your own income and live in your own private residence?" countered Pons.

---

62   The *Institutio Canonicorum*, or Rule of Aachen, was drawn up at the Council of Aachen in 816–817 AD.

"Apparently so. At least that's what the chapter agreed to do, to live communally so long as they could each own their own property, including their own houses," responded Jordan.

"Now, let's bear in mind," interjected Bernard, who returned carrying another manuscript, "that this issue was by no means new or unique here but follows on a long history throughout the Western church. The oldest traditions of the church fathers, the *Instituta Patrum,* permitted clerics to own private property. From very early on, it was only local statutes and codes agreed upon by the secular clergy themselves that governed the groups of them living communally next to the cathedrals and collegiate churches, just as it is now. These local codes did not impose poverty, so many clergy chose to live in private dwellings rather than living communally. Many lived quite well."

"But did the local codes permit the clergy to have wives too?" demanded Pons.

"Not really, at least not overtly," responded Bernard. "But since they were living in private comfort, they frequently took wives in marriage or kept mistresses, particularly in the lower ranks of the clergy."

"And the Church permitted this? Did the Church ever try to change this?" asked Jordan.

"It has long been trying to change this, but frankly, it is a real struggle to change conventions and traditions that have been going on for centuries," Bernard responded sharply. "For quite some time now, since the latter half of the last century, a strong reform movement has been growing within the Church. Its most forceful advocate was Pope Gregory VII.[63] Even before becoming pope, when he was still known as Hildebrand, he called for the clergy to return to a more rigorous imitation of the communal life of the apostles in the primitive church."

"The communal life of the apostles in the primitive church . . ." repeated Pons thoughtfully, recollecting Peter of Bruys's rant.

"And he tried to get priests to give up their wives?" Jordan demanded.

"Yes, and I do understand that's the issue you two young men are really now most interested in, or struggling with," Bernard answered, winking, with a knowing but very kindly smile. "Pope Gregory demanded compulsory

....

63   Pope Gregory VII (1073–1085) called for the clergy to adopt communal life at the Lateran Synod of 1059, and in an encyclical letter of 1074 he annulled the oaths of obedience for bishops who permitted priests to marry.

celibacy among the clergy. He insisted that priests give up their wives and mistresses, and he even annulled the oaths of fealty to any bishops who permitted priests to be married."

"So, Pope Gregory tried to ban wives and to enforce celibacy," Pons added thoughtfully.

"Yes, but his vision of reform was much broader and more all-encompassing than the one issue of priests taking wives," Bernard continued. "Pope Gregory wanted to reform the whole Church; he wanted to restore its original purity as the Church of the apostles."

"So he was seeking both communal living and celibacy?" queried Pons, frowning.

"Yes, but oh, so much more than that!" old Bernard continued, inhaling a big breath. "Remember, secular and church authority had become so intermixed that secular rulers were exercising a lot of power within the Church. Pope Gregory challenged this. He really focused on two issues: moral integrity and independence. He wanted to reform the moral integrity of the clergy and make them independent of secular rulers."

"Well, I certainly understand one aspect about moral integrity and independence of the clergy," Pons offered with a smirk. "Even excommunication is meaningless as a punishment if a noble can simply buy back his redemption!"

"That's one small part of it, for sure," Bernard admitted, scratching his jowl. "Pope Gregory did attack the sale of tithes and absolution. But he also fought against simony, the selling of offices and spiritual authority.

"You see, Pope Gregory pushed hard for reforms to make the Church and the clergy independent of the state and rulers of the state," Bernard repeated. "He wanted to free the Church from any influence or abuse by secular rulers, so he simply stripped those rulers of most of the power and authority they had previously held in the Church. With his reforms, secular rulers could no longer invest or install church officials. Secular rulers could no longer appoint bishops and abbots. Pope Gregory insisted instead on canonical elections, that we priests could elect our own bishops, provosts, priors, and abbots."

"So now the Church elects and appoints its own officials," Jordan confirmed with a nod.

"Yes. Pope Gregory simply insisted that because the Church was founded by God, it has higher authority, higher power, than any secular state," Bernard responded calmly. "And he insisted that because the pope is the absolute head of the Church, he has the highest authority of all, higher than any secular ruler."

"Well, he wasn't able to wrest much real power from secular rulers, any more than he was able to stop priests from taking wives and mistresses!" Pons cried out.

"Remember, my son, Pope Gregory was not trying to take away the territorial rights of secular rulers, but only their rights with respect to Church offices," Bernard gently corrected the young canon. "And yes, he was able to do this. He did it."

"But what about his other focus?" Pons muttered. "He was trying to promote the moral integrity of the clergy, but he did not, or could not, stop priests from living privately in their own homes and taking wives and mistresses."

"Very true," admitted Bernard.

"And all of this," concluded Jordan, "all of this reform movement was going on decades ago, and just around the time that our chapter considered revising their rules of conduct, when they reviewed this copy of the ninth-century *Institutio Canonicorum*."

"And that was when they finally opted to live communally, and to build a refectory, but let everyone retain their own private property and houses," added Pons, "as was permitted by the *Institutio Canonicorum*."

"Yes," answered the elderly Bernard quietly. "But many reformers were arguing specifically against canons owning private property. They argued that renunciation of personal possessions was necessary to live the apostolic life Christ required of the apostles in the Bible. Here, go ahead and read aloud once again this passage I found for you," he ordered, pointing to and then opening a Bible on the table. "This is what the reformers focused on. It's from Acts of the Apostles. Here it is: 4:32–35."

Pons found the appropriate passage and read aloud:

"Multitudinis autem credentium erat cor et anima una nec quisquam eorum quae possidebant aliquid suum esse dicebat sed erant illis omnia communia

"And the multitude of believers had but one heart and one soul. Neither did any one say that aught of the things which we possessed were his own: but all things were common unto them.

Et virtute magna reddebant apostoli testimonium resurrectionis Iesu Christi Domini et gratia magna erat in omnibus illis	And with great power did the apostles give testimony of the resurrection of Jesus Christ our Lord and great grace was in them all.
Neque enim quisquam egens erat inter illos quotquot enim possessores agrorum aut domorum erant vendentes adferebant pretia eorum quae vendebant	For neither was there any one needy among them. For as many as were owners of lands or houses sold them and brought the price of the things they sold
Et ponebant ante pedes apostolorum dividebantur autem singulis prout cuique opus erat"	And laid it down before the feet of the apostles. And distribution was made to every one, according as he had need."
(*Actus* 4:32–35)	(Acts 4:32–35)

"With that passage in mind," suggested Bernard, "you might want to look at what the reformer Peter Damian had to say about all this." He offered the young canons the volume he had brought in. "I have marked some passages for you, but I'm afraid this is about all the help I can give you. You'll have to continue your investigations on your own. This is all a bit too much for me at my age, and I simply must go lie down to rest. You will find, however, that not long after Pope Gregory's efforts, Peter Damian was urging that clerics who served the Church as canons should live communally and should not own private property."

Pons flashed the aged Bernard a warm smile of admiration and real appreciation and patted him gently on the back as Jordan took the volume from him. They both sincerely thanked the old canon before he shuffled away, muttering to himself inaudibly as he left.

Smiling while gently nodding his head in admiration of the elderly canon, Pons opened the volume to the passages carefully marked and began reading from Peter Damian, sometimes stopping to read aloud.[64]

....

64   Peter Damian, *Contra clericos regulares proprietarios,* in Migne, *Patrologia Latina,* vol.
       145, 485-486. Translation is reorganized from that of Pierre Mandonnet, O.P. (trans.
       Sister Mary Benedicta Larkin, O.P.), "The Role of St. Augustine, Teacher of the
       Apostolic Life" in *St. Dominic and His Work* (St. Louis: Herder, 1945), chap 23.

"Constat itaque, et perspicuum est, quod canonicorum regula ab apostolicae vitae norma prodierit: et dum spiritualis quisque conventus rectam sui tenet ordinis disciplinam, teneram quadammodo lactantis Ecclesiae imitatur infantiam.

"Audiamus ergo quam conversationem, quem vivendi ordinem sub apostolis noviter ad fidem veniens tenebat Ecclesia: "Multitudinis, ut Lucas ait (Act. IV), credentium erat cor unum, et anima una, nec quisquam eorum, quae possidebat aliquid, suum esse dicebat: sed erant illis omnia communia . . . .

"Quisquis ergo clericus proprietatis conatur habere peculium, non valet apostolorum tenere vestigia: quia non erit illi cum fratribus cor unum et anima una . . . .

"An praerogabitur clericis, quod non permisit Christus apostolis? Nam cum eos ad praedicandum mitteret, sicut Marcus ait, praecepit eis, ne quid tollerent in via, nisi virgam tantum, non peram, non panem, neque in zonis aes (Marc VI); tibi vero ad aeris, hoc est pecuniae receptaculum, non dicam zona, sed utinam arca sufficiat . . . ."

"Evidently the rule of the canons followed from the norm of the apostolic life; and while any member of a spiritual society follows the discipline of his own order, he in a certain way imitates the child of the infant Church.

"Let us, therefore, regard the form which the Church, newly clothed in the faith under the apostles, maintained as the way of life. 'The multitudes of the believers,' as St. Luke says (Acts 4:32), 'had but one heart and one soul; neither did any one say that aught of the things which be possessed were his own; but all things were common unto them' . . . .

"Any cleric, therefore, who attempts to enjoy the revenues of property, will not be able to keep to the course of the apostles . . .

"Or will clerics ask for what Christ did not permit to His apostles? For when He sent them to preach, as Mark says (Mark 6:8), 'He commanded that they should take nothing for the way but a staff only; no scrip, no bread, nor money in their purse' . . . ."

Pons stopped reading. "So, it's the 'apostolic life,' the *vita apostolica*, that's the real key here. What the reformers were appealing for was for the clergy to adopt the life of the apostles of the primitive church that Jesus Christ had taught His followers. For the reformers, the key to the *vita apostolica* was giving up private ownership of property so they would hold everything in common."

Their conversation was abruptly cut short, however, by a loud commotion in the far south end of the chapter's enclosure, at the canons' portal, which led from the enclosure into the city through one of the ancient Roman city walls. The two young canons had been so preoccupied with their examination of the copy of the old Rule of Aachen, so involved in their interaction with Bernard, that they had completely forgotten, if only briefly, that the chapter was expecting the return home of the archbishop from his journey to Rome, where he had just attended the Second Lateran Council.

Pope Innocent II had called the Second Lateran Council after finally winning sole undisputed claim to the papacy and emerging victorious over the antipope, Victor IV. The victory came after the divisive turmoil of a long schism that had begun in 1130 with the death of Pope Honorius II, when first Innocent II and then only hours later Anacletus II were each elected as successor pope, each vying for the position, causing the split. Now that Pope Innocent II had finally emerged victorious, he had called the Second Lateran Council in large part to remove any fallout resulting from the schism. It was well attended, with almost 1,000 participants.[65]

The newly arriving group at the portal was boisterous and larger than expected. As their carts and horses were being handed off to local servants to care for, several of the group immediately disappeared, moving either quickly toward the privy or down the street toward town. As the two young canons watched, their eyes popped open wide with surprise. There was Archbishop William Monachus, leading one fellow traveler by the arm, respectfully, almost deferentially, as if he were a distinguished visitor, and ushering him into the enclosure, past the archbishop's palace, toward the chapter house. Jordan and Pons quickly jumped to their feet and moved to greet them and to attend them politely.

"Greetings, brethren," began the archbishop. "Blessed be the Lord, Our Father, for bringing us home safely from our strenuous but most enlightening

---

65   See "Tenth Ecumenical Council: Lateran II, 1139" in *Medieval Sourcebook*, http://www.fordham.edu/halsall/basis/lateran2.html

trip to Rome. Brother Peter, these are two of the dedicated young canons I had hoped would be here to greet you, Pons de Baucio and Jordan.

"Canons Pons and Jordan, my sons, we have the honor of receiving, albeit only very briefly, the Venerable Brother Peter of Montboissier, Abbot of Cluny. Brother Peter and I have spent much time conversing while traveling together from Rome, and he has asked to meet briefly and to speak informally with some of your chapter members before departing again to continue his own journey westward.

"Brother Peter, please excuse me now while I leave you to gather as many of our chapter as possible to come to join you."

The Venerable Peter, the Abbot of Cluny, dressed in his black monk's garb, greeted them politely and warmly, with a gentleness and friendly openness that seemed to belie his elevated position. The monastic Order of Cluny was then the chief center of religious influence in Western Europe. As head of this powerful order, Abbot Peter led an ever-growing congregation of hundreds of monastic houses throughout Europe, and all the houses that belonged to the order, whether they were originally founded by the order or later incorporated into it, were absolutely subject to Cluny and to Peter as its abbot. The Abbot of Cluny was probably then second only to the pope in the real power and scope of his religious command and authority in western Europe.

"Please excuse both the abruptness of my arrival and the shortness of my visit with you, my sons. I am stopping here at Arles only briefly, so my staff and I can refresh ourselves before continuing on our long journey into Catalonia."

While the group was gathering, Abbot Peter began speaking informally to whoever was there.

"I would stay here this evening with you if I could do so, but it is imperative that I continue on to visit the abbey of Saint-Gilles today, where I want to see the construction now well underway on the new abbey church. Praise be to God, the abbey has now finally accepted the Rule of our order. They long refused to be administered by us, and even after the abbey was given to our order for reform well over a decade ago, they were rebellious, refusing to pay their tithes to our Cluny treasury.[66]

....

66   On the relationship of the abbey of Saint-Gilles to Cluny, see Stoddard, *Façade*, 130–131, 158. See also Dominique Iogna-Prat, *Order and Exclusion, Cluny and Christendom Face Heresy, Judaism, and Islam (1000–1150)*, trans. Graham Robert Edwards (Ithaca: Cornell University Press, 2002), 113ff.

"We are so pleased that they have finally embraced our order, praise be to God. We certainly want to encourage them to continue their spiritual progress in finding *pax,* peace, by embracing the Rule of St. Benedict as their guide to spiritual growth and individual salvation through a balance of *ora et labora,* through prayer and work. And we are so pleased that the monks have invited us to visit and view their progress on building their new basilica, a project in which we are now encouraging and supporting them.

"So I apologize deeply for not staying here overnight as planned, but I would be very pleased to take a short rest in the shade of the porch of your chapter house and would be grateful to learn from you here by discussing some issues of faith."

Pons was immediately impressed by both the genuine sincerity and gentle affability of this powerful abbot, in whom he recognized some of the personal qualities that must have helped him earn his reputation as a gently persuasive and very successful politician, yet as a man of peace, serenity, and charity.

Others were joining the small group that walked toward the chapter house, and following Abbot Peter's lead, everyone seated themselves within the wooden-roofed porch just outside the chapter house. One of the other canons left to seek out the provost, whom he knew was busy with other members of the chapter in one of the private homes, to inform them of the arrival and bring them back.

Pons quietly remarked to himself how subtly effective Peter was. As a visitor who did not have a permanent seat in chapter, Peter might not have been permitted to enter the chapter house to partake of any official proceedings. Although no proceedings were being carried out at that moment, by quietly seating himself under the porch outside the chapter house, this all-powerful abbot had shown the canons his respect and gained their respect and admiration in return. By sitting here, he was also ensuring that anyone present and within earshot—even novices, the unprofessed, or workers and laymen—would be able to join the group.

When Peter began speaking almost immediately to the small but growing group, Pons saw that this personable yet powerful abbot did not waste words in idle chatter. Making the sign of the cross, Peter gave them an oral blessing before beginning.

"My sons, I want to speak briefly with you in person about some issues deeply troubling to our Church: the heresies of Peter of Bruys, a former priest who is one of the most dangerous of heretics. Your archbishop and I have just returned from participating this April in an ecumenical council convened by Pope Innocent, the Second Lateran Council. Our discussions there included not only the need to reform errors and abuses among the clergy, errors such as dressing immodestly, getting married, and keeping mistresses, but also the pressing need to fight heresy. We strongly condemned the heresies of both Peter of Bruys who was active here and Arnold of Brescia, who is a threat in Lombardy.[67]

"For almost two decades the demon Peter of Bruys was spreading his evil doctrines near here, in this area, and throughout Provence, before he was put to death in the town of Saint-Gilles a couple of years ago. Unfortunately, many have gravely endangered their souls by listening to his foul untruths, and even after his death, the heresy continues, almost unabated. It continues! It continues to endanger Christian souls!

"The local bishops have been working hard to try to suppress this heresy. But although some have had some small measures of success within their own local areas, their success is far too limited. The heresy still continues to spread. It is now being spread near here by Henry of Lausanne, a former Cluniac monk. A former monk of my own Order of Cluny! I urge you as canons to help teach the errors of this heresy."

He stopped for a moment to assess the impact of his words, when Pons, barely able to contain his excited distress, burst in and spoke up. "I heard the heretic Peter of Bruys speak at Saint-Gilles! I was there. I saw him put to death. A former priest burned to death under a cross! It was ghastly! The murderousness of the crowd. It was appalling! It was terrible, simply horrible!

"Such blasphemies! He rejected what we believe about the Eucharist, that the bread and wine are changed into Christ's body and blood. He said that Christ gave his body and blood only once, and that priests cannot repeat this with simple bread and wine."

Very kindly, but with the absolute firmness of a teacher who is also a good listener, Abbot Peter responded, "You must teach the people in this diocese otherwise."

He continued. "My sons, I recently finished drafting a treatise, *Contra Petrobrusianos*, against those who mistakenly follow what Peter of Bruys

67   See "Canons" in *Medieval Sourcebook*, http://www.fordham.edu/halsall/basis/lateran2.html.

preached. In it I have described something that I have been told of and finally now expect soon to be able to see with my own eyes.[68]

". . . in Orientalibus Hispaniae partibus . . . miraculum, quod prius audiens vix credidi; sed post, quod audieram videns, dubitare non potui. Exstant in regionibus illis salita, ut ita dicam, vel salsa montana, quae pro saxis vel rupibus lapideum sal continent, sicque perlucidum, ut quia gemmeam pretiosorum lapidum claritatem aemulatur, salis gemma vocetur. Quod tam perspicuitate quam utilitate, marino puteali, omnique sali praepositum, de montanis illis multo labore ab incolis eruitur, et remotis quibusque pro magno munere datur, aut pro magno lucro uenditur. De quibus montibus cum diutinus rusticorum labor lucri avidus, multam lucidi illius lapidis quantitatem eruerit et eruendo fossas multas eo sale inanes reliquerit, processu temporis pluviali inundatione fossarum illa vacuitas repletur, ac repleta, post paululum in naturam illius cui admiscetur lapidis commutatur.

". . . there is in eastern Spain an extraordinary mountain of salt that I have been told of . . . . This mountain has rocks and cliffs made not of stone, but of hard, shining white rock salt (sal gemma) that is superior in purity to the salt recovered from the sea or springs, and that has, in fact, become a large-scale profitable trade for the local inhabitants. However, although deep shafts are sunk daily into the mountainside to mine the salt, every year during the rainy season the excavated holes refill with water that hardens into salt, completely replacing whatever has been removed. As with the Eucharist, an element from heaven can be transformed on earth into a different physical substance. Hot water can be transformed from a liquid into a solid substance, ice, and just as astoundingly, in the Spanish mountain, into salt."

---

68   Migne, *Patrologia Latina*, vol 189, cols. 805-6. Translation is from Petri Venerabilis, *Contra Petrobrusianos hereticos* (Corpus Christianorum, Continuatio Mediaevalis, X), ed. James Fearns (Turnhout, Belgium: 1968), 109–110 (c. 184). See Bishko, "Peter . . . Some Further Observations."

Tali recompensatione effossus
mons pene annuatim damna illata
restaurat, et quidquid de lapide
amisit, aqua in lapidem conversa
compensat. Fit ergo coelestis
aqua lapis terrenus, quae licet
naturalem mollitiem in lapideam
duritiam commutans, in alienam
substantiam transeat, formam
tamen priorem et speciem, sicut de
crystallo supra dixi, conservat. Sed
sicut de omni glacie nec de omni
crystallo, haec dixi: sic nec de
omni montis illius lapide hoc dico,
sed de illo qui non de coenosa, sed
de limpidissima concretus aqua,
originis suae claritatem etiam in
aliud mutatatus non mutat."

"If water can be so transformed by nature, who can doubt that wine can be transformed during the Holy Eucharist? If water can become salt, who can doubt that wine can become the blood of our Lord? Or that the bread can become the body of our Lord, Jesus Christ, when solemnly blessed during the celebration of the Mass by the priest, who is God's own representative here on earth?"

Very hesitantly, Jordan now politely asked, "May we have a copy of your treatise, *Contra Petrobrusianos*, to help us in refuting this heresy?"

Gratified that his message had been heard, Abbot Peter responded warmly. "Of course. I am dedicating my treatise to some of the local bishops, including your archbishop, and I have already promised to send him a copy.[69] I will ask him to make it available for your chapter to use, to help guide you in fighting this heresy."

....

69   See Iogna-Prat, *Order*, 108–119 for a thorough discussion of the treatise, and 111ff for Peter's prefatory letter dedicating the treatise to the archbishops of Arles and Embrun and to the bishops of Die and Gap.

Having focused intently on the abbot's words like an adoring child, Pons now continued to press him.

"Peter of Bruys proclaimed so many distressing things, disturbing things. He refused to venerate the Cross. He desecrated it because he said it was the instrument of Christ's death. He condemned all church buildings, saying the Church consists of the community of the faithful rather than walls and special buildings with altars. In fact, he condemned all forms of worship, ceremonies and chant. He insisted baptism of infants is useless, claiming that baptism must be accompanied by personal faith for salvation."

Shaking his head ever so slightly, Abbot Peter again responded kindly and gently, but firmly.

"As canons, you carry out the cathedral liturgy. You attend to the duties of Divine Office and carry out your service in the choir, in service to God and on behalf of His people. The souls of His people are at risk! I urge you as canons to help your bishop teach the people the errors of this heresy and to lead them to the truth.

"Remember, it was Christ Himself who, after His death and resurrection, gave the Mission to His apostles to teach His word and to baptize all in His name. The Gospel of Matthew tells us that after Christ died and arose from the dead, He appeared to His disciples, some of whom doubted it was He until He said:

'. . . Data est mihi omnis potestas in caelo et in terra.

Euntes ergo docete omnes gentes baptizantes eos in nomine Patris et Filii et Spiritus Sancti.

Docentes eos servare omnia quaecumque mandavi vobis . . . .'

(*secundum Matthaeum* 28:18–20)

'. . . All power is given to me in heaven and in earth.

Going therefore, teach ye all nations; baptizing them in the name of the Father and of the Son and of the Holy Ghost.

Teaching them to observe all things whatsoever I have commanded you . . . .'

(Matthew 28:18–20)

"And the Gospel of Mark tells us that the risen Christ appeared to his disciples and said:

'... Euntes in mundum
universum praedicate evangelium
omni creaturae.

Qui crediderit, et baptizatus
fuerit salvus erit qui vero non
crediderit condemnabitur.'"

(*secundum Marcum* 16:15–16)

'... Go ye into the whole world and
preach the gospel to every creature.

He that believeth and is
baptized shall be saved: but
he that believeth not shall
be condemned.'"

(Mark 16:15–16)

"That's the mission Christ gave to His apostles," offered Pons.

"Yes," continued Abbot Peter. "I once devised a pictorial interpretation of this theme, the Mission of the Apostles, which, thanks be to God, was then carved as sculptural decoration, oh, maybe about ten years or so ago, on the inner west portals in the narthex at the abbey church at Vézelay in Burgundy, where earlier I had served as prior. Above the central portal the lunette-shaped tympanum shows Christ giving the Mission to the Apostles.[70] Each apostle holds the Gospel, and around them are shown the nations, the peoples to whom they will bring the True Word.

Vézelay. Abbey church. Narthex. Central portal, tympanum, Christ's Mission to the Apostles.

....

70   Because of widespread illiteracy among the general populace, the church used religious imagery to instruct, earlier through frescoes, earlier and elsewhere through mosaics, and by the twelfth century in France and elsewhere, through stone sculpture and stained glass, which became the Bible of the illiterate.

"On the two lunette tympana of the flanking side portals are shown the central core truths of our faith, which the apostles are to teach to the nations. On the tympanum above the south portal to the right is the mystery of the Nativity and events surrounding the birth of Christ, including the Adoration of the Three Magi.

"But on the tympanum above the north portal to the left are mysteries occurring after the death and resurrection of Christ, with the Ascension above, and below, the story of Christ appearing to two disciples on the road to Emmaus. At first, they did not recognize Him, and it was not until later that the revelation occurred, when 'whilst he was at table with them, he took bread and blessed and brake and gave to them. And their eyes were opened: and they knew him.'"[71]

Vézelay. Abbey church narthex.
North side portal tympanum,
Pilgrims at Emmaus.

Vézelay. Abbey church narthex.
South side portal tympanum,
Nativity and Adoration of Magi.

"This breaking of the bread at Emmaus is seen as being like the Eucharist," Canon Jordan suggested.

"Yes," Abbot Peter confirmed softly. "As Christ was revealed to the two disciples at Emmaus in 'the blessing and breaking of the bread,' are the eyes of the faithful not also opened to the truth when receiving His body and blood in the Holy Eucharist?"

"I have seen those portals in the narthex at Vézelay!" exclaimed Canon Ugo Amelius. "All three. They are wonderful!"

"And just as Christ gave his Mission to the Apostles to teach and spread the True Word," Abbot Peter continued with a smile, "so it is the mission of the

71   Luke 24:30–31. See Luke 24:13–32 for the whole story.

Church to teach the truth. Here in Provence, where first Peter of Bruys and now Henry of Lausanne have spread such insidious, pernicious, evil untruths, we have to teach and spread the truth. But here, we are fighting for the souls of those being led astray! Here in Provence, the Church must even more stridently proclaim the truth! Here we need a stronger, bolder visual statement for the many illiterate, to guide the illiterate faithful—much stronger, firmer, and bolder even than at Vézelay!

"My sons, I must share something with you. I must tell you I have seen the remarkable new jamb figures that now adorn the façade on the abbey church of Saint-Denis up north in the French domain, column figures of Old Testament kings, queens, prophets, and patriarchs. They are remarkable, unbelievably beautiful! Absolutely magnificent! I wish every one of you could see those remarkable figures.

Saint-Denis. Drawings of the now destroyed column figures from the west portal. Bibliothèque nationale de France.[72]   *Chartres. West portal. Column figures (that would soon be erected 1145–1155).*

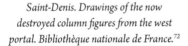

72   All the column figures were removed from the façade of Saint-Denis in 1771 and destroyed, and little remains. However, drawings of them were made by Antoine Benoit and included by Dom Bernard de Montfaucon in his *Les Monumens de la Monarchie Françoise* (Paris, France 1729), vol. I, plates XVI, XVII, XVIII.
Photo: Montfaucon, *Les Monumens,* vol. I, Plate XVII, used with permission of BnF.

"Abbot Suger placed the Old Testament kings and queens there. Sugar has long worked to strengthen the French monarchy and Saint-Denis has long been the burial place of the French kings. But these figures suggest much more than the concept of royal lineage.

"The Old Testament figures are placed at the church portal there to convey a subtle theological message of the Old Testament's relationship to the New, to suggest that the Old Testament leads to the New Testament, and to suggest that the Old Testament kings and queens were the lineage of our Lord. Those figures are truly magnificent. They are so effective, so subtly effective, that frankly, we believe they will undoubtedly use figures like them for the column figures that hopefully may one day adorn the new portals that are going to be erected for the new west front now under construction for the Cathedral at Chartres.

"But that is up north in the French Royal Domain, in the lands around the Île de France securely held by the French king directly or through his vassals. The situation is very different there. The use of Old Testament kings and queens to convey the subtle theological message is appropriate there.

"But not here! Not in Provence. Not in the County of Toulouse. Here the situation is dire; we cannot be subtle here! We are fighting Peter of Bruys's heresies. We are fighting the demons! Fighting the heretics! We are fighting to save the souls of the many, many faithful who are being led astray.

"So when the abbot and monks at Saint-Gilles told us they, too, were going to put large figure sculptures on their façade, not Old Testament kings and queens, but figures of the apostles, who would serve as guards—guards!—to the entrance of their new abbey church, we were at first taken aback. They seemed to be rebelling—rejecting the concept of royalty. But quite frankly, the situation is quite different here, and rather than benefiting from a strong monarchy, the abbey of Saint-Gilles has long suffered at the hands of local lords. So the abbot and monks wanted to promote the apostles as defenders of the faith and church, and after we thought about it, we were pleased with the idea!

"The monks noted that many of the ancient early Christian sarcophagi, or stone coffins, here show rows of apostle figures each standing in an individual niche separated by piers or columns, and the apostle figure usually holds a scroll or codex.[73] The monks wanted to use these figures on the sarcophagi as sculptural models for the stone carvers.

73   A sculptural motif on early Christian sarcophagi from the end of the fourth century. See, for examples, those at the Musée d'Art Chrétien, Arles, nos. 10, 17, 6, all depicted in Stoddard, Façade, figs. 18, 19, 20.

Arles. Early Christian sarcophagus, 4th century.[74]

"We encouraged and supported them. We said, 'Yes, put apostle figures as guardians on the façade of the new abbey church, because this will visually proclaim that Christ gave the apostles the mission to spread the True Word and that what the Church teaches is that divine Truth!'

"The apostle figures on the church façade here in Provence, the guardians, have to be bigger and bolder than the Old Testament kings and queens on columns at Saint-Denis. And I am told they are! They are huge, bold pier figures. They are large imposing apostle figures that challenge everyone who visits there. Large apostle pier figures like these will remind all visitors—both the illiterate and the literate who have been misguided alike, and errant monks and clergy as well—that the apostles received their mission to spread the truth from Christ Himself. That what the apostles spread was the True Word of Christ. That what the Church teaches is that divine Truth!

"We are now encouraging the abbey to expand the design of their portal and to include other sculptures portraying that divine Truth on the portal as well—on the tympana, on the lintels, all across the portals. Those sculptures will directly refute the heresies we are fighting here in Provence.[75]

. . . .

74   This fourth-century sarcophagus is now in the Arles Musée Antique, #6. It is often called the Sarcophagus of Hydria Tertulla because the lid now sitting on top of it names that person as the deceased. According to tradition, the sarcophagus originally held the body of St. Genest, who was martyred at Trinquetaille and buried at Les Alyscamps. In medieval times the sarcophagus was in the crypt of the Church of St. Honorat at Les Alyscamps. The sarcophagus shows Christ in the centre, gesturing and teaching one apostle, and they are flanked by six more apostles, each in a niche separated by columns.

75   On the interpretation of the scenes depicted at Saint-Gilles, especially the entombment and resurrection scenes, as a visual refutation of the Petrobrusian heresy by visually proclaiming that the Crucifixion represents triumph over sin and death, see M.L. Colish, "Peter of Bruys, Henry of Lausanne, and the Façade of St-Gilles," *Traditio* 28 (1972): 451–460. See discussion of Colish's premise in Stoddard, *Façade*, 140–148.

"When completed, those other sculptures will portray Christ's Passion. They will prominently show the Last Supper where Christ instituted the Eucharist that the Petrobrusians, the followers of Petrus Brunus, reject. They will prominently show the Crucifixion with Christ on the cross, the cross that the Petrobrusians abhor, but which we true Christians venerate because on it Christ gave his life for our salvation. We have to portray all this visually for the illiterate and for those who are uncertain, who are too easily led astray by the smooth-talking heretics. We have to fight these demon heretics! We have to rid this region of these heresies!

"You, as canons in the cathedral at Arles, deal more directly and more regularly with the people, both with the faithful and with those poor souls who are being led astray by these heresies. Your mission is that of the apostles. As the apostles spread the True Word, so should you as canons follow the way of the apostles, follow the *vita apostolica*, by teaching people the truth and leading them away from the errors of this heresy."

At the mention of the term *vita apostolica*, Pons was startled momentarily. He straightened up visibly, leaping intellectually to what seemed to him to be a new topic. He vigorously pressed the abbot further.

"Are you suggesting that we canons should adopt the *vita apostolica* to carry out our mission? Several of us have been learning about the reformers who would urge us to embrace the *vita apostolica* that requires a fully communal life, and that requires us to renounce all personal wealth and property and to embrace the strict monastic life.

"But how can we as canons live the *vita apostolica* yet carry out our mission? How can we as canons live a monastic life? We as canons cannot cloister ourselves away in isolation like the monks," he continued plaintively. "We carry out the liturgy and service in the choir. We carry out the business of the Church. We work on behalf of the Church, negotiating and documenting donations and gifts.

"And what about the wealth of the Church itself? What about the chapter's business? Is it right for us to carry on business solely to enhance the wealth of the Church?" he cried softly.

Looking directly at Pons, Peter smiled very kindly and continued softly, consolingly.

"Your archbishop has spoken to me about you and your concerns, about your probing questions. I should tell you that our own Order of Cluny was in need of reform when I was first elected general, and because of this, I wrote and promoted clear rules for the monastic Order of Cluny."[76]

After a moment, pressing his hands together and touching his lips, as if in prayer, Abbot Peter continued, responding slowly and thoughtfully.

"The monk and the canon regular[77] may both live a communal life. However, the monk is a 'learner' whose sole responsibility is for his own salvation and who adheres to the Rule of St. Benedict as a guide to achieving his goal. The canon regular is both a 'learner' and a 'teacher,' who not only learns to grow toward God, but who also has the responsibility to *docere* or *instruere*—teach or educate— his fellow men, both by what he says and by what he does—*verbo et exemplo*—as a *forma et exemplum*—pattern and example.[78]

"Canons regular, who are priests, are clerics who stand in the choir and sanctuary as representatives of the Church before God, performing a service on behalf of the people, and only secondarily are they responding to the Rule they have adopted."

Still not satisfied, Pons pressed him further. "But we do carry out business on behalf of the Church, negotiating and documenting donations and gifts. Is it wrong to work for the wealth of the Church? Is it wrong for the Church to be so wealthy, to own so much property?

"Peter of Bruys condemned all church buildings, and I have heard that the other man you mentioned earlier as a heretic, Arnold of Brescia, is a canon who has called on the Church to renounce its ownership of property."

After first slowly inhaling a deep breath, Abbot Peter then smiled kindly once again at Pons before gently responding.

"My son, did not the three Magi worship and adore the Christ child by presenting Him with gifts, with expensive gifts of gold, frankincense, and myrrh? And does this not teach us to worship Christ by presenting gifts of value to His Church? We portrayed this on one of the portals at Vézelay. Perhaps we should suggest to the monks at Saint-Gilles to more prominently portray the three Magi adoring Christ and presenting their gifts.

....

76   See "Blessed Peter of Montboissier" in *The Catholic Encyclopedia*.

77   The canon regular is one who has adopted a strict Rule that governs his conduct.

78   These comments are not taken directly from Peter the Venerable but from a collection of eleventh- and twelfth-century writers, all from Caroline W. Bynum, "The Spirituality of Regular Canons in the Twelfth Century: A New Approach," *Medievalia et Humanistica* 4 (1973).

"This confusion is not yours alone, my son. We monks, too, struggle with the dilemma of property and wealth. My worthy brother Bernard of Clairvaux and I hold strongly differing, if not opposing, views on this issue. We have disputed vigorously with each other about the monastery's ownership of property, trying to resolve this. Bernard challenges what he calls the worldly practices of some monasteries, such as ours. He attacks them for owning and keeping secular possessions of value, specifically for owning towns, villas, and servants; for collecting tolls and duties; and for keeping serfs to work on their properties. He questions whether this violates the Rule of St. Benedict, under which both our monasteries live.

"But, as I have responded to my brother Bernard, the Rule of St. Benedict itself says that when a monastery is accepting a novice, if he has any posses- sions, he should first either distribute them to the poor, or give them to the monastery as a donation. Moreover, the words of the Blessed Gregory himself agree with this, because he forbade any bishop or secular leader to try to curtail in any way the income, property, or charters of the monasteries.[79] So it is right and appropriate for the Church, for the chapter of canons, or for the monastery to collectively own property. It is God's will, as shown us by our blessed fathers.

"As for church property or church structures, is not a magnificent stone church, beautifully built, superbly vaulted, and elegantly decorated with beautiful sculptured or painted renderings of biblical images, completely appropriate as a house for God? And is it not a gloriously inspiring surround- ing for the liturgy with which we praise and worship Him?

"Less than a decade ago we finally completed construction of our own church up in Burgundy, at the home of our monastic order. It is the largest church in all of Christendom, the greatest and most magnificent church structure ever built. It has a huge nave of massive stone walls and arches, a soaring cupola at its transept crossing, a sanctuary profusely decorated with religious carved sculptures of biblical stories and religious imagery. It is a

---

79   On these discussions, see "Peter the Venerable vs. St. Bernard of Clairvaux: *On the Keeping of Serfs,* c. 1120" in *Medieval Sourcebook,* https://sourcebooks.fordham.edu/ source/1120Petebern.asp.

church structure that is a monumental tribute to God and to our monastic Order of Cluny.[80]

"My brother Bernard of Clairvaux has challenged this as opulence. He calls for stark austerity in church and claustral buildings. But should we not construct such a glorious surrounding as a loving tribute to our God? Is not such a magnificently beautiful structure an appropriate house for God? Should we not make God's house as beautiful as we possibly can?"

Just as the abbot was finishing, there was another commotion at the southwest portal leading to the town, where his entourage had returned. His two companions rose, as did he, and after giving the canons his personal blessing and bidding them farewell, Abbot Peter quickly walked to the portal and disappeared from sight.

The other canons who had been in attendance slowly dispersed, but Pons and Jordan walked back into the chapter house. Pons's head was reeling at first, but slowly things began to sort themselves out as he focused on everything he had heard, everything he had just learned about, especially the *vita apostolica*. They sat in silence for a while.

Slowly rising from his seat, with the quiet determination of someone who was working toward a difficult decision, Pons exited the central portal of the chapter house and turned immediately. He looked once again for quite a long time at the carved capital with the figure of the siren, the beautiful half-woman, whose fleshy torso, breasts, and abdomen were so beautiful, so tempting, so seductive, and so . . . destructive. Walking westward a few paces, he then fixed his gaze for a much longer time on the revolting counterpart, the female figure with identical face and hair and lips, whose breasts were being sucked by demonic serpents from hell.

It had taken him some time after returning from his encounter with Beatrice, but by now he finally accepted and understood that what he had experienced was nothing but *luxuria*—lust, base urgings of the flesh. His encounter with Beatrice that fateful day at Saint-Gilles had been a test in which he had failed. He had failed his God. He now vowed he would not fail again.

....

80   The huge, magnificently decorated church of Cluny III is now destroyed, and only remnants remain. Its original structure and decoration are known, however, through the thorough excavations and extensive study of K. J. Conant. See, for example, K. J. Conant, "Cluny, Les églises et la maison du chef d'ordre," *Bulletin Monumental* 127, no. 2, année 1969: 183–186.

"Jordan," he suddenly cried out as Jordan turned to rejoin him. "I just recognized for the first time that these two figures are one and the same! This luscious, beautiful, so very desirable woman is also *Luxuria*. They are not good and bad counterparts; they are one and the same. Woman is the temptress. Woman leads man astray. Woman leads man . . . to hell."

Pons had long been drawn to these carved figures of warning and admonition. And this warning, these images that would guide him, that would help keep him anchored, were right here on capitals outside the chapter house, right where Peter the Venerable had just helped to open his eyes.

For months and months and months, Pons had persevered so clumsily through soul-searching inquiry and nagging doubts, sustained only by his blind conviction that God somehow intended him to struggle with this. Yet answers had remained elusive. Until now.

God had now sent Abbot Peter of Cluny to light the spark that would now give the answers—answers that would change Pons's life forever. Certainly, Abbot Peter had reaffirmed for Pons the need to build beautiful buildings that glorified God. He had reaffirmed the need for canons to defend all the Church rites and rituals that brought man closer to God. But it was much more than that. Much more significantly, by sending Abbot Peter, God had spoken directly to him. God had answered his prayers. Pons had now been shown a new path and the way forward.

Pons slowly sat down again with Jordan. God was now once again speaking clearly to Pons. If Pons had ever been certain of anything, he knew he was now certain of God's message.

"Jordan, God wants our chapter to live the *vita apostolica*. We must all live the true communal life, as did the apostles. We must each of us renounce all personal wealth, give up all our personal belongings to the chapter. We must all renounce women. We must live celibate lives. Even those with wives and families must give them up to live like the apostles. We will carry out the liturgy and service in the choir and carry out the business of the chapter, but we will live the *vita apostolica* and teach the people by both word and deed.

"This is what God wants me to bring about. This is the task God has given me to accomplish. This is God's will."

Aghast, totally astounded, Jordan finally gasped, "Pons, are you serious? I don't think you realize what you are proposing! Are you certain you want to take this on?"

"This is the task God has given me," Pons responded quietly.

"It is probably impossible," Jordan continued. "And even if it were possible, it would be extremely difficult."

"Well, of course . . ." Jordan stumbled on, after some thought, "maybe you could get the chapter to discuss formally changing our chapter's rules. That, at least, would probably not be too difficult, at least to start the discussion. But after the discussion . . . Well . . . Yes, maybe the archbishop would see some benefits in promoting the reform movement and strengthening relationships with Rome. After all, our archbishop is William Monachus, William the Monk.

"But the provost, the dean, the chapter . . . That's an entirely different thing! Getting all the canons to renounce and give up their own personal wealth, to give it all to the chapter will be . . . Well, it may be impossible. Some are very wealthy. Some live very comfortably—very, very comfortably."

"I am one of them," Pons countered.

"But what about the canons who are married? Who have mistresses? Pons, do you understand what you are proposing? You are going to make enemies. Bad enemies."

"Marriages of canons have been annulled," Pons responded determinedly.

"Of course, we know that marriages of canons have been annulled, but . . . Maybe if you could begin by speaking privately with some of those who have wives and families, try to convince them it is in their own best interest. But why would they agree? Pons, please reconsider all this!

"Oh! And watch out for Peter Villelmus! He will be especially furious, having taken you into his own dwelling to live with his family. How will you ever be able to speak with him to convince him? I just don't know. So please, please! I beg you to reconsider, to think long and carefully about all this before starting anything," Jordan gasped.

But Pons had made his decision.

"This is the task God has given me. I will do it."

With the clarity of vision and vigorousness of purpose reserved only for the young, the twenty-nine-year-old canon was now embarking on a mission to carry out what God had told him to do. God had now clarified for him that for the canons at Arles, the common life, the *vita apostolica* described in the Acts of the Apostles, should be the guiding principle. Pons's task was to make it so.

*   *   *

Pons immediately threw himself wholeheartedly into his task.

He began by bringing up the issue of the *vita apostolica* twice daily in chapter, where the brothers gathered to take counsel, to hear the daily readings, and to deliberate over infringements to their own rules of governance. Of course, he always started from the premise that their own rules, loosely modeled after the Rule of Aachen, were less restrictive than they should be, less restrictive than they ever should have been. As the canons discussed issues arising from their own rules, Pons would raise the concept of what the *vita canonica* should be, and he would champion the notion that the ideal *vita canonica* should emulate the life of the apostles, clarifying that the *vita apostolica* required both the renunciation of private property and living the celibate life.

Most of the chapter initially tolerated with patience and forbearance Pons's new focus on the *vita apostolica*, viewing it as a new phase of his previous intensely personal trials and tribulations. Some quietly dismissed his campaign as idealistic but not at all realistic, expecting that with time he would mature and that his interest would slowly but eventually wane.

Most found the discussions interesting, at least, if not entertaining. Many frankly actually enjoyed the discussions, in part because often they were quite titillating when they focused on celibacy. Celibacy had not previously been a major issue in chapter, not an important issue for discussion, and the new discussions on the subject permitted verbal explorations of a wide range of temptations of the flesh, and of carnal activities and improprieties, as well as that of fornication itself. Moreover, there were few secrets among these men, and Pons would relate his own story as a "fable," naïvely describing his own seduction with such openness and innocence that most became charmed by his genuine idealism, even while they were vicariously enjoying his sinful exploit.

Some were immediately and violently openly opposed to this campaign, however, especially those who had wives and families, including, as Jordan had predicted, Peter Villelmus.

"If we are to emulate the apostles, to live communally, we must not only renounce personal wealth and personal belongings; we must give up wives and families," Pons would begin. "We cannot bring wives into a communal complex. We cannot bring wives into a common dormitory. We must all isolate ourselves from women. It is women who arouse all base urgings of the flesh in men. Women arouse lust in us as men, and another canon's wife must not become a whore in our thoughts!"

"And where would you be if I had not taken you as a child into my own dwelling, you pious little prig? My wife and I fed you and raised you like one of our own, and you repay us by calling my wife a whore! I swear I wish we had not . . ." spat Peter Villelmus.

"But I know whereof I speak," whispered Pons, with some chagrin. "Who among us can look at a beautiful woman without wanting to kiss her lips, to touch the soft flesh of her breasts, to caress and stroke the yielding flesh of her abdomen, to feel her thighs against your own, to taste her body, to press . . . No! None of us would be able to restrain ourselves! None of us would be able to refrain from these thoughts. And this is lust! The thoughts alone are lust. Woman leads us into temptation. Woman is the temptress!"

To this Peter Villelmus retorted heatedly, "When God created woman, did he not intend for man to enjoy her? We would not be here today if God intended man to keep to his own bed and refrain from knowing women. God sanctifies sexual union with the sacrament of marriage.

"Now, your whores, that's a different thing," Peter Villelmus continued, pointing toward young Bertrand. "Like you over there, Bertrand, with your concubine whore, who has known half the men in this chapter house! Now that's fornication. That's wrong! And I've told you so in chapter. But within holy marriage, for us to have conjugal union with our wives is right and proper. It's God's will!"

Pons continued faithfully with his campaign to win over his fellow canons, but the campaign was fated to be cut short. Not long after the visit of Peter the Venerable, the Archbishop of Arles, William Monachus, was appointed papal legate to Barcelona in Catalonia[81] and was to leave for Barcelona. The archbishop asked Pons to accompany him and to serve and assist him there as his *subdiachonus*, or subdeacon, an administrator who would assist the archbishop with specific lay duties and faithfully draft documents.[82]

....

81   Albanes and Chevalier, *Arles*, no. 3228. See also Schneider, "Sculptures," 73.

82   On Poncius de Baucio's accompanying Archbishop Willelmus Monachus to Catalonia, see Schneider, "Sculptures," 73 and Albanes and Chevalier, *Arles*, nos. 3228, 535, 538.

This would not only be an honor for Pons, it would be an exciting trip. So although he was truly conflicted, feeling somehow that his real mission was being postponed, he certainly accepted the invitation. After all, there would be lots of time after he had returned to chapter.

* * *

And so within but a few months of beginning his mission to reform the chapter, Pons found himself on the road, traveling on horseback, accompanying Archbishop William Monachus and his large entourage to Catalonia. The group had not been traveling long, following a well-used section of the *Via Domitia,* the ancient road the Romans had built to connect Italia with Hispania through Gallia Narbonensis, and they had just passed the bridge at Ambrussum, between Nîmes and Montpellier. Pons acknowledged to himself, with some regret, that once again he would not be turning westward at Montpellier to continue on one of the pilgrimage routes into and across the Iberian Peninsula to Santiago de Compostela. No, they were going southward, following the route along the Mediterranean coast through Perpignan to Barcelona, where he would assist the archbishop.

To pass the time while traveling, Pons struck up a conversation with another member of the large group, a new man whom he did not know.

"I am Canon Pons de Baux of the cathedral at Arles. Do you have any idea what we can expect when we get to Narbonne? I have heard it is as important a center as Arles or Marseille."

"Indeed, I believe I do. I am Canon Nicolaus of Saint-Ruf, and I have been to Narbonne. It is now becoming a thriving cultural center, but it has also long been a major Jewish center of learning. Frankly, it is now so important a center that many are now eagerly trying to take control of it. The Count of Toulouse, the Count of Barcelona, the viscounts of Carcassonne, and the lords of Montpellier, they all want to take control of it. In fact, the archbishop there has been trying to get the Count of Toulouse to take control by force, since the Viscountess Ermengarde of Narbonne is only a child. I only hope we do not encounter any hostilities while passing through."

"You are from Saint-Ruf, but you seem very well acquainted not only with this route, but with the power struggles here," responded Pons.

"Yes, our community of canons regular at Saint-Ruf, Avignon have a strong relationship with other chapters of canons regular in Catalonia."

"Tell me about the canons regular of Saint-Ruf," said Pons, more out of politeness and to make conversation than genuine curiosity.

"Certainly, and with pleasure! Quite some time ago, maybe a century ago," began Nicolaus, "four members of the cathedral chapter at Avignon left to go to Saint-Ruf because they wanted to live a more austere life in emulation of the apostles. As usual they devised their own chapter's rules of conduct. They first tried to model them on the Rule of Aachen, but then decided it was not strict enough."

"Really?" interjected Pons, his ears pricking up.

"Yes," Nicolaus continued. "And after deciding it was not strict enough, not austere enough, they formally adopted the Rule of St. Augustine. Then, toward the end of the last century, the influence of our house really started to spread, especially in Catalonia. That was where papal reforms of the clergy first began to take hold. I think reform was slow at first, but communities eventually began adopting our constitution. Then Pope Urban II finally recognized our order." Nicolaus cautiously awaited his listener's response.[83]

Pons now pulled down his hood completely, to get a better look at his traveling companion. He asked hesitantly, "How was this reform able to succeed, to take hold in Catalonia?"

It was now obvious to Nicolaus that he had piqued Pons's curiosity, and that Pons as a canon had not taken offense at the concept of the need for reform among the clergy but was instead receptive to a fuller discussion. Nicolaus responded warmly, eagerly, and effusively.

"Good question. Well, papal influence was strong there, of course, and, as I'm sure you already know, it was Pope Gregory who first sparked real papal reform of the clergy around then. Catalonia was already under papal influence. Count Berenguer Ramon II of Barcelona got himself into serious

....

83   For the influence of the canons regular of Saint-Ruf, Avignon, see Paul Freedman, "Review of Ursula Vones- Liebenstein, Saint-Ruf und Spanien: Studien zur Verbreitung und zum Wirken der Regularkanoniker von Saint-Ruf in Avignon auf der iberischen Halbinsel (11. und 12. Jahrhundert)," *Speculum* 74, no. 2 (April 1999): 527–529. See also J. C. Dickinson, *The Origins of the Austin Canons and their Introduction into England* (London: SPCK, 1950), 42.

The first Catalan priory of Saint-Ruf at Santa Maria de Besalu was established in 1084. Pope Urban II recognized the order in 1095.

trouble—he was accused of murdering his twin brother—and to gain some assistance in his troubles, he placed his lands under papal control. So papal influence was really strong.

"Then our canons of Saint-Ruf from Avignon were already active there, of course, and the first Catalan priory of Saint-Ruf at Santa Maria de Besalu was established.

"But I think it was probably the canon regular Olegarius, who embraced reform, who really played the key role. Many of us have heard stories about Olegarius because he was a canon regular at our house. He came from a noble family in Barcelona that had long been friendly with the Counts of Barcelona, and when Olegarius eventually became the Archbishop of Tarragona, the count granted him and the church full control over Tarragona and the surrounding land, making him virtually a secular ruler. So Olegarius was able to develop an alliance between the house of Saint-Ruf and the Count of Barcelona, and this certainly strengthened the reforming influence of Saint-Ruf.[84]

"So to answer your question, how was papal reform of the clergy able to take hold in Catalonia? Well, I guess we might say it was because it was an area under strong papal control, where the political difficulties of the secular rulers were turned to good use, so that an enlightened and politically astute church leader, who was himself a reformed canon, could use his position of power to inspire and promote reform under the Order of Saint-Ruf.

"Oh, but more importantly, of course, the spirit of reform and the desire for the truly spiritual life was growing by then and still continues now to grow ever stronger," Nicolaus added quickly, with a touch of chagrin, as a pious afterthought.

Pons was visibly taken aback at what he was hearing. "One reformed canon turning secular political difficulty to good use . . ." He thought about the reluctance of members of his chapter to embrace the *vita apostolica*, but this fellow was telling him about canons who had taken the difficult decision, who had chosen to live an austere life.

....

84   Olegarius rose through the ranks of the church, starting as a young canon at the Cathedral of Barcelona, then abbot of Saint-Ruf in Avignon, then Bishop of Barcelona, and finally Archbishop of Tarragona. It was in 1118 that Count Ramon Berenger III granted Olegarius as Archbishop of Tarragona full control over Tarragona. See Freedman, "Review."

Pons tentatively queried, "The Order of Saint-Ruf encourages an austere life in emulation of the apostles?"

Nicolaus responded quietly. "Yes, we canons of Saint-Ruf adopted the Rule of St. Augustine. We want to dedicate ourselves to the spiritual life, and we seek a religious life of simplicity, austerity, and humility. We embrace the full communal life. We hold all things in common. We seek to follow the *vita apostolica*. We are not monks—we do not shelter ourselves away; we do not follow the strongly ascetic rules of many monasteries. Rather, we serve the Church as canons regular, who live by the Rule of St. Augustine, who live in emulation of the Apostles by holding all things in common."[85]

Euphoria now swept over Pons. He was overcome with joy. His spirit and his soul soared. Praise be to God! Here was the answer to his dilemma. Here was the key, the tool that could unblock some of the barriers and obstacles to his moving forward on his mission. The Rule of St. Augustine—that he could reasonably put forth as the model to define the canons' *vita apostolica* for his chapter.

"Thank You, God!" he said aloud. Then he continued silently to himself, "Thank You, God, for sending me on this journey with the archbishop. Thank You, God, for putting me here, on this horse, with this traveling companion from Saint-Ruf. Thank You, God, for sending this canon regular from whom I can learn."

"Can you teach me about the Rule of St. Augustine?" he then asked Nicolaus, somewhat impatiently.

"Certainly," replied Nicolaus, trying to contain his own growing excitement at Pons's obviously genuine interest and enthusiasm. "We should be able to examine a copy of the Rule together after we reach Barcelona. I know that the archbishop has asked you to assist him there as *subdiachonus*, drafting documents. I, too, will be assisting him later, after I have completed some other work for our order,[86] but we should have some overlapping time in Barcelona. I'll find a copy of the Rule there, and we can examine it together. Perhaps you will want to make a copy of it."

....

85   Freedman, "Review."

86   A "Nicolaus, canonicus Sancti Rufi" was in the company of Archbishop Willilmus Monachus in Spain, where Nicolaus penned and witnessed a charter. See Schneider, "Sculptures," 65. See also Albanes and Chevalier, *Arles,* no. 537.

As they continued talking and chatting while proceeding on their journey, they soon became friends. How could two such energetic young men, equally fired up about the same issue, not become friends once they had found each other? Pons spoke to Nicolaus about the visit of Peter the Venerable, about witnessing the burning of Peter of Bruys. He confided to him about succumbing to temptations of the flesh with Beatrice, about repenting his sinful fall from innocence, and about how difficult it had been to try to keep thoughts about the pleasure of her from his dreams. They talked and talked of many things. Nicolaus told him all about himself, and he was pleased also to relate what he knew about the places they passed, their history, and their politics.

*   *   *

It was November, and Pons was in Barcelona. The city had long been the capital of the Count of Barcelona, who also laid claim to Provence, but who ruled much more securely over all of Catalonia.[87]

Barcelona, this ancient Roman walled city, was a well-chosen capital, situated on a plateau with its magnificent harbor facing the Mediterranean Sea. With its ancient Roman monuments and grid planning, overlaid with a strong Hispanic flavor and strong Arab presence, the lively old city was rich in culture. Conquered by the Arabs during their conquest of the Iberian Peninsula in the eighth century, Barcelona had been reconquered a century later by Charlemagne's son, Louis the Pious, when it was established as the seat of the Carolingian "Spanish Marches," the defensive barrier between the Frankish kingdom and the Muslims.

By now, Barcelona was but one of the exciting centers in Iberia where Muslim and Christian cultures coexisted, mingled, and thrived, where Latin scholars could come to study. For centuries, learning and scholarship had mostly stagnated and declined in the Latin West, with few and limited exceptions. However, Muslim scholars had long embraced and preserved the classical scientific learning of antiquity—Plato, Aristotle, Euclid, Ptolemy, and all the Greek philosophers—translating them into Arabic while also

87   Within a decade or so the dynasty's territory would also include Aragon as well because two years earlier, in 1137, Ramon Berenguer IV, Count of Barcelona, also called Ramond Berengar the Holy, had married one-year-old Petronilla of Aragon, the heir to the Kingdom of Aragon, and their future progeny would eventually merge those two dynasties.

pursuing their own Arabic scholarship as well. Jewish scholars had also played a critically important role in preserving classical works, translating them from Greek and Latin into Arabic and Hebrew. Consequently, much classical learning had been preserved and still existed in the Iberian centers, mostly in Arabic. Once Toledo was reconquered by the Christians in 1085, its renowned library was destined to attract myriad Latin scholars, but there were many other centers with impressive classical scholarly collections, transmitted by Muslim and Jewish scholars, that now drew these Latin scholars. Barcelona was one of them.[88]

Canon Pons had not been here very long, but he thoroughly enjoyed this beautiful, thriving, exciting, polyglot city. He took great delight in wandering aimlessly and exploring its delights whenever he could get the chance, although he was usually too busy to do so, just as now he was busily drafting documents on behalf of the archbishop. He was just completing one,[89] the last of a huge pile of work.

Putting down his quill, he rose, scratched his head, and stepped away from his desk before stretching and then walking to the window opening, apparently waiting for someone. He was gazing out on the courtyard, lit by the early afternoon sun, when two men quietly entered: Fernando, a local cleric in Barcelona who usually served as an assistant to the archbishop's delegation, and a stranger, a dark-skinned, turbaned Arab, who was carrying several manuscripts.

"I see you are awaiting us, Brother Pons," began Fernando. "Please let me introduce Mohammed Al Hasany, whom I have mentioned to you.

"*As-salamu alaikum wa rahmatullahi wa barakatuh.* Peace be upon you with Allah's mercy and blessings," Mohammed began.

"God be with you, and thank you for coming" responded Pons.

"Fernando has told me that your family considers itself to be descendants of Balthazar, one of the three Arabic astronomers, or wise men, who followed the star to Bethlehem," noted Mohammed, then adding with an ironic smile, "but I see you are not Arab."

---

88   See "Latin Translations of the 12th century," *Wikipedia.*

89   For the document drafted by "Poncius subdiachonus," see Albanes and Chevalier, *Arles,* no. 535. See also Schneider, "Sculptures," 73.

"No, I am not," Pons answered confidently but politely. "My family has long lived in Provence, just north of Arles, but we nevertheless pride ourselves in having descended from one of the Magi."

"*Allahu Akbar*. God is great," Mohammed responded with a nod. "It is said that the stars control all our lives. Nevertheless, your ancestor was indeed a wise man to understand their call to follow that one star."

"You are most gracious," Pons responded politely with a deep nod.

"As you may already know," Mohammed continued, "Abbot Peter of Cluny came to our land a few months ago. He was so pleased to be able to be here in our land where Arab scholars have kept alive classical Greek learning. He spoke with some of our scholars and said he was amazed at the strength of the tradition of scholarship that our Arab culture has long embraced. I was but one of the interpreters who participated in some of those meetings, and although I am not a scholar, being but an interpreter, Abbot Peter and I also spoke together privately several times.

"What you may not yet know is that during his sojourn here, Abbot Peter became very interested in our Muslim culture, in Mohammedanism. I will admit I was skeptical at first about his intentions. After all, I was born during your First Crusade and grew up in its aftermath, learning of hard necessity not only to speak your Latin language but to read and write it, as well. But when I mentioned my experience of the Crusade to Abbot Peter, he responded that Muslims should be met not with armies seeking battle, but with scholars ready to discuss ideas."[90]

"Abbot Peter of Cluny is a very wise man," responded Pons, humbly.

"Abbot Peter stated that if he is able to do so, he would like sometime in the near future to have our Qur'an translated into Latin. He said he wished that Christians like himself could come to truly understand our culture by reading what we truly believe, instead of forging their own mistaken concepts and misinterpretations. So if Abbot Peter is successful, you may be able one day to read our Qur'an yourself, if you are interested in doing so.

"But for today, Fernando has told me about you, about your finding some curious inscriptions back home. When he told me about your wanting to understand what you called a curious use of little 'circles' with numerals,

....

90 See James E. Kiefer, "The Early Abbots of Cluny," in *Biological sketches of memorable Christians of the Past*, http://justus.anglican.org/resources/bio/151.html.

I agreed to offer my services to you, if you would like to learn about our number system."

Pons was thrilled and jumped with delight at the offer. Frankly, he was rather tired of preparing and copying documents. Although he knew that it was God's work and important, he also knew it was not the special mission God had entrusted to him. Moreover, the idea of doing something totally different, of learning something absolutely new, was both exciting and a great relief.

"Oh, yes, I would be so grateful," Pons responded enthusiastically.

"I would be deeply honored to explain our number system,"[91] Mohammed began. "Our number system is not at all new. In fact, it is very old, but it is only now being received more enthusiastically in the West and becoming accepted by the West.

"I have brought copies of three important scholarly works kept here in Barcelona to show you, and we can all look briefly at them," he began, laying them very carefully out on a table. "I selected them and brought them here today to demonstrate to you the scholarly tradition of learning that our Arabic culture has long embraced and promoted.

"First, I have something very special I thought you simply might like to see, even though it is much too complex for our purposes today. It's a copy in Latin of an Arabic astronomical treatise, the *Sententiae astrolabii* that was translated two centuries ago by Lupitus of Barcelona at the request of Gerbert of Aurillac. Apparently Gerbert had been here in Catalonia studying, learning about the astrolabe and calculating with Hindu-Arabic numbers. Much later, after returning to France, he became your Pope, named Sylvester II. So like you, he was interested in our number system."

"Yes!" exclaimed Pons. "During my early schooling my teacher, old Bernard, mentioned that Pope Sylvester II was interested in your Hindu numbers and tried to promote them, but your number system still never caught on. Apparently, no one really understood what benefit there might be in using your numerals."

"Well, I do expect that you may come to think otherwise after we speak today. Here we have the two works we will examine a little more closely,"

91   For more on Hindu-Arabic numerals, see "Hindu–Arabic numeral system," *Wikipedia*, and J. J. O'Connor and E. F. Robertson, "Indian numerals," *MacTutor* (2000), https:// mathshistory.st-andrews.ac.uk/HistTopics/Indian_numerals/.

Mohammed continued. "We have a copy in Arabic of *The Book of Addition and Subtraction according to the Hindu Calculation,* by Muhammed ibn Musa al-Khwarizmi, who was a most influential and famous Arab scholar and mathematician.[92] And we also have a copy in Arabic of a work by Al-Biruni, an important Islamic astronomer and mathematician of a century ago."

Before even looking at these works, Pons admitted to himself that he simply could not envision a more efficient numbering system than the Roman one, where each symbol has its own unique value: I is one, V is five, X is ten, L is fifty, C is 100, D is 500, M is 1,000, and to compose a number, you simply keep adding symbols in a string with the biggest number to the left with the smaller add-ons to its right, each in descending value. Of course, some numbers are composed as a smaller take-away, that is, with a smaller symbol to the immediate left of the next larger one, such as IV, but that was never a problem.

"The Roman system is so simple," Pons explained politely, "you simply string all the symbols together until you have represented the full value you want. So for example, MMCCCXXXVIII would be the Roman number for two thousand three hundred thirty-eight."

"Yes, Roman numbers are cumulative or additive" Mohammed agreed, "but they are also very cumbersome in comparison with our Arabic number system."

"And adding Roman numerals together or subtracting one number from another can be quite a chore," Fernando suggested.

"Not if you use the abacus,"[93] Pons suggested.

"We'll see," Mohammed suggested with a wry smile as he opened one of the volumes and began writing ten symbols onto a scrap of vellum with his quill. "Our Arabic number system uses Hindu numerals, a series of nine unique symbols, representing the values one through nine, plus a little circle whose use I will describe shortly. Here are the symbols most commonly used here now, beginning with the little circle.

. . . .

92   Muhammed ibn Musa al-Khwarizmi (c. 780–850 AD).

93   The Greek or Roman type of abacus was used for trade and calculation through the twelfth century. It had two vertically aligned slots for each Roman numeral, a lower longer one with four beads, and a shorter upper one with one bead, which when moved indicated five of its lower units. See "Medieval Mathematics," *The Story of Mathematics,* http://www.storyofmathematics.com/medieval.html.

Hindu-Arabic numerals, twelfth century.[94]

"Using only these ten symbols, you can write any number. The value of each symbol depends on its place or position, so the symbol stands for different values, depending on its position within the series. This is a place-value system. The little 'circle' is especially important because it is a placeholder.

"Using our place-value system, we count with each Hindu numeral: 'one, two, three, four, five, six, seven, eight, nine.' For the number ten, the 'one' moves over to the next place to the left, and a little 'circle' is added to hold the initial place. As al-Khwarizmi here explained," he added, pointing to the volume, "if no number appears in the position for 'ten,' a little circle should be used to 'keep the rows.'"

"There's your little 'circles,' Pons," Fernando suggested.

Mohammed smiled and patiently continued. "The ten series then continues with each of the numerals replacing the little circle in sequence until we reach nineteen. Then, a 'two' is inserted into the left place and the little 'circle' again holds the initial place, and we have 'twenty.' And this continues to thirty, with a 'three' in the left place and the circle in the initial place, and on and on, eventually to 'ninety-nine,' after which a 'one' moves over into the next place further left, and two little circles are added to hold two places."

"So the little circle is the placeholder that keeps the numerals in their correct rows," exclaimed Pons.

"Yes," answered Mohammed. "We Arabs call this little circle *sifr*, which means 'empty.' The *sifr* is extremely important as a placeholder. But it's much more important than that. As al-Khwarizmi clarified, the *sifr* is also our numeral indicating 'nothing.'[95] Your Latin Christian scholars have no Roman numeral for 'nothing.' They have to write it out as *nulla* or *nihil*, or sometimes they abbreviate it with *N*.

. . . .

94   These Hindu-Arabic numerals are modelled after the examples presented in several sources, most notably O'Connor and Robertson, "Indian," and "Devanagari," *Wikipedia*. In the first of these two sources, it is argued that the Indian Gupta numerals had evolved into this form of Nagari numerals by the eleventh century, when they were known to the Arab world in this form.

95   See "0," *Wikipedia*, https://en.wikipedia.org/wiki/0. Fibonacci (1170–1250) used the term *zephyrum*, which became *zefiro* and then *zero*.

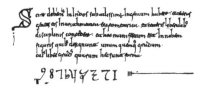

Codex Vigilanus.[96] *Excerpt from page.*

"Here's something that may surprise you," he continued. "It's a copy of a single page from a Western manuscript that was copied on parchment especially for me. When I was in Pamplona, in the Rioja, working on another translation project, I was surprised to see a Western manuscript into which Hindu-Arabic numerals had been copied long ago: The *Codex Vigilanus.* I was told the codex is from the tenth century. One of the monks I was working with at that time agreed to make this copy of the page for me, painstakingly reproducing the numerals. Here it is." He showed them the page on the desk.

"But there is no little circle, no *sifr*, here!" Pons exclaimed. "And the forms of the numbers are quite different from those you just showed me!" Pons exclaimed.

"Yes, you are correct," responded Mohammed. "Although the scribe was aware of Hindu numerals and copied them into the codex, he did not include the *sifr*, and he copied the numbers from right to left. We cannot know for certain, of course, but the scribe who copied the numbers most probably did not know about the *sifr*, and did not understand its use, just as he probably did not understand how the other numbers were used because he simply copied them from right to left, as they undoubtedly appeared on the original document. Even now, many who know about Hindu numerals do not fully understand the use of the *sifr*."

"And the difference in the forms . . . ?" Pons pressed.

"Well," Mohammed began, "the Arab mathematician Al-Biruni once wrote that the numerals we use are the best and most regular of the Indian forms,[97] but there are many local variants of the forms of the numbers. Hindu number

96   From the *Codex Vigilanus*, a manuscript preserved in the library of the Monasterio del Escorial in Madrid, Spain (Escorialensis d 1 2.) It contains a collection of diverse historical documents that were copied into one codex by the scribe Vigila and two associates in the Riojan monastery of San Martin de Albelda. The *Codex Vigilanus* is dated 976 and contains Arabic numerals, possibly their first appearance in the West.

97   O'Connor and Robertson, "Indian."

symbols are used in many lands, not only in India, but also elsewhere in the Far East, as well as in Arab lands. And as is to be expected, everywhere they are used, they have evolved. Different sets of symbols have evolved with the different peoples in the different lands."

Opening the other volume and leafing through several pages, Pons noted, "Even here in this copy of al-Khwarizmi's work, the Hindu-Arabic figures seem to be a little bit different."

"Yes," Mohammed replied. "As long as the Hindu numbers are handwritten by individuals, there will be variations—even in so important a manuscript as this one. Hindu numbers will never be standardized because, well, what could ever replace the handwritten manuscript or codex?

"Quite frankly, I was told that Gerbert, your Pope Sylvester II, may have inadvertently added to the confusion. Apparently, when he tried to introduce our Hindu-Arabic numbers into Western use, he devised a new kind of abacus, a counting board, with many sets of special counter pieces, jetons, that each had one of our nine numerals on them, but no *sifr*. The counter pieces were movable for adding and subtracting. The jetons also rotated, however, so people became confused about how the numeral was supposed to be written. For example, using only these two variants of the numeral six we see here, the numeral six could appear in many forms.

"Here, let me copy these two variant sets of the Hindu-Arabic numerals onto this little piece of vellum for you," Mohammed offered, quickly copying them down.

"But now let's choose the *Codex Vigilanus* numerals to review how the system works," he continued, as he began writing each symbol as he spoke of it. "If we write one numeral 'four' all alone, it indicates four, whereas if we place the numeral 'seven' to the left of it, it indicates seventy-four. Or, if we place the numeral 'eight' to the left of the other two, it indicates eight hundred seventy-four."

"Yet in Roman numerals those numbers would be IV, and LXXIV, and DCCCLXXIV," exclaimed Pons.

"Yes. And as you will see," Mohammed continued, again opening the al-Khwarizmi book, "if you give up the abacus, you can write the numerals down onto vellum or parchment and line them up with others. Because of the simplicity and order of the place-value system, and using the *sifr*, you can manipulate the numbers effectively and efficiently for manipulations like addition and subtraction. That is what our esteemed Arabic mathematician, al-Khwarizmi, has shown. See here . . ." he began as he pointed to an example of addition, patiently vocalizing and pointing to each step.

"Our Arab mathematicians also do much more complex operations with them," he added. "They use them for astronomy, for example, but I'm afraid I do not understand those complex operations well enough to try to explain them."

"I think I am beginning to see that the system would be very useful for addition and subtraction, once you were familiar with the Hindu-Arabic numbers," suggested Pons. "But I am afraid anything more complicated is beyond me too," he admitted.

The three men then looked briefly at the materials, until Mohammed told Pons he could keep the scrap of vellum with the numerals he had written today, but the other documents had to be returned to the library.

"Are you interested in pursuing this further?" Fernando then asked Pons. "Remember, Barcelona is now attracting Latin scholars interested in both classical philosophy and Arabic scholarship.

"There's an Italian working here now," Fernando continued rather excitedly, "a mathematician and astronomer named Plato of Tivoli, who is working with a Jewish mathematician, Abraham bar Hiyya ha-Nasi. The two scholars are busy translating classical mathematical and astronomical texts from the Arabic and the Hebrew. They are always working in the cathedral library. I could try to arrange a meeting with them for you."

"I have another suggestion," interjected Mohammed with a look of discomfort if not slight distress. "Let's all walk together to the library now with these volumes. Perhaps the two of them will be working there, and you can meet them and decide yourself whether to pursue the issue with them. I know them, you see. They are now translating an astronomical treatise, and, well, they are deeply involved in what they are doing. They are. . . Well . . . I suspect you may find them rather difficult to approach if you are not an accomplished mathematician."

Pons and Fernando agreed to Mohammed's suggestion, and the three men walked to the library together. As they walked, Pons profusely thanked them both: Mohammed for his generosity in sharing his knowledge and for his remarkably clear explanation of the Arabic number system and Fernando for his insight and kindness in finding and introducing this Arab teacher to Pons.

As they entered the library, they encountered Plato of Tivoli and Abraham bar Hiyya ha-Nasi.[98] The two scholars were noisily arguing with each other, both talking at the same time in raised voices in what sounded like two different languages, both incomprehensible to Pons, while flailing their arms in disagreement, and punctuating what they were saying by slamming piles of vellum and parchment pages onto a large desk. When they finally saw and recognized Fernando and Mohammed, they stopped arguing momentarily.

"Plato of Tivoli and Abraham bar Hiyya ha-Nasi," began Fernando, "may I introduce Canon Pons de Baucio, who is here in Barcelona assisting Archbishop William Monachus, the papal legate here. And I believe you already know Mohammed."

"Hello," they both responded.

"Canon Pons, are you a mathematician astronomer?" demanded Plato.

"Well," responded Pons, "I am very interested . . ."

"Good!" interrupted Plato abruptly and rudely. "We need another mathematician astronomer to resolve an absolutely crucial issue of terminology! Absolutely crucial! Absolutely!! We are working on translating into Latin this copy of Al-Battani's late ninth-century *Kitab al-Zij*," he said, pointing to a huge corpus of work. "As you must know, it's his astronomical treatise with tables, called *De motu stellarum* or *On the Motion of the Stars*."[99]

"You certainly must understand the vital importance of the issue!" interrupted Abraham.

"But of course they do," Plato cut in again. "Everyone knows that all natural processes are governed by the movement of the heavenly bodies in the celestial sphere! All natural processes! That's why we astronomers study the movement of the stars, which is mathematical science, *mathematica speculatio*. That's why we astronomers study the effects of the movement of the stars, which is physical science, *naturalis speculatio*."

....

98   Plato of Tivoli was a known early scientist scholar who worked in Barcelona at that time, transmitting Greek authors to the Latin West. Plato of Tivoli and Abraham bar Hiyya ha-Nasi collaborated on translating into Latin copies of Greek and Hebrew scholarly works that had been transmitted to them in Arabic or Hebrew. See "Plato of Tivoli," *Encyclopedia.com*, http://www.encyclopedia.com/doc/1G2-2830903444.html.

99   For more on Al-Battani's Kitab al-Zij, see J. J. O'Connor and E F. Robertson, "Abu Abdallah Mohammad ibn Jabir Al-Battani," *MacTutor* (1999), https://mathshistory.st-andrews.ac.uk/Biographies/Al-Battani/.

"But this fool here is being stupidly stubborn, bull-headed. He and I cannot agree on terminology." Abraham interjected.

"Hah! Really?" Plato retorted. "The scholar Al-Battani, for his complex calculations, uses formulae for functions as mathematical tools. He provides formulae and tables for the function of an angle in a right triangle—you know, of course, the ratio of the length of the side opposite the angle to the length of the hypotenuse. al-Battani uses the term *jiba* or *jyb* of a right-angled triangle.

"This bull-headed fellow here," Plato continued excitedly, pointing at Abraham, "this absolute fool here insists this *jiba* may refer to a Hindu term, *jya-ardha* or *jya*, whereas I know—know for sure, know and am *absolutely* certain—that it refers to the Arabic word *jaib*, as in a fold or opening of a garment at the neck. The eminent Robert of Chester and I both agreed on that when he was studying here."[100]

"So," Abraham broke in, pointing to Plato, "this perverse fool has translated it badly as the Latin *sinus,* meaning 'fold' of a garment—or 'bosom,' or 'bay,' or 'curve'—and abbreviated it *sin* to distinguish it from the term *sine,* or 'less' that we use in simple subtraction."[101]

"Tell me!" demanded Plato in raised loud voice. "Am I not correct? Am I? Should the terminology be *sinus* and abbreviated as *sin*? Is this bull-headed ignoramus not mistaken? Tell me! How do you translate the term?"

"I am afraid I cannot answer . . ." began Pons before Plato rudely cut him off again.

"But why? You must! You . . ." Plato began.

"Do you not understand the importance of this?" interrupted Abraham. "You must understand! This is important! We need to provide absolute clarity for these calculations. Absolute clarity. We are talking about the science of the

---

100   For Robert of Chester studying in Barcelona with Plato of Tivoli in 1136, see Louis Karpinski, *Robert of Chester's Latin Translation of the Algebra of al-Khowarizmi* (New York: 1915), 28; but Karpinski here suggests that Robert of Chester and Robert of Ketton were one and the same.

101   On the origin of the term *sin* in trigonometry, see "Trigonometric functions," *Wikipedia,* https://en.wikipedia.org/wiki/Trigonometric_functions, and "Sine," *Wikipedia,* https://en.wikipedia.org/wiki/Sine. The concept originated in India around 500 AD, but when the Hindu term *jya-ardha* or *jya* reached the Arabs in the eighth century, the term *jya* was transliterated into *jiba* or *jyb*. In Arabic, as in Hebrew, vowels are omitted, and *jiba* was mistaken for the Arabic *jaib* by early Latin translators of Arabic mathematical treatises. This misinterpretation is often attributed to Robert of Chester.

movement of the stars. We need absolute clarity to ensure firm command of mathematics if we are to understand precisely how all natural processes are governed by the heavenly bodies in the celestial sphere!"

"Gentlemen, gentlemen, please," Mohammed finally interrupted loudly and firmly. "Canon Pons is not a mathematician astronomer. Nor is Fernando. Nor am I. We are sorry, but we cannot help you because we do not understand what you are arguing about. We are not capable of helping you in this."

"But . . ." gasped Plato.

"Then why . . . ?" cried the two scholars almost simultaneously.

"We do apologize for interrupting your most important work," offered Fernando politely with a smile, but in exasperation. "And we will take our leave now, so you can carry on with it without further interruption." He and his two companions turned and quickly left the room.

Once outside, the three men first reassured each other not to worry about the embarrassingly rude, but certainly rather comical, academic feud they had just witnessed. They all agreed this was but a prototypic disagreement between academics. After enjoying prolonged hearty chuckles about the encounter, they each bid the others farewell before all going their own separate ways.

Pons returned to his study, sat down at the table, and thought about what he had learned. He did not understand at all what the two mathematician astronomers were arguing about—something about a *sinus*, a curved fold, and a triangle. However, he did understand what Mohammed had just shown him about the ten Arabic numerals and about the importance of the *sifr*, the circle '0.' It was a numeral for "empty, nothing," but most importantly now for Pons, it was a placeholder.

He thought back to the carved inscription he had seen on the outer crypt wall of the church at Saint-Gilles. He was certain it had read "*ANNO DOMINI M° C° XVI°*" with three little 0s, one above the M, one above the C, and one above the I.

"I think I understand what they mean," he thought to himself. "The stone carver, or whoever commissioned the stone carver, was trying to show that he knew about the new Arab way of writing numbers. He knew that the Arabs use 0s to hold numeral positions, but he had not gotten it quite right. He used the little 0 to indicate the place position for the thousand, for the hundred, and for the singles, but maybe he did not know also to use it for the tens. I wonder why? I think the Arab sixteen should use two place positions, so that it should have been X°VI°."

Pons continued thinking about the Arab number system for some time, becoming rather excited as he began envisioning some of its potential advantages for record-keeping for the business of the canons.

"If you can manipulate numbers as easily as seems to be true with the new Arabic system using the *sifr*, or 0," he conjectured, "you could sum up totals from many donations quickly on a document without first having to transpose everything onto an abacus and then back. Oh, I cannot wait to show these figures to Jordan and William Boso and explain to them all about the Arab number system when I return home!"

Three days later, Pons returned to his desk early in the morning shortly after the hour of *Prime* to begin again his work assisting the archbishop in his assignment as legate. Barely had Pons picked up his quill to begin drafting his first document when Nicolaus of Saint-Ruf enthusiastically burst into the room. He was carrying two manuscripts, both obviously old. Placing them carefully on a desk, Nicolaus immediately began explaining.

"Here it is! Just as I promised you. Here is a copy of the Rule of St. Augustine. It is really two separate short pieces. The first is called, *Disciplina monasterii*; the second is a commentary or supplement, called the *Praeceptum*. Both of them are late eleventh-century copies."[102]

An excited Pons picked up the copy of the Rule and held in his hands. He was thrilled to be able to finally examine these documents. Bending over the *Disciplina monasterii*,[103] he quickly read aloud the opening exhortation: "*Let God be loved above all things, dearest brethren, and then our neighbor, because these are the principal commands given to us.*"

The two canons then began reading silently the short, precise rules: for prayers, psalms, and choral office; hours of work, meals, and reading; doing nothing for personal benefit; having a non-murmuring, or non-complaining,

....

102   On the Rule of St. Augustine, see Mandonnet, *St. Dominic*, Part two, especially the Introduction and chapters 20 and 21. St. Augustine (354-430 AD) was Bishop of Hippo.

103   Quotations from the *Disciplina monasterii* are from Mandonnet, *St. Dominic*, chap. 21. Mandonnet accepts the published transcription of Donatien de Bruyne, *La première règle de saint Benoît* (1930), 318–326.

attitude; obedience; deportment at meals; behavior outside the communal grounds; silence rather than idle chatter; and correction of faults.

After a moment, Nicolaus called out in recognition, "Aha! Here it is. Here is the crucial piece. 'Let no one do anything for himself alone, whether for clothing or anything else; for we desire to live the apostolic life.' This is the prohibition against personal possessions, cited by the reformers as necessary for the apostolic life Christ required of the apostles in the Bible, in the *Acts of the Apostles* 4:32–35."

The two young canons were quiet for a few moments before Nicolaus began speculating.

"This really is the key. The apostolic life really requires the renunciation of private ownership, the giving up of owning things oneself, the renunciation of personal wealth, the adoption of poverty. The individual who has no personal wealth of his own, who owns no personal possessions, will not be tempted by gifts or offers of bribes to sell indulgences. He will not be tempted to live his own life, with his own family. He will obey only his superior within the community. He will be dependent on his community. He will think only of the good of his community."

Nodding his head, Pons agreed.

"Our chapter would have great difficulty accepting and adopting this Rule," Pons admitted. "Many of our canons come from wealthy families and they do not want to give up living apart, in their own homes, where they can live well and even have their own families. As I have told you, when I was first brought to the chapter as a child, Canon Peter Villelmus took me into his own home where I lived as a member of his family with him and his wife and children."

Nicolaus asked, "And did it not seem wrong to you at the time, or in any way inappropriate?"

"Of course not. Not at all." Pons continued. "But if we are to model ourselves after the apostles and truly live communally the *vita apostolica* as defined here, we will have to adopt religious poverty and renounce all personal wealth and possessions. Frankly, I am beginning to suspect that communal life can truly succeed only if it involves the adoption of religious poverty and the renunciation of personal wealth. Because with personal wealth comes private residences, and then privacy. And with privacy comes the temptation of the flesh, the temptation of women . . ."

The two canons moved on to the second short document, a supplement to the first. Pons again read aloud the beginning: "*These are the things which we command you who are assembled in the monastery to observe.*"[104]

While the *Disciplina monasterii* appeared to be a concise list of rules, this expanded commentary appeared to be a more detailed guide for religious life that followed, in general, the order and concepts of the shorter list. The commentary included eight main areas of guidance for communal life, beginning with the all-important communal sharing of property with no private property as the purpose and basis of common life, and then continuing with appropriate prayer; moderation and self-denial with respect to food and drink; safeguarding chastity and fraternal correction with respect to women; care of community goods and treatment of the sick; asking pardon and forgiving offenses; governance and obedience of superiors; and loving observance of the Rule.

Pons noted wryly, with some chagrin, "One of the two longest and most detailed sections in this guide list is on 'safeguarding chastity and fraternal correction.' Apparently, I am not alone in my weaknesses."

"Indeed, you are not alone in them," chuckled Nicolaus with a kindly smile. "Remember," Nicolaus continued, "at the First Lateran Council,[105] the bishops and abbots discussed church reforms and recognized they needed again to ratify rules to forbid priests, deacons, subdeacons, and monks to keep mistresses or women other than their mother or sisters in their houses. They needed rules to absolutely forbid marriages of priests and to declare any such marriages null and void."

"And yet," Pons added with a gentle shake of his head, "at the Second Lateran Council held in spring earlier this year, it was recognized as necessary again to ratify rules to deprive clerics of their office if they were living with women and to forbid anyone to attend masses celebrated by clerics who have

....

104   Quotations from the *Praeceptum* or Supplement are from St. Augustine, *The Rule of our Holy Father St. Augustine* trans. Robert P. Russell (Province of St. Thomas of Villanova, 1976). This edition is based on the critical text of Luc Verheijen, O.S.A., *La règle de saint Augustin,* (Paris: Études Augustiniennes, 1967).

105   See "Ninth Ecumenical Council: Lateran I 1123, The Canons of the First Lateran Council, 1123," *Medieval Sourcebook,* http://www.fordham.edu/halsall/basis/lateran1.html.

wives or concubines.[106] Here in the supplement to the Rule are the injunctions." He began to read them aloud.[107]

"4. *Although your eyes may chance to rest upon some woman or other, you must not fix your gaze upon any woman. Seeing women when you go out is not forbidden, but it is sinful to desire them or to wish them to desire you, for it is not by thought or passionate feeling alone but by one's gaze also that lustful desires mutually arise. And do not say that your hearts are pure if there is immodesty of the eye, because the unchaste eye carries the message of an impure heart. And when such hearts disclose their unchaste desires in a mutual gaze, even without saying a word, then it is that chastity suddenly goes out of their life, even though their bodies remain unsullied by unchaste acts.*

"5. *And whoever fixes his gaze upon a woman and likes to have hers fixed upon him must not suppose that others do not see what he is doing . . . . Let the religious man then have such fear of God that he will not want to be an occasion of sinful pleasure to a woman. Ever mindful that God sees all things, let him not desire to look at a woman lustfully. For it is on this point that fear of the Lord is recommended, where it is written: An abomination to the Lord is he who fixes his gaze (Prov. 27:20)*

"6. *So when you are together in church and anywhere else where women are present, exercise a mutual care over purity of life. Thus, by mutual vigilance over one another will God, who dwells in you, grant you his protection.*"

After a long silence, Nicolaus said softly, "The communal life is how God protects us from such temptation."

After a much longer silence, Pons responded quietly, his voice cracking with emotion, "We as canons must remove ourselves as much as possible from the temptation of women. We as canons cannot live the *vita apostolica* unless we adopt a truly communal life. We as canons cannot effectively live communally unless we renounce all private property."

Then, in a strong, clear voice, filled with resolve, he slowly proclaimed, "The Church needs this reform. Our chapter at Arles must adopt the Rule of St. Augustine."

....

106   See "Tenth Ecumenical Council: Lateran II 1139," *Medieval Sourcebook*, http://www. fordham.edu/halsall/basis/lateran2.html.

107   Quotation from Augustine, *Rule*.

Terce
Mid-morning—third-hour bells

Anno Domini MCXLII

Arles, 1142

———————

After returning from Barcelona three years ago, Pons had immediately thrown himself wholeheartedly once again into the task of convincing the chapter to emulate the *vita apostolica*, but this time he had the Rule of St. Augustine in hand. For three years he pursued his mission, and this time, armed with the copy he had made of this respected model for a new code of conduct, his task was much more focused.

Within the chapter, his efforts were recognized and respected, if still deemed a bit idealistic, and by 1142 he was elected *capud scole*,[108] chancellor or rector, in charge of the cathedral chant school. Archbishop William Monachus had been very supportive of Pons's mission, and with the arrival of the new archbishop, Raymond de Monte Rotundo, in 1142, Pons continued to enjoy strong support.

Just a year ago, Archbishop William Monachus had strengthened Arles's relationship with Conrad III of Hohenstaufen, King of the Romans and claimant to the crown of Holy Roman Emperor. Pope Innocent II, known to be a man of irreproachable character, was vigorously promoting reform, and it was

----

108   See the *Authentique,* Arles, MS 1242, fol. 125, no. 70. See also Schneider, "Sculptures," 74.

clear that if the Arles chapter would agree to reform by formally and visibly adopting the Rule, this would help to maintain balance in Arles' relationships with these two political rivals, papacy and empire.

But first of all, the canons had to agree to adopt the Rule of St. Augustine, to emulate the *vita apostolica*, to live communally—fully communally—by renouncing their own private property and living a celibate life, giving up wives or mistresses. As Jordan had predicted, convincing them was not an easy task.

As earlier, those canons who did not have any personal wealth and property tended to be more receptive to the concept of adopting the Rule and were more easily convinced about its merits. So, too, were those who were unattached and had no wives or families. Many of the canons now agreed, at least in principle, but some wavered. Many remained unsure, preferring to continue the discussions while awaiting their outcome.

Those canons who were personally very wealthy and those who were married or attached to a woman often either refused to discuss the issue or posed strenuous objections. Some seemed truly to vacillate, or at least to adopt different faces, speaking in chapter as if they agreed in principle and recognized the validity of the concept, but then retiring as usual to their comfortable homes and the welcoming arms of their wives or mistresses. Some were genuinely torn between what they seemed to recognize as the correct path for their chapter to take and the path they would prefer personally to choose instead. Some threatened to leave Arles in search of a more reasonable chapter. Of course, some remained violently opposed, especially those with loving wives and families.

Just after the chapter had finished celebrating *Terce* at the third hour after dawn, one of the canons opposed to the idea pulled Pons aside and began his tirade.

"And are you proud of yourself, you God-forsaken hypocrite?" boomed Bernard Aiguillus, an ill-tempered, somewhat older canon. "We are going to lose all this! We will lose the close community we enjoy here!"

"No," responded Pons calmly. "We will live more closely, living the truly communal life together, as the apostles lived."

"You ass! You're an idiot!" Bernard shot back angrily. "We are already a community. We all live well. Our chapter is prospering. We are prospering.

We want for nothing. Why are you causing such trouble? What on earth's the matter with you?"

As his voice continued rising, he began taunting Pons. "Do you really think we are going to share everything in common, to love one another, to eat together at one table, and to sleep together in the same dormitory? You're either an idiot or a fool!

"No! Oh, no. Wait a minute . . . I think I understand. You like men! You're a sodomite! You like it *a tergo*, from the rear, with a man! You're one of those freaks who like that Greek style of love, and since you can't have it, you don't want anyone to have any. Why else would you want us to give up the warmth of our wives and mistresses? You're a damned pervert! You're a damned freak! You're a damned sodomite!"

Bernard turned and stormed angrily away as Pons stood frozen with rage, livid with anger, desperately gripping his hands together tightly to restrain himself. Finally, after several minutes, he loosened them to pray.

"Forgive me, Lord, I would have . . . I wanted so badly to strike him! Sometimes I think this will never end," he whispered. He took a slow, deep breath and quietly shook his head in despair.

But finally, finally, it seemed that it could end. Improbable as it had seemed, the chapter had finally just agreed to adopt the Rule, but with the clear *proviso* that they would adopt and adhere to it as soon as they were able to do so—that is, as soon as Pons had arranged everything to enable them to do so. No small *proviso* this, for as Pons freely admitted, they needed to build a full claustral complex to be able to live communally.

In thinking about that *proviso*, Pons now began to realize the enormity of the task before him: to be able to live fully communally, the chapter would have to construct a whole new set of buildings for the communal life. None of the many smaller dwellings then being used by the canons, some as shared housing among the brethren, some as private dwellings, could accommodate the full chapter living, eating, and sleeping communally. In addition to their existing chapter house, they would need a larger refectory that could accommodate everyone, and they would certainly need a large new dormitory for sleeping, all arranged, in accordance with longstanding tradition, around a quiet garden for reflection and contemplation. What was needed was an entire complex of permanent buildings for communal living, a complex of claustral buildings built around a central cloister.

Moreover, building the claustral complex itself would now be only part of the task. The previous year, when the chapter had begun seriously discussing adopting the Rule, the archbishop, then William Monachus, had called both Pons and William Garnerius, who was then *caput scole*, or chancellor, to the archbishop's palace to clarify his position.

"My brothers," he had said, "we want you to know that we are aware of Canon Pons's efforts to bring the chapter to adopt the Rule of St. Augustine and to adopt the communal life. We want you to know that we fully support this effort.

"However, we remind you that when we do finally undertake the necessary building campaign, we must not only construct a new claustral complex, but we must also reconstruct the east end of our church. And then we will also have to have a new bell tower and decorated west portal. After all, now that I have pledged submission and faithfulness to King Conrad III, who expects to become Holy Roman Emperor, we expect to become an imperial church.[109] I do want your solemn word that the church will be completed."

So, the task before Pons now was truly enormous. Nevertheless—praise be to God!—the chapter had endorsed the *vita apostolica* and had agreed eventually to follow it, so Pons had completed the first step in the plan with which God had entrusted him.

At the same time that Pons had been busily carrying out his mission to get the chapter to agree to adopt the Rule, his brother had his own designs and was putting in place the means to achieve them. As one of the most powerful local lords in Provence who controlled towns and lands centered around Arles and Marignane, Raymond of Baux was finally setting the stage to mount a challenge for control of the region, a challenge he fully expected would culminate in open warfare between his House of Baux and the House of Barcelona.[110]

The ambitions of the two brothers were not only in synchrony, they were now about to coalesce to enable each to help the other in achieving their goals. Raymond's territorial ambitions to control the region would assist Pons in bringing the *vita apostolica* to the chapter at Arles.

....

109   See Jean-Pierre Poly, *La Provence et la Societe Feodale (879–1166)* (Paris: Bordas, 1976), 273–275, and Albanes and Chevalier, *Arles,* nos. 531, 538.

110   The conflict would eventually be called the Baux wars (1144–1162).

At this time, the region of Provence was under the titular control of the Holy Roman Emperor, who held it as King of Burgundy, which was a large swath of counties, including Provence and extending southward from the County of Burgundy to the Mediterranean Sea.[111] The Emperor's authority over the region of Provence was in name only, however, and the lower Rhône Valley was divided with real authority and influence fragmented primarily between two clans of counts and viscounts, warlords all. Conflicting territorial rights were claimed by two strong rival houses: the house of Toulouse—that is, by Raymond of Saint-Gilles, Count of Toulouse and Marquis of Provence—and the Catalan House of Barcelona, whose powerful Count Ramon Berenguer claimed them through marriage.

In 1112 Ramon Berenguer III had married Douce, who was the heiress of Provence as daughter of Countess Gerberga. This permitted the Catalan house to claim control of most of Provence, but it put them in conflict with the local house of Toulouse. A treaty between the warring claimants in 1125 formally recognized the claim of Alphonse Jourdain, who was then Count of Toulouse and also acknowledged his traditional title, Margrave of Provence. Under the treaty, the region was formally divided, albeit unequally, between the two rival houses.[112] The Count of Toulouse was to hold the Margraviate of Provence and the County of Forcalquier, which was the lesser piece comprising all the land north and west of the lower Durance River. The Catalan Counts of Provence were to hold the County of Provence, which was the greater piece comprising all the land between the Durance and the Mediterranean, from the Rhône to the Alps, with Arles as its capital.

However, by 1131 both Douce and Ramon Berenguer III had died, so the Catalan-controlled portion of Provence that had been inherited by Douce passed to their younger son, Berenguer Ramon I, who claimed the title Count of Provence.[113] Now Raymond of Baux could hope to mount his own claim to the territory in Provence through his own marriage because he had earlier married Stephanie of Gevauden, who was the younger sister of Douce. Raymond of Baux, who was allied in fealty to the house of Toulouse, though never merely its vassal, was an independent and powerful local

111   See map, page 4.

112   See map, page 4.

113   Berengar Raymond I was the younger brother of Ramond Berengar IV, Count of Barcelona.

lord with extensive holdings that he now hoped to expand within Catalan-controlled Provence.

Within this hotbed of territorial dispute at that time, the city and church at Arles managed to prosper and thrive, though they were within the boundary of the Catalan-controlled portion. Wary of the looming dispute between the local lords and the House of Barcelona, the people of Arles appointed a consulate and urged the archbishop to make changes so as to prepare for possible war, and in 1131 Archbishop Bernard was instrumental in founding the Consulate of Arles and in drawing up its Charter of the Consulate, or Code of Rights.[114]

The Consulate of Arles remained largely under the control of the archbishop and was mostly independent of the Catalan Count of Provence. The town of Arles, though still the capital of Provence, was essentially divided into districts, each controlled by different feudal lords, including the archbishop, the Count of Toulouse, and other noble families, as well as the Catalan Count of Provence, who maintained his own residence within the city, the *Palais de la Trouille*, at the site of the antique baths.[115]

The Consulate of Arles recognized only the power of the Holy Roman Emperor, but this was in name only. It was the archbishop who exercised real authority, control, and power over the Consulate,[116] so the Archbishop of Arles exercised substantial secular power in addition to his religious authority. In fact, by 1136 the Emperor Lothair had written to Archbishop Bernard, revealing his desire to establish his imperial authority in Arles by reinstituting an imperial church there if the archbishop would pledge submission and faithfulness to him.[117] So in 1141, King Conrad III of Hohenstaufen received this recognition from Archbishop William Monachus, thereby establishing imperial authority while also enhancing further the power of the archbishop.[118]

114   For this history of Arles and Provence, see Edouard Baratier, *Histoire de la Provence* (Toulouse, France: Privat, 1969), 131–137. See also Louis Mathieu Anibert, *Mémoires historiques et critiques sur l'ancienne République d'Arles* (Yverdon, 1779).

115   The Count of Barcelona maintained a residence and set up court in Arles in the *Cité* at the *Palais de la Trouille,* Constantine's baths. See Poly, *La Provence,* 80, 99, 293 and Albanes and Chevalier, *Arles,* no. 941, in which the palace is mentioned.

116   In a bull of 1144, Emperor Conrad III formally ceded to the archbishop his authority and jurisdiction over the *Cité,* the quarter of Arles that was the heart of the old Roman castrum, because the archbishop acted like a "lieutenant-general." See Anibert, vol. I, 300–340, and vol. II, 81–95. See also Albanes and Chevalier, *Arles,* no. 551.

117   See Poly, *La Provence,* 273–275; and Albanes and Chevalier, *Arles,* nos. 531, 538.

118   See Poly, *La Provence,* 273–275; and Albanes and Chevalier, *Arles,* no. 531, 538.

By 1142 the archbishop was crucial to Raymond of Baux's plan to mount all-out war to press his own claim, through his marriage to Stephanie, to the territory in Provence and to take control of it. Not only did the archbishop control the Consulate and city of Arles, but he also represented the claimant to the crown of Holy Roman Emperor in Arles and its immediately surrounding territory.[119] Raymond of Baux not only needed the city of Arles on his side as support during the war he was going to mount, he wanted formal recognition and sanction of his right to the territory in Provence from the would-be Holy Roman Emperor, Conrad III, who held titular control, and it was the archbishop who represented the emperor in Arles. What Raymond of Baux intended to do was to appeal to King Conrad III to ask him to recognize Stephanie's rights as daughter and heir to Gerberda's possessions in Provence.

Raymond of Baux was no fool. Before mounting his war to seize control of Provence and wrest the territory from the House of Barcelona, he entered into a formal feudal relationship and agreement with the archbishop and church of Arles. Raymond of Baux's war coalition already included other local lords from the region under the control of the House of Barcelona—Peter de Lambesco, Guy IV de Fos, and William de Rians, who were related to the House of Baux by marriage and were vassals of the Count of Toulouse. Together with their liege lord, Raymond of Saint-Gilles, Count of Toulouse, they intended to battle against Berenguer Ramon, the Catalan Count of Provence.[120] To gain formal support from the city of Arles, and to strengthen his alliance, Raymond of Baux was now instigating pledges of fealty between these allies and the archbishop and church of Arles.

Pons was now standing just outside the canons' enclosure, next to the canons' portal at the old Roman city wall. He was waiting for his older brother, who had asked to meet there to speak in private, before the arrival of all the others who would be participating in the pledge. At the sound of some commotion at the portal, Pons looked up.

"Greetings and welcome, Raymond, Lord of Baux," said Pons. "I am truly pleased to see you again, my beloved brother."

. . . .

119   See Poly, *La Provence*, 219f, 290f.
120   See Paul Fournier, *Le Royaume d'Arles et de Vienne sous le règne de Frédéric II (1214-1250)* (Grenoble: G. Dupont, 1885), 8, and Paul Turc, *Hyeres et les seigneurs de Fos: fin Xe siècle-1257,* (Toulon, France : Centre archéologique du Var, 2003), 69.

"Greetings to you, my brother, Canon Pons," Raymond responded. The pair embraced warmly before they turned to proceed slowly up the public path toward the antique theater, talking together as they walked.

"I am pleased that we can meet to speak briefly," Raymond continued. "I want to thank you for working this out with the archbishop. I must confess that I was a bit worried at first, when the new Archbishop Raymond de Monte Rotundo arrived this year, about whether he would be receptive to this proposal, and whether I could count on you to set it up. I knew that you were well respected by your previous archbishop. I understand William Monachus took you with him three years ago when he was sent to Barcelona."

"That's right," Pons replied proudly. "We became good friends after returning here, and he started calling me *Balcherio capellano meo*,[121] his special chaplain, last year."

"It pays me to keep my eye on you here, you know!" said Raymond with a grin. "But your fellow canons here who are distant relatives of our Baux clan have assured me that your views are indeed valued by the current archbishop, who often confers with you."

"They are too kind," returned Pons. "But I must admit that in fact both archbishops have been very supportive of my efforts to get the canons here to reform. They recognized the benefits of our adopting this reform—benefits not only to the souls of us clerics, but also to the health, wealth, and well-being of our church at Arles."

"As you know," continued the Lord of Baux, "the pledge we are making today is only the first of several that I predict will be made within this year and the next as we firm up our bonds and relationship with the archbishop and the imperial church. First, my man will today cede his rights to prime lands important to the archbishop, will receive in fief from the archbishop two important fortified towns, and will pledge fealty to the church, thereby firming up his obligation to defend and protect it. Following that, if all goes according to plan, both Alphonse Jourdain, the Count of Toulouse, and I will pledge ourselves to be faithful supporters and defenders of the archbishop and the church.[122]

....

121   Albanes and Chevalier, *Arles,* no. 538.

122   See Florian Mazel, "Seigneurie épiscopale, aristocratie laïque et structures féodo-vassaliques en Provence au XIIe siècle : le sens d'une féodalisation limitée." *Aspects du pouvoir seigneurial de la Catalogne à l'Italie (IXe-XIVe siècles), Rives nord-méditerranéennes* 2, no. 7 (2001), 27–36.

"So today, my son-in-law Peter de Lambesco, who is married to your niece Azalaxis, plans to cede his rights to the fortified town and territory of Salon to your Archbishop Raymond, who in return will give to Peter de Lambesco, in fief, the fortified sites of Alvernico and Avallone. For this, Peter de Lambesco will pledge an oath of fealty to the church at Arles, promising to honor and serve it, to provide twenty mounted knights each year, and, upon the archbishop's request, to return the two fortified sites with all their munitions,"[123] Raymond clarified.

"And we want to ensure that it is documented that this exchange and pledge were made with the consent of all Lambisco relatives and successors too—that it was made by Peter with the consent and counsel of his wife, their three sons, his brother Ugo de Lambisco, myself as his liege lord, and the two canons at the church who are from the Lambisco clan, William Peter de Lambisco and Ugo de la Berbe."

Pons interjected at this point. "Yes, we will be glad to document the exchange and pledge as having consent from all Lambisco relatives and successors, but not all of them can be present today, so to avoid any future, uh, misunderstandings and, um, to ensure the exchange is honored by one and all, I suggest—and I'm sure the archbishop will agree—that we ask for the cession of the Salon lands to be confirmed again, independently and in person, both by Azalaxis and by Ugo."

Inhaling deeply and opening his eyes widely, Raymond immediately recognized his young brother's cleverness in asking for a confirmation of the pledge directly from Peter de Lambisco's wife and brother. This would certainly help ensure the exchange and transaction were honored, regardless of the outcome of war hostilities. Keeping his thoughts to himself, Raymond of Baux stopped walking for a few moments, but then quickly resumed and nodded his head in agreement.

Pons now reminded Raymond what he wanted out of this arrangement. If Raymond was going to use their family's connections to the chapter at Arles to realize his territorial ambitions, Pons wanted to ensure this would also help him to realize his own vision and God's mission. Pons now reminded his brother that the feudal pledges and donations were to be made not only to the church at Arles, but also to the cloistered community of canons who were soon to begin to live the *vita apostolica*.

....

123   Albanes and Chevalier, *Arles,* no. 543.

"These communal buildings we plan to build will be permanent stone structures, and very costly," Pons explained. "The building construction and decoration will be paid for out of our collective pooled funds, which we will be further augmenting."

"Which our House of Baux is helping to augment," Raymond reminded him, interrupting.

"Yes. Yes, of course. But we canons, and our archbishop, also want assurance that our church and claustral complex will be secure, safe from the ravages of war and safe from possible usurpation by, uh, any other . . . local warlords. We do insist that the oaths be made to honor and defend the '*claustrum et ecclesiam Arlelatensem . . . et omnem Arlelatensis ecclesie*' (the cloistered community and church of Arles ... and everything belonging to the church)."

Raymond of Baux appeared skeptical for a moment, then said, "You will be giving over to the chapter your entire personal endowment of land and income. Are you certain you are willing to do this now, while you are still alive? Yours was a very generous and substantial inheritance charter. You will lose all control over it, and . . ." He sighed. "I will not give you any additional endowment in future, especially if you are just giving it all away to support your canons living together!

"Remember, my wife and I already, just two years ago, made a large donation of land for a new Cistercian monastery, Le Thoronet, to be built. And I may soon make a donation to building the cloister and church of Arles. So you know that I do support building churches and monasteries, but I am careful with any donations I make. If you decide to give away your own personal endowment to your fellow canons, Brother, that is your affair, not mine, and I'll not give you any more."

"Yes, I am certain. I know this is what I am to do," responded Pons gently. "In fact, I will not even attend the ceremony today, because I do not want anyone to misunderstand and entertain the possibility that Peter de Lambisco, my relative by marriage, might be making this exchange with the archbishop for my personal benefit rather than for the cloistered community of canons and church at Arles.

"Instead, my new friend and colleague, Canon William Aicardus Rufus,[124] will represent me and join many of the canons to witness the exchange.

---

124 Vilelmus Aicardi Rufus begins to appear among the witnesses in the documents at Arles from 1141 on. See Schneider, "Sculptures," 66.

William came here last year from the chapter of Saint-Ruf in Avignon, which has been a powerful force for canonical reform for several decades. William was sent to us by my dear friend, Nicolaus of Saint-Ruf, whom I came to know well in Barcelona, and to whom I am deeply indebted for helping me with my plans."

"Whatever. Do as you wish," retorted Raymond dryly, with more than a hint of exasperation.

The pair turned and walked at a quick pace back down the path, entering at the canons' portal. A small crowd was gathering in the courtyard outside the bishop's palace. Curious local townspeople, men, women and children, had slipped in to see the local nobility who were arriving, and the canons who were to be involved were gathering. Pons hesitated for a moment, wondering if he should accompany his brother further, and for but a brief moment he thought he recognized Beatrice among the many women and children in the melee. Flushing with embarrassment, and unsure whether or not he had actually seen her, he turned quickly, to get away from the crowd, away from Beatrice, and to return to the chapter house.

With the arrival of Raymond of Baux, those involved in the oaths and exchange began entering the bishop's palace, and eventually the exchange began and was carefully recorded.

"I, Peter de Lambisco, with the counsel of my wife Azalaxis; and my sons, Pons, Peter and Raymond; and Ugo de Lambisco, my brother; and Raymond de Baux, and William Peter de Lambisco; and Ugo de la Berbe do hereby release, give, and cede to the Lord God and the most blessed St. Trophime, and St. Stephen, and to you, Raymond, Archbishop of the holy church at Arles, and to your successors all that we hold in the *castrum* and territory of Sallone."

"In return, I, Raymond de MonteRotundo, Archbishop of Arles, do hereby give in fief to Peter de Lambisco and to his posterity the *castrum* of Alvernico, the *castrum* of Avalone, and everything pertaining to them."

"For this honor, I, Peter de Lambisco and all my successors do hereby pledge ourselves to honor and defend the *claustrum et ecclesiam Arelatensem et omnen Arelatensis ecclesie* (the cloistered community and church of Arles and everything belonging to the church)."[125]

....

125   Albanes and Chevalier, *Arles,* no. 543, and Schneider, "Sculptures," 26–28.

The canon scribe carefully recorded that the pledge was made in the presence of witnesses, and he carefully recorded the names of the thirty-seven present, the majority of them canons, including William Aicardus Rufus.[126] Before the group dispersed, the archbishop noted that the pledge and exchange would be formally confirmed within the next few weeks by Peter's wife and brother, as Pons had suggested.

As the oaths were taking place, Pons sat on the porch outside the chapter house, patiently awaiting the arrival of a report about the proceedings. When his friend William Aicardus Rufus approached bearing a huge grin, Pons perked up.

"Well?" asked Pons, so hopeful he seemed about to burst. "Did it all go as we had hoped and expected?"

"Absolutely," responded William Rufus. "As promised, Peter de Lambisco pledged to honor and defend the *claustrum* and church at Arles, and more oaths and pledges of support can be expected from Alphonse, Count of Toulouse, and from Raymond of Baux himself within the weeks and months ahead."

"Yes," responded Pons victoriously. "And most of the canons have finally announced their intention to renounce their personal property by donating it to the cathedral chapter coffers, so we are making real progress there as well. We should soon have both the revenue and the assurances of security we need before proceeding."

"The chapter certainly knew what they were doing when they elected you to be responsible for getting the buildings built and supervising the construction," noted William with a wry smile. "They certainly entrusted you with a big task."

"Yes," gasped Pons. "They agreed to adopt the Rule of St. Augustine if and when they could live communally—but only if someone else would do all the work to make it happen. And because it was I who had started the whole thing, it naturally became my job to do everything necessary for us to live communally. And now I am responsible not only for overseeing construction of the claustral buildings, but for the reconstruction of the church, too," he added with a sigh.

Pons did not really resent having this huge task thrust on him, because he recognized that the chapter and the archbishop were simply acting as most

. . . .

126   See Schneider, "Sculptures," 28, footnote 1.

people do in such situations, especially when they were at all ambivalent about the task—passing the real work on to whoever else would do it. Frankly, he was simply relieved that the chapter had finally taken the first step forward on the path down which God had entrusted him to lead them. However, the path certainly now appeared much longer and more tortuous than he had first thought it would be.

"Let me try to show you what I can envision so far," Pons began with a smile, as he turned toward the chapter house. "Our chapter house with its two bays will remain here, of course, along the south flank of the cathedral, and we will certainly need the passageway descending into the transept of the cathedral from the room in the west corner."[127]

Spinning around and thrusting his arms out toward the south, he continued, "The new cloister will be positioned here somehow, directly south of the chapter house, with the communal buildings somehow grouped around a central cloister. All the existing private dwellings here will have to be torn down, of course. But the terrain here poses such a huge problem! It is so severely inclined here, and that will somehow have to be dealt with.

"Frankly, I desperately need professional help with the plans. We want to begin construction as soon as possible, and I wish I could now seek out some advice from the Guild of Masons and Carpenters, but we cannot do so yet. We cannot start construction until we are sure both of the funding and of the support of the Baux coalition, so we won't become a target in any hostilities that may come.

. . . .

127   The chapter must have had a stairway and passage leading from the chapter house into the church in the twelfth century. They would have needed a direct passage for the celebration of hours, etc. The steep slope of the immediately surrounding topography would have made walking around to the west entrance of the church prohibitively cumbersome. There is now a stairway along the west end of the chapter house leading directly into the church, but the church was smaller in the twelfth century, so if this stairway existed then, it would have opened onto the grounds beyond the transept and near the apse, not into the church. The small room directly west of the chapter house opens directly into the transept through what is a late eleventh- or early twelfth-century wall, and even though the opening has been obscured by much later renovation, it is most probable that this passageway existed in the twelfth century. For a ground plan diagram showing the construction history of the church, see "Cathédrale Saint-Trophime d'Arles," *Wikipedia*, https://fr.wikipedia.org/wiki/Cathédrale_Saint-Trophime_d%27Arles.

"I have been warned about those *magistri comacini*, the Lombard master masons, with their monopoly on labor and their binding contracts. We do not dare engage a master mason or his workshop until the support of the coalition is firmed up.

"But I am now discussing the sculptural decoration with the other canons in chapter. All I am certain of so far is that we must keep the two carved capitals showing the siren and *luxuria*. They will serve as a reminder to the canons not to be tempted by women. I just don't know how I could have made it through my trial with a temptress without those figures," admitted Pons with an embarrassed smile.

*   *   *

Within weeks, a smaller group of local nobility convened in Berbe, where Azalaxis confirmed the exchange and pledge in the presence of eleven named witnesses, including Ugo Amelius, dean of the chapter at Arles, and a couple other canons.[128]

"I, Azalaxis, wife of Peter de Lambisco, and my sons, Pons, Peter, and Raymond, praise and confirm ..."[129]

And not long after, another small group convened again at Arles, in the archbishop's chamber, where Ugo de Lambisco likewise praised and confirmed the cession in the presence of thirteen named men, again including Ugo Amelius, William Aicardus Rufus, and several other canons.[130]

Raymond of Baux's war alliance was firming up. The safety and security of Pons de Baux's yet-to-be-built claustral buildings were firming up too but were not yet a certainty. Raymond of Baux and Alphonse Jourdain had not yet made their own pledges.

Several weeks after the initial pledges, Pons was seated outside the chapter house at Arles, bemoaning the delay in the final pledges and wondering when he would finally be able to begin some real work on his mission, when he heard a boisterous group enter through the canons' portal. Jumping to his feet, he walked toward them and immediately recognized his brother and the

....

128   See Schneider, "Sculptures," 27.

129   Albanes and Chevalier, *Arles,* no. 543. See also Schneider, "Sculptures," 27.

130   Albanes and Chevalier, *Arles,* no. 543. See also Schneider, "Sculptures," 27–28.

Count of Toulouse amidst what appeared to be a gang of at least ten or twelve elegantly dressed strongmen.

"Hello, Canon Pons, my brother," began Raymond of Baux, clarifying the relationship for his entourage. "My lord, Alphonse, Count of Toulouse, and I are meeting with your Archbishop Raymond de Monte Rotundo today to discuss the terms of the pledges of fealty and cessions that each of us will make with the other within the months ahead. So our coalition for war is strong and will soon be very firm indeed. But the Count of Toulouse has something he wants to bring to you himself."

"Yes, Canon Pons," began the Count of Toulouse, rather haughtily. "First of all, bravo to you and your archbishop and your chapter! It is such a pleasure to work with clerics who understand the real value of . . . *protection* by good friends. Protection against foreigners, against foreign usurpers. The protection that comes from solid and mutually beneficial relationships.

"What I have brought you today are a couple of stone carvers," he continued very arrogantly. "This one calls himself Guillelmo," he began, as he pointed toward one of a pair of somewhat disheveled young men wearing dust-laden tunics. "He seems to be in charge. The other one doesn't seem to talk very much. They just arrived in Toulouse after working for several years in the Lombard region in the workshop of a well-known master sculptor and architect there, a Master Niccolo. Guillelmo and his associate are now starting up their own workshop, and they came to me seeking a commission. I thought of your project here.

"Guillelmo is originally from Toulouse, where he started as an apprentice," he continued, "so he knows all the beautiful cloisters there. You know them yourself, of course—the cloister of Saint-Sernin and the cloister and chapter house of the Cathedral Saint-Étienne. When Master Niccolo visited Toulouse—oh, I guess it was at least ten years ago that I received him there—he accepted Guillelmo as an apprentice and took him back with him back to teach him. So I assume the young stone carver's work must be more impressive than his scruffy appearance would suggest.

"Anyway, I thought they might be of some use to you," he added nonchalantly. "Or at least that you might want to talk to them about your cloister project. But if you do decide to go ahead with them, make sure you make your own arrangements with them, because this is not at all my affair." The count turned dismissively and walked away with Raymond of Baux and the strongmen without bothering to take proper leave of the canon.

"I am honored to meet you, Canon Pons," began the scruffy younger of the two sculptors, who now boldly approached Pons as the other one turned shyly and walked away quietly.

"It is a pleasure to meet you. Tell me about yourself and your colleague," Pons began, probing to try to see whether they might be capable of undertaking his project. "How large is your workshop? What was your apprenticeship training? Your journeyman training? As sculptors, are you members of the Goldsmiths' Guild?"

"There are but three of us now, sir, two master stone carvers and one assistant. My colleague, Master Pietro, and I are just starting out on our own, and though we are not yet established or well-known, we have been very well trained. As the count, his lordship, indicated, I first began my training in Toulouse as an apprentice in Master Gilabertus's workshop, just as he was finishing his sculptures for the chapter house and cloister of the Cathedral of Saint-Étienne there.[131] I was mostly assigned to finishing decorative edges and repetitive details, but I began working on decorative sculpture too.

"Master Niccolo came through the region then and visited Toulouse about a decade ago.[132] He was very impressed with Master Gilabertus's pier figures in the chapter house there, with the soft, gentle elegance of his figure style, but especially with the way Master Gilabertus had carved some of the pier figures out of the salient corner of the pier, as if the figure were emerging from inside a tall niche.

. . . .

131   Gilabertus's apostle figures and this cloister capital should probably be dated around 1130.

132   It has long been postulated that Master Niccolo travelled to France and must have seen the apostle figures from the chapter house of Saint-Étienne, Toulouse. This contentious issue is still debated.

Toulouse, Musée des Augustins. Capital from the cloister of Saint-Étienne, Toulouse. Death of Saint John the Baptist.[133]

Toulouse, Musée des Augustins. Pier figure from chapter house of Saint-Étienne, Toulouse, originally signed by Gilabertus. St. Andrew.[134]

"Master Niccolo also liked the decorative sculpture I had been working on, and he agreed to accept me as an apprentice in his own workshop and to train me further. So not long afterwards I followed him back to the Emilia Romagna region and joined him there."

"Come walk up the hill with me so we two can talk further," Pons suggested, and thinking it might be worthwhile to learn about this scruffy master sculptor and his workshop, he took the sculptor lightly by the arm to guide

. . . .

133   Photo provided and used with permission of Musée des Augustins. Photo Daniel Martin. Capital depicting the Death of Saint John the Baptist, here showing the Feast of Herod with Salome Presenting the Head of John the Baptist, attributed to Gilabertus, is usually dated 1120–140.

134   Photo provided and used with permission of Musée des Augustins. Photo Daniel Martin. Pier figure of St. Andrew, the Apostle, originally signed by the sculptor, Gilabertus, is usually dated 1120–1140.

him toward the portal and out into the town. "What about your colleague, Pietro? Did he train at Toulouse?"

"No, Pietro was already working with Master Niccolo as an apprentice when I arrived in Piacenza. Pietro was originally from a small town near there but had earlier joined Master Niccolo's workshop in Piacenza. We quickly became friends and colleagues, working and training under the same master, first as apprentices, then as journeymen."

"So, it was at Piacenza that you were trained?" queried Pons,

"Oh, no, that was only the beginning! You see, Pietro had already been training there for a few years. He had already worked with Master Niccolo earlier on the porch at the small parish church of Sant'Eufemia in Piacenza,[135] where Pietro carved some of the foliate capitals and some of the animal sculpture.

Church of Sant'Eufemia, Piacenza.
Porch. Capital.

"Before I arrived there, Pietro had already learned—learned from Master Niccolo—and demonstrated at Sant'Eufemia his remarkable ability to use figural and animal shapes, even acanthus foliage shapes, to emphasize the structure of the capital, to create the shape of the capital, by building it out of the contorted organic forms that push against its upper and lower. This was a very different approach to figure sculpture from what we had been doing on the capitals at Saint-Étienne, Toulouse, where we simply lined up strings of little figures on the faces of the capital.

"By the time I arrived, Master Niccolo was working on another project at the Cathedral of Piacenza, where he and his workshop were constructing three new double-storied porch portals for the façade.[136] Pietro had joined the workshop to work on much of the ornamental decorative work on the

---

135   The porch capitals were attributed to Niccolo and his workshop in Bornstein, "Capitals," 15–26.

136   The lower portion of the façade of Piacenza Cathedral is dated after 1122 because of an inscription, but the inscription has been challenged, and the complicated building history is further complicated by its extensive renovations. Consequently, how and when Piacenza Cathedral's earliest sculpture fits within the chronology of Niccolo's workshop is problematic.

archivolts curving directly above two portals, while Master Niccolo himself carved the horizontal lintel of the south portal with scenes from the Life of Christ."

"This way," Pons interrupted the sculptor after they were through the portal, taking his arm lightly again, to guide him left and up the hill.

"You see, Master Niccolo makes extensive use of decorative sculpture— he particularly likes certain repetitive motifs, such as raised pearls in a line, twisted rope, braided strands, and especially rows of tongue and dart. He is not only a skilled master, but a very good teacher. He always starts his apprentices on this repetitive decoration, but if you demonstrate some skill, he then lets you help with more complicated work, foliate or figural, and he trains you as you work. He heads a huge workshop with other master sculptors, as well as journeymen and assistants, who always work under his close supervision. We learned directly from Master Niccolo himself, as well as from the other master sculptors working with him, so we are well trained."

Piacenza Cathedral. South portal of façade. Lintel (attributed to Niccolo) with scenes of Life and Temptations of Christ; and archivolts with acanthus vine scrolls and decorative motifs.

"Pietro and I became very adept at the foliate sculpture. Master Niccolo always encouraged me in this work, and he himself has acknowledged that I now excel at it. I am a master of rinceaux, acanthus vine scrolls. I excel at carving both lush acanthus leaf rinceaux and undulating acanthus vines filled with floral motifs, or sometimes even inhabited with animals and little figures."

"So you carve mostly decorative and foliate sculpture?" the now somewhat disappointed canon asked, as they were approaching the old Roman theater. "Did you also learn how to carve larger animals? Or figures? What other kinds of things do you carve?" Pons had never seen any of the monuments Guillelmo mentioned but was trying to visualize their work.

"When I first arrived there from Toulouse, I joined the ongoing project at the Cathedral of Piacenza, where I helped finish some of the foliate and decorative work, but Master Niccolo then let me help Pietro finish some figures on the lintel of the north portal that had been started by someone else. We helped with the shepherds in the field and the three Magi there.

Piacenza Cathedral. North portal of façade. Lintel with scenes from Nativity of Christ; and archivolts with inhabited vine scrolls and decorative motifs.

"But the workshop soon moved on to a big, exciting, new project at Ferrara. You see, Master Niccolo had been inspired! And at the Cathedral at Ferrara,[137] where he was in charge of creating the new west portal, work had not yet been begun, so he could create what he was envisioning. He wanted to create a magnificent, truly new kind of sculpture-decorated church façade, incorporating new ideas that he had seen elsewhere, on his distant travels to Toulouse and through Burgundy and Aquitaine—ideas like filling the tympanum above the portal with carved figural sculpture and inserting large carved pier figures into the salient corners of piers, ideas that had never

....

137   Ferrara Cathedral is now traditionally considered to have been begun in 1135.

before appeared closer to home in Emilia, or in Lombardy, or anywhere in the Veneto! He would still use the traditional porch supported by columns resting on recumbent lions, so beloved throughout his homeland, but he wanted to adapt this by adding the new ideas to create his own completely new vision of a beautiful church façade."

"And you helped him carve those figures?" Pons asked hopefully. "I have never been in Lombardy or Emilia, and I am trying to envision what you did there. Come, sit here on this bench with me and tell me what you did."

Ferrara Cathedral.
West portal.

Ferrara Cathedral. West portal.
Tympanum, St. George and Dragon.

"Thank you. Well, Master Niccolo filled the half-moon lunette of the tympanum above the door at Ferrara with carved figural sculpture—just like what he had seen in Burgundy and Aquitaine.[138] While he worked on filling the lunette of the tympanum with carved figures of St. George and the Dragon, he had Pietro and me work on the wide strip of lush, inhabited vine scroll, with animals intertwined with acanthus leaves curving around above the tympanum. And although we started out doing only foliate sculpture there, Master Niccolo began blocking out figures and animals for us to finish and finally letting us carve them ourselves under his supervision.

....

138   It has long been postulated that Master Niccolo may have adopted both the concept of filling the tympanum above the portal with figure sculpture and the concept of inserting pier figures into the salient angles of piers on the jambs of a portal after seeing them during travels in France.

"Another sculptor began carving the lintel below with the Visitation and Nativity scenes from the Life of Christ, but Master Niccolo finally roughed out the remaining scenes himself, and then let Pietro and me finish the lintel. We finished the figures and animals in the scenes of the shepherds and sheep, the Flight into Egypt with a donkey, and the Baptism by John the Baptist.

Ferrara Cathedral. West portal. Detail of archivolt.   *Ferrara Cathedral. West portal. Detail of lintel frieze. Life of Christ: Flight into Egypt, Baptism by John the Baptist.*

"But Master Niccolo also envisioned decorating his west façade portal at Ferrara, the main entrance to the cathedral, with pier figures carved deeply into the angles of the piers, fairly large figures—half the size of a man[139]—like those he had just seen at the chapter house at Saint-Étienne, Toulouse. Master Gilabertus had used such figures for a chapter house, but Master Niccolo wanted to put them on the entranceway to a cathedral! You see, for Master Niccolo, figure sculpture is, at least in part, just another kind of decorative sculpture. So, he carved many of those pier figures into the jambs at the entrance to the cathedral. He first did it at Ferrara. He had Master Pietro and me help with a couple of figures and finish details, but he was so enthusiastic about the concept that he carved many of those jamb figures himself."

....

139   The Ferrara apostle figures are about 1 meter high, while the Toulouse apostle figures are no more than 1.15 meters high. See Kain, *Sculpture*, 111.

Ferrara Cathedral. West portal.   *Ferrara Cathedral. West portal.*
Pier figure. Daniel.   *Pier figure. Jeremiah.*

"So you mostly carved decorative foliage but helped finish details of figures at Ferrara," Pons probed, somewhat disappointed that this experience seemed rather limited, "but did you train further and work on other projects?"

"Oh, yes," Guillelmo responded enthusiastically. "We then moved on to Verona. At the Church of San Zeno in Verona[140] Master Niccolo wanted to try to blend elements of the new foreign style with some elements of the local old style. He wanted to use the new sculpture-filled tympanum, but to try flanking the portal with stacked rows of scenes with carved relief figures. His own mentor, Master Wiligelmo, had twenty years earlier decorated the Cathedral of Modena with strips of carved reliefs depicting the Genesis stories, when Niccolo was in training with him there.

"It was in Verona that we completed our training as journeymen, under Master Niccolo. At San Zeno he guided and encouraged us to really develop, to truly come into our own. He entrusted us there with much of the carving, and had us carve figures, in addition to animals and foliage, of course.

. . . .

140   Most scholars recognize most of the sculpture on the lower central section of the façade of San Zeno (i.e., the porch, portal, and façade) as work of Niccolo and his workshop that can be dated around 1138 because of the inscriptions, but there is disagreement.

"Master Niccolo again carved the tympanum himself there, this time a figure of San Zeno flanked by the soldiers and cavalry of Verona. At first Pietro and I again worked on the foliate decoration, including the strip of inhabited vine scroll surrounding the tympanum and several panels of elegant acanthus.

"But at San Zeno Master Niccolo wanted relief panels instead of jamb figures, as I just mentioned, and it was Pietro and I who carved many of those reliefs. We worked on the panels showing the Life of Christ from the New Testament, including the three adoring Magi, the shepherds, Herod, and the Flight into Egypt, and Pietro carved the Baptism by John the Baptist.[141] And although Master Niccolo planned and carved most of the Creation panels himself, and signed them, he let me sign the panels showing the Life of Christ because I had carved so much of them—along with Pietro, of course.

Basilica of San Zeno, Verona. West portal, north panels. New Testament scenes of Life of Christ.   *Basilica of San Zeno, Verona. West portal, south panels. Creation scenes.*

. . . .

141   Many have remarked on the stylistic differences in the New Testament Life of Christ reliefs, often attributed to another sculptor, Guglielmus, whose signature is inscribed above:
QUI LEGIS ISTA PIE NATUM PLACATO MARIE
SALVET I ETERNU QUI SCULPSERIT ISTA GUILLELMUM
INTRANTES CONCTI SUCURRANT HUIC PEREUNTI.

"Pietro helped Master Niccolo finish the Creation panels, where he carved the panel with Adam and Eve after the Fall, and he did some of the animals in the Creation of the Animals."

Basilica of San Zeno, Verona. North panel detail. Adoration of Magi.

Basilica of San Zeno, Verona. South panel detail. Creation of animals.

"You must have had major responsibility at San Zeno if Master Niccolo permitted you to sign the work," Pons suggested encouragingly, now beginning to hope that this young sculptor and his colleague might be able to help him begin pursuing his mission. "Tell me more, as we walk back."

They stood up to return as the sculptor continued talking. Pons looked up briefly, however, and what filled his view were the remains of the Roman theater, the monumentality of those antique remains. His momentary hopefulness turned to dismay. He realized he needed much more than sculptors. He first needed builders!

"It was at San Zeno that we began thinking about starting up our own workshop once we had finished our training," Guillelmo continued unremittingly, even after noticing the canon's dismay. "You see, before we had finished our work at San Zeno, Master Niccolo began another huge project nearby at the Cathedral of Verona,[142] where he returned to the new idea of jamb figures flanking the portal with a tympanum filled with figure sculpture, all in high relief. Master Niccolo again carved most of the tympanum himself there, the Virgin and Child with the Annunciation to the Shepherds and Adoration

142   Documents report the construction of the Cathedral of Verona in 1139, and the sculpture is now usually dated 1139–1145.

of the Magi. Pietro carved one of the pier figures himself, King David, but Master Niccolo and others carved most of the rest of the pier figures. Pietro and I worked on some of the foliate sculpture there.

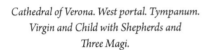

Cathedral of Verona. West portal. Tympanum. Virgin and Child with Shepherds and Three Magi.

Cathedral of Verona. West portal, north jamb. Pier Figures of Malachi, King David, Jeremiah, and Isaiah.

"We decided to leave to start up our own workshop, and Master Niccolo encouraged us to do. So you see, we are very well trained. Master Pietro and I finished our training as journeymen in Verona under Master Niccolo, and we are now master sculptors and members of the Goldsmiths' Guild. We excel at small figural and decorative foliage sculpture, and it is time for us to undertake our own projects.

"As for our assistant, he was a member of the workshop in Piacenza. He is still rather limited in the range of what he can carve, but he can do simple decorative carving, finish foliage and vine scrolls, and even finish little figures and animals. He is particularly proud of some new floral motifs we learned from Master Niccolo, such as the five-petal rosette, and especially portraying the underside of the flower with the vine stem emerging from it.[143] Frankly, Master Niccolo has such a big workshop that he was willing to let him go, so we invited him to join our new workshop and brought him here with us.

"May I ask what kind of project you are envisioning?" the young sculptor asked.

"Well," replied Pons rather hesitantly, having returned to the cathedral area and beginning to walk toward the chapter house with the sculptor in tow,

....

143   Both of these motifs, the five-petal flower and portrayal of a flower from the underside with the vine stem emerging from it, appear on Niccolo's "Portale dello Zodiaco" at the Sagra di San Michele.

"we will be building a new claustral complex as well as reconstructing much of the cathedral, so we will be looking for a master mason qualified to develop and carry out an overall building plan. I'm afraid I didn't get the impression that you are qualified to do that."

"I understand, and I can appreciate that," responded Guillelmo calmly. "Both Pietro and I have been very well trained, but we are master stone carvers. We are not master masons nor builders. But we are very good stone carvers. Frankly, we came back to this region at Master Niccolo's suggestion, hoping to find work with Master Brunus's workshop at the abbey of Saint-Gilles, where they have been working for several years on an elaborately carved façade with lots of decorative foliage and huge stone pier figures[144]— absolutely huge, even larger than life-sized, twice the size of Master Niccolo's pier figures! Master Niccolo had recently heard that Master Brunus may be expanding his sculptural project, adding carved friezes, and might want more sculptors. But Master Brunus told us he doesn't need any additional carvers now," Guillelmo admitted rather forlornly.

"But we are here, we want to work, and we want to strike out on our own, to prove ourselves. Could you tell me what sort of building you will be doing and what stone carvings you may eventually need?"

"Well," began Pons rather hesitantly, having reached the chapter house, "I do not yet have it worked out, but eventually we will be building an entire communal complex around a cloister. Our chapter house will remain here, along the south flank of the cathedral. The new cloister will be here, directly south of the chapter house, with the communal buildings constructed around the cloister. Unfortunately, we cannot begin those communal buildings quite yet—not until we have certain assurances . . . I don't want to go into all that. But we do wish we could begin somehow."

....

144   The pier figures at Saint-Gilles are all about two meters in height. This is twice the size of the pier figures at Toulouse, Ferrara, and Verona.

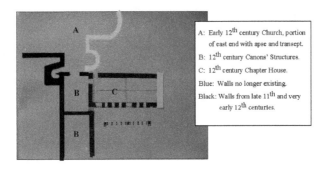

A: Early 12th century Church, portion of east end with apse and transept.

B: 12th century Canons' Structures.

C: 12th century Chapter House.

Blue: Walls no longer existing.

Black: Walls from late 11th and very early 12th centuries.

Arles. Cloister. Ground plan. Earliest proposal. Sloped wooden-roofed porch to be supported by row of piers and double columns in front of chapter house.

"We certainly do wish we were able to begin," repeated Jordan, who had just sauntered up to the pair.

"Canon Jordan," said Pons, "this is Master Guillelmo, a stone carver introduced to me by the Count of Toulouse, and we are discussing the project here. Master Guillelmo, Canon Jordan."

"Deeply honored to meet you, Canon Jordan," said the carver. Then he turned to Pons and asked, directly and rather boldly, "Could you perhaps begin work here, on the porch to the chapter house?" Guillelmo pressed forward, apparently buoyed in his hopeful expectations. "From what you have described, this wooden-roofed porch we are now standing under will become the north gallery of the new cloister, so we could begin by enhancing the porch while you wait for your . . . 'assurances,'" he added, very discretely and with surprising confidence.

"Oh, my, that's very clever," responded Pons, somewhat more receptively.

"The façade of the chapter house is already very beautiful, with its central main portal, an arcade supported on double colonnettes, and arched open windows on each side.[145] And several of the carved capitals are really

. . . .

145   On the north façade wall, and the original façade being comprised of the large portal flanked by three window openings to the west and two to the east, see Schneider, "Sculptures," 106–115. It was Hans-Adalbert von Stockhausen who provided the first thorough examination of the north wall, and noting the horizontal break in the masonry above the western arches of this façade, he concluded it probably belonged to an earlier design with a flat, wooden-roofed gallery. See Hans-Adalbert von Stockhausen, "Die Romanischen Kreuzgänge der Provence: I. Teil: Die Architektur," *Marburger Jahrbuch für Kunstwissenschaft* 7 (1933), 142–144.

quite beautiful!" exclaimed Guillelmo. "Especially these two with siren and *luxuria* figures.

"Canon Pons, could it have been Master Niccolo himself who carved these two figures, perhaps when he first passed through this region on his way to Toulouse? Or perhaps it was a member of the workshop he took with him. One of Master Niccolo's capitals on the porch at Sant'Eufemia in Piacenza shows sirens whose physical bodies closely resemble this siren here.

Church of Sant'Eufemia, Piacenza. Porch. Capital. Siren by Niccolo.

Arles. Chapter House, Façade. Capital. Siren. (Unfortunately, quite damaged)

"And not only the siren figures," Guillelmo realized. "There are also strong similarities between some of the foliate capitals at the two sites, at Sant'Eufemia, Piacenza, and here on the façade of the chapter house—both large, broad, erect acanthus leaves and smaller acanthus mixed with interlace. Could Master Niccolo and his traveling companions have carved the façade here?

"Master Niccolo had told us that while on his journey, he had undertaken a couple of projects on the *Via Francigena*, including one at the Sagra di San Michele after passing through Torino in the Val di Susa. I think this may have been another, here at Arles, and this may be his work!

"Moreover, when Pietro and I were journeying here, we, too, passed through the Val di Susa and sought refuge overnight at the Sagra di San Michele, where we saw what I now recognize must be a very crude copy of this *luxuria* capital, here at Arles. The capital here is more fully articulated; the carving of the figure and drapery is more subtly done; the body is more physically dynamic; even the petals on the drum behind the figure are more refined. The *luxuria* capital at the Sagra must have been copied from this one by one of the less skilled assistants in Nicolo's workshop.

Sagra di San Michele. Capital.
Luxuria (lust) by an assistant in
Niccolo's workshop.

Arles. Chapter House, Façade. Capital. Luxuria
(lust). (Unfortunately, very damaged.)

"Will you want to keep these beautiful carved capitals and the façade?" continued Guillelmo, unable to restrain his admiration for the beautiful carving or his adulation for his mentor.

"Oh, yes, we have to keep these two carved capitals!" responded Pons firmly, energized with excitement at the young sculptor's genuine interest in the two carvings. "In fact, we want to keep this entire arcade," he added as he calmed down a bit.

"We need to keep this arcade of *balcones*—window openings—onto what will eventually be the cloister," explained Jordan, "because they will permit unregularized canons who have not yet adopted our Rule, laymen, and all visitors who would not be permitted into the chapter house to stand in the cloister gallery and participate in portions of the chapter meetings."[146]

"Well, we could begin by making a beautiful porch here for you, and it can eventually become the north gallery of the cloister," offered Guillelmo confidently. "Since you are keeping this façade arcade, the porch or gallery should also have two bays, to line up with the chapter house. The gallery will certainly have to have a lean-to wooden roof. I may not be a builder, but I certainly don't think anyone could possibly erect a stone vault over this north wall façade, with its arcade openings and large portal. And with a lean-to wooden roof, we can put elegant supports on the garden side."

"Oh, we would want small double colonnettes with beautiful carved capitals, like the elegant cloisters in Toulouse," Pons interjected. "Would you be able to do those?"

"Certainly," Guillelmo offered. "Perhaps we could even reuse some of the smaller Roman colonnettes from the old Roman ruins nearby."

"You may have trouble finding any that have not already been appropriated for use elsewhere," interjected Jordan.

"As for the choice of type and shape of the capital, we will follow what appears here on the *luxuria* capital. After all, it is one of the shapes used by Master Niccolo's workshop at the Sagra di San Michele, and we used it at Verona. Now, at the corners of the new gallery, would you like slender piers with double engaged columns, like the beautiful cloisters in Toulouse?"[147] Guillelmo prodded encouragingly. "And will you want some figure carving on the capitals?" Guillelmo continued without missing a beat, not waiting for Pons's response. "I know you will want some decorative acanthus vines and rinceau scrolls. But we can also carve charming little figures as well as beautiful acanthus vine scrolls."

....

146   A standard feature of early Cluniac end Cistercian chapter house architecture was a series of openings in the wall linking the chapter house to a gallery in the cloister. These arcade openings onto the cloister were to permit the unprofessed and those who did not have a permanent seat in chapter to partake of some parts of chapter without entering the chapter house by standing outside under the protection of the cloister gallery. The *balcones*, or arcades supported on double columns, permitted novices, *pueri*, *laici*, and visiting monks to witness the first parts of the proceedings, to hear the reading of the Rule, the martyrology, and the sermon, and to participate in part of the routine, the recitation of the prayers and collects. See Schneider, "Sculptures," 117ff.

147   On the double engaged columns, see Schneider, "Sculptures," 166–178.

"Oh, figure carving, most certainly," answered Pons, now deep in thought. "We definitely want historiated capitals. And I know what stories we want depicted."

"Just a moment, my friend," interjected Jordan, pulling Pons aside for a moment for a private comment. "Remember, we have been discussing this in chapter for some time, and even though the chapter has thrust all the responsibility on you, they still want to be part of this sort of decision."

"Yes, of course!" retorted Pons with a hissed whisper that betrayed his irritation. "But I have finally won approval with almost everyone in chapter, even with William Garnerius, who had his own strong ideas at first but now supports our proposal."

Turning back to the sculptor, Pons began, "We will be enclosed here in the privacy of our own cloistered compound," he explained, "so we want sculptures depicting biblical stories that will strengthen and nurture our faith."

"Would you want Creation scenes or a Nativity cycle, like those we did with Master Niccolo at San Zeno?" Guillelmo asked hesitantly, not understanding which biblical stories might be considered to strengthen the canons' faith.

"No," answered Pons firmly.

"Or a Passion series," Guillelmo asked even more hesitantly, "with a Last Supper scene and a Crucifixion scene? We know that's what they are now planning for Saint-Gilles."

"No!" Pons retorted more abruptly and a bit too vigorously. "We are not fighting the Petrobrusian heresy here within our own cloister! We do not need those images in here."

Then, taking a deep breath and regaining his composure, he adopted a calmer tone and continued. "We want biblical images here that will confirm and portray the central truths of our faith, but we want subtle images that will engage us in thinking about those essential core issues and about our faith. So we want images that have several layers of meanings for us to contemplate.

"We want well-known biblical stories that foretell, or rather prefigure, the important events that are the central truths of our Christian faith: the Annunciation, the Nativity, the Crucifixion, and the Resurrection. These are the indisputable core certainties of our Christian belief.

"First, for the Annunciation to Mary of Christ's birth, we want one capital showing the Old Testament story of the annunciation to Abraham after the three angels visited him at Mambre.[148] Abraham ordered that a calf be slaughtered for a feast. Then the angel announced to Abraham and Sarah that the aged, childless woman, who was much too old to give birth, would nonetheless miraculously give birth. This story is well-known as prefiguring the Annunciation of the miraculous birth of our Lord Jesus Christ."

"I think I understand," the young sculptor responded hopefully.

"Then, to suggest the Nativity and Birth of Christ," Pons continued, "we want one capital showing the Old Testament story of Balaam, because it was Balaam who prophesized 'There shall come a Star out of Jacob,'[149] which was the prophecy of the birth of Christ and the Nativity. Balaam was an astrologer, an early ancestor of the three magi who followed the star to Bethlehem."[150]

"Of course, we all know that means he could have been an early ancestor of your family as well," Jordan added as an aside, with a wry smile.

"Well, perhaps, yes, but that is unimportant. What is important here is that he prophesized the star of the Nativity," Pons retorted, a bit unnerved. After returning his attention to the sculptor, Pons asked, "You did say your workshop can do animals, so could you do a capital of Balaam and his ass with the angel stopping him?"

"Of course!" responded Guillelmo. "As I've told you, we excel at animals! Pietro began assisting Master Niccolo with animals at Sant'Eufemia and Ferrara. Then there were all the animals in the scene of the Creation of the Animals at San Zeno in Verona. And remember, we trained with Master Niccolo, who–just like his mentor Wiligelmo at the Cathedral of Modena— put stately lions at his church portals. Well, we helped with the paired lions supporting the porches at all three churches we worked on in Ferrara and Verona. And, quite frankly, anyone who hopes to work as a sculptor anywhere in the Veneto learns to carve the lion, the triumphant recumbent lion, the symbol of St. Mark, patron of Venice."

"Good!" responded Pons enthusiastically, though unable to envision any of the depictions mentioned by the young sculptor and wondering if all those

....

148   Genesis 18:1–14.

149   Numbers 24:17.

150   On Balaam and the Magi, see Tim Hegedus, "The Magi and the Star in the Gospel of Matthew and Early Christian Tradition," *Laval théologique et philosophique* 59, no. 1 (February 2003), 81–95.

carved animals included an ass. "Because we would want to show Balaam when he is on his ass, with the angel stopping him,"[151] Pons emphasized.

Suddenly perceiving a puzzled look on the sculptor's face, Pons kindly took the time to explain. "You do not seem to know or understand that story, so I'll tell it to you. Although Balaam had been instructed not to do so, he defiantly set off on his ass on a journey to curse the Israelites. When an angel tried to stop him, Balaam did not recognize the angel, and it was only when the ass recognized the angel and then turned aside and spoke to Balaam that the man finally saw the angel. The angel then commanded him to change what he had intended to do and to bless the Israelites instead, and Balaam finally continued on and obeyed this command."

"And as William Garnerius suggested in chapter," Jordan continued support-ively, now looking directly at his friend, "given the major change our chapter will be undertaking in adopting the Rule, this image of Balaam on his ass will not only prefigure, as usual, the birth of Christ, but it may also subtly suggest to our canons here the issue of obedience and changing one's path once one recognizes God's true commands. So it is a very appropriate image choice."

"Yes," answered Pons with a grateful smile.

Pons then quickly turned away for a moment, remembering with a silent chuckle, "And of course, as both Peter Villelmus and Bernard Aiguillus shouted out during the discussion in chapter, they think this story appro-priate because they think I am an ass for bringing in communal life and the *vita apostolica*."

"Oh, forgive me, Father," Pons voiced silently to himself with remorse, as he made the sign of the cross. "*Mea culpa, mea culpa.* I do know it is wrong for me to find that humorous! I'm indulging myself. I shall confess it and do penance for my self-indulgence."

After once again composing himself and turning to the sculptor, Pons resumed speaking again with more command. "Let's continue. To suggest the Crucifixion of Christ, we want one capital depicting the Old Testament story of Abraham's sacrifice of his son Isaac.[152] That image is very well-known as foretelling our Father's sacrifice of his own Son, and the Crucifixion of our Lord Jesus Christ."

....

151   Numbers 22:21–35.

152   Genesis 22:1–14.

"And as you and I have already noted in private," Jordan added confidentially, turning directly to Pons, "that particular image may also perhaps resonate strongly with our chapter as we adopt the communal life, particularly with those who will have to sacrifice living with their own wives and families."

"Yes," murmured Pons quietly.

"And finally, to suggest our Lord's resurrection and triumph over death, we certainly should have one capital depicting the New Testament story of Christ's Raising of Lazarus from the dead,"[153] Pons concluded.

"That's four capitals with biblical scenes," offered Guillelmo. "Judging by the length of what will be the gallery here, we could probably put three sets of colonnettes between the piers in each of the two bays, so you could select more biblical scenes for the other capitals."

"We'll think about that," responded Pons. "We may eventually decide in chapter for other scenes, but let's start with those four that prefigure the central truths of our faith. They have been endorsed by the chapter."

"And you want simple piers, flanked with paired colonettes?" Guillelmo pressed.

"Well, must we?" retorted Pons. "We know in some other cloisters there are larger figures carved in low relief on the piers. We should have a large figure of St. Stephen here. After all, our church is now dedicated to St. Stephen. Could we get a figure of St. Stephen in low relief, perhaps on the pier at the west corner near the entrance to the church?"

"So far I have worked only on much smaller figures and on finishing the detail on larger figures," admitted Guillelmo. "But Pietro worked directly with Master Niccolo in carving and finishing the large pier figure of King David at Verona. But why shallow, low relief? The pier figures that Master Gilabertus carved at the chapter house of Saint-Étienne, Toulouse and that Master Niccolo carved at the Cathedral of Ferrara are in high relief, deeply carved into the corners of piers. Would you want us to try one of those?"

"Oh, if that were possible it would be wonderful!" Pons cried with a huge grin.

"I am certain our Pietro would be thrilled at the opportunity and the challenge of carving a large figure of St. Stephen in high relief on the corner

....

153   John 11:1–45.

pier here entirely by himself, from blocking it out to finishing it," admitted Guillelmo.

"Canon Pons, I am really enthusiastic about this opportunity to prove ourselves here," exclaimed Guillelmo. "This would be our first big project as our own workshop, our first commission. We can negotiate our own price, and we can work much more reasonably than a well-known master or a large, well-established workshop. If you give us a chance to prove ourselves, I promise you will not be disappointed."

"Master Guillelmo, let's be clear here," said Pons "First of all, we will, of course, have to see the quality of your workshop's carving before entering into a formal agreement for a larger program, but from what you have said, with your training in the workshops of two well-known masters, and given that it was the Count of Toulouse who introduced you to us, I am willing to let you begin, to prove your workshop's capability. You will begin with what we have just discussed, as soon as we have agreed on payment for that initial work. If your work proves acceptable, we will then discuss how we will move ahead on the rest of the project. Is this acceptable to you?

"Yes, yes, yes! We would be thrilled to start work immediately."

"Be forewarned that I want to be kept fully apprised of all your plans, any changes to them, or problems that arise. Let's sit down under the porch to begin working out the details for this initial work—cost, payment, procurement of stone. . . " Although Pons was fully aware of the magnitude and seriousness of the task before them, excitement and euphoria now swept through him because he was finally beginning that task. He was beginning down the path toward his goal in the mission given him by God. Clapping the sculptor on the shoulder, Pons added warmly, "Master Guillelmo, my young new friend, this will be the start of something beautiful."

*　　*　　*

Details were worked out, and because they were able to procure the stone quickly with the help of the abbot at Saint-Gilles, work began within a few weeks. Although the workshop was very small, and the carvers were all fairly young, they seemed to be working collaboratively, which surprised Pons, who observed them from a courteous distance. He surmised that perhaps it was because they were young and relatively inexperienced at giving orders that they seemed to be able to work so well together, each learning from the others as each worked on his own carving. Naïvely, the inexperienced Pons resolved at first to let them work fairly independently.

To prove themselves, they began with work on the four historiated figural capitals Pons had requested, with Pietro immediately beginning on the capital with the annunciation to Abraham and Sarah. Soon Pietro had finished much but not all of the capital, and Pons came for the first time to inspect their work, bringing Jordan with him.

After looking at the capital for a moment, Pons immediately gasped in distress. "No! No! No! This is wrong! This is terrible! I cannot approve this! There should be three angels. Three! That is why this scene is associated with the Trinity!"[154]

Visibly distressed and crushed by the criticism, the master sculptor Pietro quickly and quietly slipped away, leaving Master Guillelmo to deal with the canons.

"Three angels? I am certain you told me *the* angel announces to Abraham that Sarah will give birth,"

Arles. North gallery, capital. Abraham and Sarah with angel at Mambre.

Guillelmo retorted defensively, "and that this is like the Annunciation to the Virgin. That's why we carved it this way," he continued, feigning confidence, "with one angel announcing the future birth filling one side of the capital. Here's Sarah on another side, and between them at the corner is Abraham leaning on a crutch to show he's very old, and the angel is speaking to him."

....

154   On the imagery of the angel's annunciation to Abraham that Sarah will give birth, see Schneider, "Sculptures," 460ff.

"No!" Pons cried. "*Three* worthies, or angels, appear to Abraham at Mambre. They symbolize the Holy Trinity! That's an important part of the meaning of the image. This is wrong! This is unacceptable!"

"Pons, wait just a moment! Calm down!" Jordan interjected. "Depictions of the story do always show three worthies appearing at Mambre, but I think it is usually only one angel that then announces that Sarah will give birth. That's another layer of meaning here. The Trinity of God, who is Father, Son, and Holy Spirit, all in one.

"And let's be fair here," Jordan continued. "I was with you when you were instructing Master Guillelmo. You did not talk about the Holy Trinity symbolism, much less emphasize it. Be fair, Pons! Be fair. Frankly, you stressed only the significance of the scene suggesting the Annunciation to Mary."

"But..."

"Besides," Jordan added, "just look at the figures on this capital. They are quite extraordinary! Really beautiful!"

"If you want more angels," Guillelmo offered hesitantly, "we can possibly adapt the carving on the one side that has barely been blocked out yet, just behind this angel, to include another angel, or ... perhaps two. And to ensure everyone recognizes the scene, we can inscribe 'SARRA' on the molding above her. Master Niccolo often put inscriptions on his sculptures to identify the scene, or the meaning, just as he sometimes included his name to identify his workshop as the carver. We can add 'SARRA.'"

"And when we canons recognize this image as the annunciation to Abraham, it will subtly invoke not only the Annunciation to the Virgin, but also recall the three worthies at Mambre who represent the Trinity," Jordan confirmed.

"All right," conceded Pons. "I guess I should accept my responsibility in this. You are correct, Jordan. I was not clear enough. Let me look at the capital again," he added as he began looking more closely at it.

"Well . . . Oh, my!" he began again with a smile. "The capital is really beautiful! Abraham looks convincingly old and decrepit. He is convincingly leaning on his crutch. And his tunic here has a realistically looped closure at the neckline.

Arles. North gallery capitals, story of Abraham and angels at Mambre:
Servant with calf; foliate capital.

"But on another side of the capital, the calf bearer, the youthful servant bearing on his shoulders the fatted calf that will be prepared as a meal for the three worthies, is truly extraordinary! He looks like an antique Roman sculpture, except that he is wearing contemporary dress, a working man's *gonelle* and little boots."

"I believe Master Pietro used a 'Good Shepherd' figure on an early Christian sarcophagus as somewhat of a model," Master Guillelmo offered.[155]

"Master Pietro is a very talented carver," Pons admitted. "I do want you and your workshop to continue, but let's proceed more carefully in the future. No more mistakes like this! If you are unsure about an image, ask me!"

"Actually, we would ask you to confer more frequently with us as we work," the stone carver responded. "We do want to do a good job, but unless we know what you are looking for, we cannot produce it for you."

"Yes," Pons admitted. "Agreed. I will work much more closely with you from now on. But will you ask Master Pietro to do what he can here?"

....

155   See Schneider, "Sculptures," 465. Rouquette earlier suggested that the Good Shepherd on an early Christian sarcophagus at Arles may have been the model for the servant bearing the fatted calf. See Jean-Maurice Rouquette, *Provence Romane: La Provence Rhodanienne* (Abbaye Sainte-Marie de la Pierre-Qui-Vire (Yonne), France: Zodiaque, 1974), 341–342.

Arles. Capitals. Abraham and angel at Mambre, with second angel; foliate capital.

"We will do what we can, but perhaps it would be better if we left this side unfinished for now, so we can think through how we might be able to best correct it,"[156] concluded Master Guillelmo without revealing his immense relief.

Arles. North gallery capital. Christ Raising Lazarus, with Martha and Mary.

From then on, Pons closely watched over their work, stopping at the construction site outside the chapter house almost every day to answer any questions, to avoid any more misunderstandings.

Master Guillelmo had begun by carving the capital depicting the Raising of Lazarus, placing the figure of Christ prominently filling one face, flanked by the two sisters and the tomb at the corners. After finishing the capital, he immediately began carving delicate acanthus rinceaux and palmettes on the

---

156   The second angel differs somewhat in style and may have been incorporated later, possibly by a different sculptor.

long abacus block that would eventually be placed atop this and the foliate capital it would be paired with.

Examining the finished capital, Pons expressed his delight. "Your figure of Christ has such a sweet and gentle demeanor in performing the miracle."

"And your realistic little details are both charming and extraordinary," praised Pons. "The overlapping flap of the tunic closure at Christ's throat, the thin end of the mantle cloth hanging over the shoulder, the parallel tubular folds of cloth encircling the waist and hips . . . Your figure carving on the capital is as fresh and charming as your acanthus rinceaux on the abacus! Both are beautifully done."

Arles. North gallery, capitals with foliate abacus.
Raising of Lazarus with Mary and onlooker; foliate capital.

"Perhaps it is because we look so closely at nature in carving foliage and animals that we notice such little details on figures too," mused Guillelmo. "And we pride ourselves in carving what we see, the details as well as the movements. But we are very pleased that you appreciate our work."

Leaving the alterations on his first capital to be completed later or by someone else, Master Pietro immediately moved on to carving capitals of the Sacrifice of Abraham and the Angel Stopping Balaam. Pons closely oversaw his work, but from a distance, stopping every day to speak with Master Guillelmo about it once he had recognized that Master Pietro was much more comfortable with carving stone than with speaking with his employer about his work.

"I would like to ask you to look more closely at our Master Pietro's work," Master Guillelmo insisted one day. "He is an extraordinarily talented stone carver. I don't want our unfortunate misunderstanding about the number of angels appearing to Abraham to dampen your enthusiasm for our work.

"Look at his capital with Abraham's Sacrifice of Isaac. Look at Abraham here with his cape circling his chest and real shoes on his feet. We call Pietro our 'Bold One,' as Master Niccolo used to call him. Pietro manages to portray real body substance. Look at the powerful shoulders swelling slightly forward on Abraham. Look at his belly and hips. Abraham is really swinging that sword! Look at the angel stopping Abraham and how the clinging drapery over his chest and leg reveals the angel's strong torso. See the little looped opening of his shirt at his throat; see how his cloak folds neatly over one shoulder but cascades down his other shoulder to be tied up at his waist. And our 'Bold One' likes to twist the folds of cloth at the waist into a roll, a rope-like belt of cloth.

Arles. North gallery capital. Sacrifice of Isaac. Angel stopping Abraham.

Arles. North gallery capital. Sacrifice of Isaac. Abraham about to sacrifice Isaac.

"But more striking than any of those charming details is that his figures seem to be so physically solid that they almost burst out of their space— something he learned from Master Niccolo! The capitals cannot contain the figures, who step out from the capitals with their feet on the abaci. I tell you, our 'Bold One' is absolutely brilliant! Remarkably talented! He produces absolutely stunning work!

"Here on the other capital is the Angel staying Balaam, stopping him from continuing on his path. Our Pietro just loves trying to show movement—another thing he shares with Master Niccolo. Look how the angel is stepping in front of Balaam's ass, raising his sword to stop the animal.

Arles. North gallery, capital. Angel staying Balaam, stopping him from continuing on his path.   *Arles, North gallery, capital. Angel staying Balaam. Balaam stopped on ass, but not recognizing angel.*

"We learned so much from working together with Master Niccolo in his workshop: how to carve both figures and drapery. Pietro now usually carves faces with sharp angular corners at the bridge of the nose to suggest the bony structure beneath—something he learned at Ferrara and began using regularly with his pier figure of King David at Verona. Frankly, I think our Pietro now vies with Master Niccolo himself at portraying the suggestion of a physical body with muscles and bones beneath the drapery."

"And let me tell you about the decorative foliate line he always carves at the upper and lower edges of the capital . . ."

But just then Rainaldo and Bernard Aiguillus stormed up, angrily interrupting them.

"Can't these men work more quietly?" Bernard Aiguillus blurted out in a huff. "We have work to do in the chapter house! We have important work to do! We are the porters. The others are trying to tell me what they need brought to them for work, what they need prepared, and I cannot even hear them! We cannot hear each other. Everyone is terribly annoyed at this infernal noise. We have work to do. Everyone asked us to come here and stop this horrid noise!"

"And it's not just the noise," added Rainaldo. "The stone chips, the dirt, the mess is everywhere. I'm supposed to move things in and out for the scribes working today, and I have to clean everything I give to them, clean anything they want removed, and even clean a place to put anything down! The mess is intolerable!"

"Rainaldo, Bernard Aiguillus, please, please let's be reasonable," Pons responded calmly, placatingly. "We all know the chapter agreed to this work being done. Stone carving is noisy and messy. We all knew this would happen.

"We all know the importance of your work here," he continued cajolingly, trying to placate them, "and we all recognized the project would place some special burdens on you because of the important tasks you are usually assigned, carrying and moving heavy volumes and implements, but we decided in chapter to proceed nonetheless. I must remember to commend you in chapter for your extra efforts.

"But I will now ask on your behalf. Is there anything we can do, Master Guillelmo, to lessen the noise and to keep the mess from getting into the chapter house?"

"There's not much we can do about the noise," Guillelmo responded. "But we can reduce the mess getting through the openings by hanging covers over them. This will cut down on the light in the room. But if you want us to do it, we will.

"Do you have any coverings we could use? Animal skins would be best, though thick cloth would also work. I know for your documents you use vellum, so perhaps you already have some poor quality or imperfect animal skins that are both tough and thin but not good enough for your work. They would be strong enough to cover the window openings yet still let in some light."

"I'll see to it," offered Pons. "Let's try the window coverings, Canon Bernard Aiguillus and Canon Rainaldo, and see if they help."

Bernard Aiguillus and Rainaldo nodded half-heartedly, with no indication of satisfaction, before turning and walking away, their heads lowered together, privately discussing their displeasure at everything.

"Let's both hope this helps," Pons offered.

"Yes," Guillelmo responded before calmly continuing, skillfully endeavoring to maintain the favor of his patron. "Let's look at our Pietro's work again. I do hope you now recognize how skillful he is at carving."

"Yes," Pons admitted. "Especially his figure sculptures. But what is the story about this little foliate edge he carved along the top and bottom of his capitals? Does he always add that?"

"Yes," Guillelmo responded with a little chuckle. "It's his signature, and I do have a little story to tell you about it.

"When we were training with Master Niccolo, we soon realized that Niccolo liked to sign his work or the work of his workshop with more than just his name. He would sign or frame his own work with a particular simple decorative motif—his signature motif— called 'egg and dart.' He insisted that we carve this particular motif around the lunette tympana he was so proud of at the cathedrals of Ferrara and Verona, and even at San Zeno, Verona, though there it was much smaller and the band narrower. For a while we thought he was just indulging his general love of decorative ornament, but then he also had us carve it vertically along the jambs and flanking some of the pier figures at Ferrara and again at Verona.

"I first mistakenly wondered whether he had adopted this signature motif after his journey to Toulouse, after seeing the petalled halos of Master Gilabertus's figures in niches that he so admired at Toulouse, because the motif does resemble a series of petals. In fact, he did have us carve petalled halos on St. Zeno and the Virgin in the two tympana at Verona, and he also had us carve petalled halos on some of his pier figures at Ferrara and the Cathedral of Verona. But no, the "egg and dart" motif is a standard decorative motif that he had already used earlier at Piacenza, where rows of egg and dart appear on an archivolt at both the north and south portals.

"We finally recognized that Master Niccolo adopted this signature decorative motif, this egg and dart, as a mark of his workshop. And he included it prominently as a frame around work he was exceptionally proud of, especially the new types of sculpture he was directing: along the edge of each of his lunette tympana filled with carved figure sculpture—something quite new in that area—or on the colonnettes flanking the jamb figures at Ferrara— something totally new and original there. We believe that Niccolo signed those pieces with this motif because he was so proud of them, just as he had inscribed his name on the monuments.

"Well, wouldn't you know it, our Pietro decided, as soon as we set out on our own, to adopt his own signature motif, derived from Master Niccolo's egg and dart. Pietro uses a series of small, stylized, foliate egg and dart, like foliate horseshoes. He always uses it. See how he has included it at both the top and bottom of his two historiated capitals—the ones with figures—and on his purely foliate capitals too. He says he got the idea for the motif because he remembered carving a thin row of stylized vertical acanthus outside the rows of egg and dart on the archivolts at Piacenza. He now has our assistant carve this decorative detail as a signature on everything either of them carves. Mark my words, in the future we will be seeing Master Pietro's signature motif on some magnificent and noteworthy sculpture!"[157]

"I must say, I am more than pleased with all of your workshop's work," Pons offered.

Pons was, in fact, thrilled. Here were some carved capitals and other stone carvings that would eventually become the beginning of work on the cloister! The cloister around which communal buildings would somehow, one day, be built. Communal buildings that would enable the chapter to adopt the *vita apostolica*. The task God had given him was now underway!

That porch would be transformed, hopefully sometime soon, into the north gallery of a cloister whose four galleries would open not only to the chapter house, but onto a dormitory and refectory. And at the heart of the complex would be the cloister, a place for reflection and restful repose, with its central greenery and four galleries, covered walkways.

These carved historiated capitals, these carved stones, would one day decorate a gallery of the cloister in which the canons would be able to stroll and sit while quietly contemplating the images. These images would strengthen and enhance the canons' faith by foretelling, suggesting, and recalling the central truths of their Christian faith. These images would also confirm the chapter's decision to adopt the Rule of St. Augustine and would help bolster the canons' intent to live the *vita apostolica* by portraying not only Balaam on

....

157   Master Pietro's signature motif will appear above pier figures at the central portal at Saint-Gilles, most notably on St. Paul. This signature motif also appears at the Cathedral of Piacenza (e.g., on a capital of the south portal). For photo, see Bornstein, "Capitals," fig. 17.

his ass discovering late that the path he had taken was not right and had to be changed, but also the pictorial admonitions against women and lust, the siren and *luxuria*.

"All praise be to God. Yes, the task You have given me is now underway," Pons proclaimed softly. "Thank You! Thank You! But when will my brother and the Count of Toulouse make their pledges that will ensure the safety of Your church and *claustrum* at Arles? When can we begin real construction?"

Despite his frustration with that delay, Pons had to admit he was absolutely delighted at the sculptors' work. The figures they had carved were not timid, static, shallow little low-relief things, lined up and wrapped arbitrarily around the capitals. No, they were instead charming, dynamic, physically active, deeply cut figures that filled the capital and that emerged out of the mass of the capital, either by completely filling the concavity on the face of the capital to support the abacus block above, or by bending into the corner to support the salient upper edge of the capital.

Master Pietro was now beginning very cautiously to block out the large pier figure of St. Stephen. The two master sculptors had also blocked out the foliate capitals that the assistant was working on, which would be placed on the garden side. Work had been going on for many weeks. Work was progressing well, with Pons closely overseeing it.

"I must say, I am more than pleased with all of your workshop's work," Pons proclaimed to Master Guillelmo one morning, just after *Terce*, at his daily meeting with the sculptor. "I am absolutely delighted with what you have done. Your figures are so lively and active. They are truly remarkable! Your rinceau vine scrolls are amazingly intricate and beautiful."

"On the two abaci above the first two capitals you can see our two preferred styles of acanthus rinceaux," Guillelmo responded. "I like to carve a more delicate and irregular vine tendril that is busily filled not only with leaves, but with birds, animals, and figures, while Pietro prefers a heavier, more substantial tendril coiling carefully around single rosettes. But frankly, we borrow from each other and sometimes carve the other type. The two foliage styles complement each other well, and we used them together at Ferrara and Verona."

"Master Guillelmo," replied Pons "We are very pleased indeed with what your workshop is doing here. I truly wish I were able to hire builders, a master mason and his workshop of masons, so I could speak with you about doing all the sculpture we will need here. I hope to be able to do so soon, but I cannot yet do so."

But Pons would not be able to undertake that discussion with the master sculptor, at least not that year.

Work was progressing fairly quickly. The chapter house still had only a porch with a lean-to wooden roof, higher on the chapter house side than on the garden side, but the porch now had most of the first of its two bays, with beautiful carved stone capitals on twin colonnettes on the garden side, where the supporting piers were also each flanked by paired colonettes.

Just days later, after the hour of *Sext*, Pons was summoned to the archbishop's palace for a meeting, along with William Garnerius, who was now *precentor*, or leading chanter, in the chapter. Upon entering the room, the archbishop introduced Pons to two other men.

"This is Brother Ugo of the abbey of Saint-Gilles, who is here representing the abbot, who is unable to make the short journey himself because of his old age. And with him is Master Brunus, whose workshop has been carving the sculptural program on the façade of the abbey church."

"It's a great honor to meet both of you," responded Pons, wondering why the renowned sculptor was meeting with them there, and trying hard not to reveal his surprise and nervousness. "Master Brunus, I have heard about your bold sculptural program with large apostle pier figures on the façade of the abbey church."

"We do thank you for seeing us," began Brother Ugo. "It is because of the building program that we are here, and we bear distressing news. You may have heard that not too long ago there was a terrible accident at the abbey church. Absolutely terrible! A section of stonework near the center of the façade collapsed along with a section of the vault near the southwest end of the crypt below, killing two men, burying them alive. Gilius and Causitus— may God have mercy on their souls!" he added, making the sign of the cross. "They had been working on the façade near the central portal when the collapse happened."

"The two men were working with me as members of my workshop," interrupted Master Brunus. "They were invaluable to us. We are all devastated at their loss."

"It is imperative that work on the sculptural program not be delayed," began the archbishop. "The expanded program there will focus on the Passion of our Lord Jesus Christ, on the events of Holy Week. The sculptural program will help fight the Petrobrusian heretics because it will proclaim to all who see it the truth of two of the most important rites of the Christian faith that the Petrobrusian heretics deny: the Eucharist and the Veneration of the Cross.[158]

"The work at Saint-Gilles must not be delayed! That was where Peter of Bruys was burned alive. That is where the Church must make a strong visual statement to keep the illiterate from falling into the throes of the heresy. That is where the Church hopes to turn the tide against this insidious heresy."

"Not to mention the fact that our abbey was counting on the revenues from pilgrims who would visit our abbey while en route to Santiago de Compostela," interjected Brother Ugo. "And we have to get the façade fixed and completed so those pilgrims can get into the church to make their donations, so we can pay our exorbitant dues to Cluny!"

"Yes, yes, of course," added Archbishop Raymond, adroitly smoothing over this little eruption of avarice. "But the truly compelling issue here is the need to complete the strong visual proclamation against the heresies of Peter of Bruys, and as soon as possible, on the façade of the church. We all know that the heresy did not die out with the burning of Peter of Bruys. Far from it!

"That Henry of Lausanne is a devil-phoenix! He has already escaped once from prison. He is spreading the heresy here in Provence, and his following is now growing especially strong in Toulouse territory, so Alphonse Jourdain now finds the problem growing right at his own doorstep," the archbishop ended.

"But what does this have to do with us and our chapter?" asked Pons meekly and with great discomfort, as he fearfully began to anticipate a possible connection.

"We want you to release Master Guillelmo and Master Pietro from their obligation here, so they can join Master Brunus's workshop at Saint-Gilles to help complete the façade sculpture there," responded Brother Ugo rather abruptly.

"But the collapse!" cried William Garnerius. "How can work continue?"

"Let's be honest here," began Brother Ugo. "The accident occurred because a portion of the old groin vault at the west end of the crypt collapsed. That's really where the only problem is. But our new builders—the ones we just brought in for this building campaign—know how to correct the problem. They know how to strengthen the crypt vault. They are very skilled Lombard masons, *Magistri Comacini.*"

....

158   See Colish, "Peter," 451–460.

"They say the groin vault there was not strong enough to support the new construction above it at the west end, which unbalanced the groin vault below," Master Brunus continued. "But they say they can rebuild and strengthen the vaulting by putting up diagonal arches, new supports, at the groins. I think some call them 'supporting ribs.'"

"They will use these ribs to solve the problem," interrupted Brother Ugo, "because they will add strength and stability in supporting a heavy vault. They say the *Magistri Comacini* have been using them for this purpose for decades, not only in Lombardy, but elsewhere too. The crypt at Saint-Gilles has to support everything above it, including the grand façade with all the stone sculpture. We need sturdy, solid support in the crypt!"

"So," added Master Brunus, "the crypt bay will soon be repaired, rebuilt, and ready for the work above to proceed. Frankly, I really didn't need more sculptors when Master Guillelmo first approached me," he added. "But having lost two men, I do need them now. We have to proceed with the sculptural program on the façade as quickly as possible, and we need your sculptors to help finish the work on the façade."

"Would it be only a temporary arrangement, until the work at Saint-Gilles is completed?" asked William Garnerius hopefully, before receiving nods of assent. "Well, by then we should have received the pledges of support we need from Raymond of Baux and from the Count of Toulouse so that you can proceed with work here, Pons."

"Canon Pons," said Master Brunus, after seeing the look of total devastation on the young canon's face. "I just looked at the work of Master Guillelmo and Master Pietro in the porch of your chapter house before meeting you here today. It is very beautiful. Very high-quality carving. You are to be commended for finding such talented young sculptors and for giving such novices an opportunity. But they are now really comfortable with carving only smaller figural and decorative sculpture. They are master carvers, but they still have much to learn, a great deal to learn. I can teach them. I can train them how to carve large life-size figural sculpture.

"I have already spoken with them," Master Brunus finally admitted. "Master Guillelmo seems to be loyal to you, his present employer, but I believe they are both really very keen to have the opportunity to work on the project at Saint-Gilles, not only on the decorative sculpture there, but Master Pietro especially is keen to work on the large pier figures he would be carving with me there.

"Canon Pons, if you agree to release Master Guillelmo and Master Pietro to me, at the end, after they have worked with me at Saint-Gilles, you will be getting much better-trained sculptors who will be able to carve really magnificent large pier figures for your cloister!"

Pons was devastated at the prospect of postponing work on the cloister, but he also remembered Guillelmo's admission that Pietro welcomed the challenge of trying to carve the large pier figure of St. Stephen because they had never before had full responsibility for such a large program. Moreover, knowing his brother to be not only ambitious but ruthless, Pons certainly wanted that most important pledge of support before forging ahead with the building project, although he could certainly never admit this to the chapter.

But if Pons were to agree to the sculptors leaving Arles to go work at Saint-Gilles, would there be a backlash from the chapter, after he had worked so hard to convince them to adopt the Rule of St. Augustine?

"I bow to the will of God and respectfully accede to your request," Pons began, looking first at William Garnerius and then at Archbishop Raymond. "And I certainly do see the necessity of it. But a few members of the chapter have already begun making arrangements for the transition to communal life under the Rule. I know it was premature, but I was so pleased, and so relieved, at their acceptance of the change that I could not bring myself to correct their misperception of how long it would take. I couldn't tell them how long it might be before the construction is completed and we can live communally. One canon has already sent away his wife and children! The chapter may be very angry about this turn of events. After disrupting their personal lives so completely, I fear this change may cause real problems—if not now, then sometime in the future."

"Remember, Canon Pons," answered the archbishop, "this will be only a temporary hiatus in work here at Arles. And as for your potential problems with one or two canons, I am sure you will be able to calm them down and reassure them if you explain the situation fully to them."

And with that, work ceased for the present in the cloister at Arles. Within a few days, Master Guillelmo, Master Pietro, and their assistant had tidied up only minimally, packed up their implements, and departed for the abbey at Saint-Gilles, leaving a partially complete porch, incomplete sculptures, piles of unused stone and wood, and heaps of heavy rubble and detritus scattered everywhere.

A few days later Pons and Jordan were leaving the chapter house together to go celebrate *Terce*, when they were accosted unexpectedly by one of the canons, Rainaldo. Grabbing Pons by the shoulder, the large, older giant spun him around and hulked down to spit out his anger directly to his face.

"Is it true what they are saying?" Rainaldo growled. "After wreaking havoc with our lives, after destroying what solace we canons were able to find while doing God's work, are you now walking away from this blasted Rule of St. Augustine? Are you giving up on the infernal communal buildings?"

"No, no!" choked Pons, trying to remain calm. "This is but a temporary stoppage, a hiatus in our building project. There is an emergency situation following a collapse at Saint-Gilles. The workshop will return as soon as the masters have assisted in completing the work there."

"You damned hypocrite!" spat Rainaldo, pulling himself up imposingly. "You damned rich boy. You just don't want to part with your money now that you realize you will be giving up your own wealth for all of us in the chapter to share. Some of us don't have much. Some of us have precious little.

"All I had, the only real happiness I ever had, was my loving Hildegard and our two sons. When they heard people talking about your schemes, I had to be honest with them and tell them about the communal living and all . . . and that they would have to leave here. They were frantic; they had nowhere to go. My Hildie was beside herself! She fell apart, fell into pieces. Her sister had just died, though, and her brother-in-law was willing to take her as his woman and to take the boys, too, as future workers. So they went! They're gone! I have nothing now! I have nothing left! Nothing at all left! And it's your fault, you God-damned rich boy! You selfish hypocrite!

"You never kept a woman here. You don't know what it's like to have a woman who'll take care of you nice-like. You've always preferred men, you God-damned pervert, you sodomite," he hissed, grabbing Pons by the throat. "I could kill you! Why I don't just break your neck here and now I don't know,"

"The only loving I've ever had, the only pleasure and happiness I've ever had is gone!" Rainaldo continued, sobbing. "Gone! Because of you! Because of your God-damned, God-forsaken schemes!"

Initially shocked at the venomous rage, Jordan at first waited for Rainaldo to vent his anger, wrongly assuming that it would diminish. But now Jordan was truly frightened at what might happen, frightened for his friend, and he tried to step in.

"Rainaldo, Rainaldo," Jordan began, speaking calmly, soothingly. "Canon Rainaldo, you are a senior and respected elder canon in our chapter. You are now suffering. You are grieving at what you have given up, grieving at the loss of your beloved woman and of your good boys. But in your heart, you know this will be for the best. Our chapter has chosen a new path, the right path, the path taken by the apostles, the path of the *vita apostolica*.

"We know how you loved your Hildie and your two sons. Your Hildie was a good woman. A good woman! Your two boys were good boys. Good sons! We would not ask you to give them up lightly," Jordan continued, trying to placate the distressed giant. "Your sacrifice will not be in vain. You are a senior, older canon. You are leading the way; you will be showing the others what to do. You are setting the example. You are going to become a leader in this among the chapter."

Pons had finally caught his breath as Rainaldo's grip eased, and, thinking the angry old canon assuaged, he joined in.

"Canon Rainaldo, I give you my sacred word—I pledge my life—that we will adopt the Rule of St. Augustine and live the *vita apostolica*. Everyone wants this change to take place. Everyone. Not only me, not only Jordan, but everyone. All the chapter. The archbishop. Everyone. It will just take a bit longer to accomplish than we had expected. But it will happen! And Canon Jordan is right—you are leading the way!"

But although Rainaldo was no longer so visibly enraged, he was also not so easily to be placated. Puffing out his chest and putting his hands on his hips, he growled threateningly at Pons in a low voice.

"So you give your word, you little pervert, and you pledge your life. Well, we shall see! You pledge your life, and I hold you to it. Your life!" And he turned sharply and left abruptly.

Pons and Jordan looked at each other but could not speak, so overcome was each by what had just happened. There was disbelief, dismay, a bit of pride, and much relief, but mostly fear. Fear—abject fear, both vague and very, very real. Jordan was overwhelmed by a vague premonition, swept through by a wave of fear for the personal safety of his good friend, whom he had long ago tried to talk out of this mission.

As for Pons, at first he had felt little concern for his own personal safety, but he now slowly began to recognize the real possibility of being physically harmed, of being so seriously hurt physically that he might be hindered in working toward achieving his goal. The fanatical Pons now froze in abject terror and panic at the realization that if he were seriously hurt or killed, he would fail in the special mission God had entrusted to him!

Without speaking, the two began walking to the church and tried wholeheartedly, but rather unsuccessfully, to focus their full attention on celebrating *Terce*.

* * *

It would be almost a year before the final pledges would be made that would ensure, despite the war to come, the safety and security of the church and claustral buildings Pons was to build for the canons to be able to adopt the Rule at Arles.

In that next year, 1143, a large and distinguished group would assemble in the town of Furcas to witness the critically important oath and pledge of Alphonse Jourdain, Count of Toulouse, made with the counsel of his barons, Raymond of Baux, Raymond's son Ugo, Peter de Lambisco, and others. A document of that year reports that after many disputes, Alphonse Jourdain (Ildefonsus) released and gave to Archbishop Raymond de Monte Rotundo and to his successors the very lucrative tithes of all the newly cleared areas in Argentia. The count pledged his fealty and swore that he and his successors were bound to honor and defend the "ecclesiam et claustrum" at Arles and the castle of Salon and the fortified town of Saint Amantio, which also belonged to the archbishop and his church.[159]

> ". . .jurare illi vitam et membra et corp[us] suum et eccl[esi] am et claustru[m] Arelat[e]n[se] et castellum de Sallone et castru[m] de S[an]c[t]o Ama[n]tio ita q[uo]d ego no[n] auferam illa neq[ue] aliq[ui]d ex illis arch[i]ep[iscop]o Arelat[e]n[se] neq[ue] homo neq[ue] femina mea ope vel meo co[n]silio. Et si homo ut femina aliq[ui]d mali in vitam et m[em]bra ut corp[us] tuu[m] comiserit ut eccl[esi]am et claustru[m] Arelat[e]n[se] ut sup[ra]dicta castra. . ."[160]

....

159   *Authentique*, Arles, Bibliothèque Municipale, MS 1242, fol. 146–146 vo. See Albanes and Chevalier, *Arles*, nos. 548, 549, where the references to the *claustrum* were inadvertently omitted in the published transcription of document no. 548. See Schneider, "Sculptures," 28–29.

160   *Authentique*, Arles, Bibliotheque Municipale, MS 1242, fol. 146–146 vo.

The document records that Alphonse Jourdain made the pledge with the "co[n] silio. . . baronu[m] meorum videlicet Raimundi de Baucio, Hugonis filii ei, . . . Petrus de Lambisco . . ."

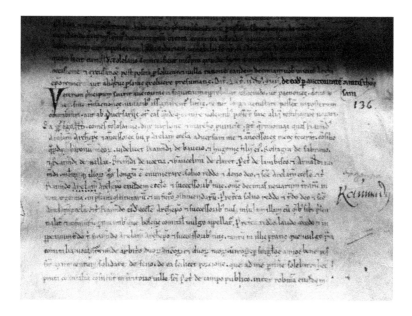

Authentique du Chapitre, Arles, Bibliothèque Municipale, MS 1242, fol 146 (lower half).

Authentique du Chapitre, Arles, Bibliothèque Municipale, MS 1242, fol 146 verso (upper half).

In return, the archbishop ceded to the count and his successors all of Argentia. He did this with the counsel of Ugo Amelius, who was dean of the chapter, and William Garnerius, who was precentor of the chapter, and other canons. The long list of witnesses to this pledge and exchange includes not only the dean and precentor of the chapter, but several consuls of the Republic of Arles, as well as Raymond of Baux, Peter de Lambisco, and many others.[161]

Having counseled his feudal lord, the Count of Toulouse, to do so, Raymond of Baux also now needed to make this pledge. So not long after, Raymond of Baux also swore to Archbishop Raymond de Monte Rotundo and pledged with his life to defend the "ecclesia et claustrum," the church and cloister of Arles, as well as Salon, Saint Amantio, and all the holdings of the church at Arles.

"I, Raymond de Baucio . . . with the counsel and willingness of my wife, Stephanie and my sons . . . return all the honors of St. Nicholas of Marignane and all honors of Saint Marie of Marignane . . ."

The ten witnesses to this oath again included Ugo Amelius, William Garnerius, and two other canons.[162]

Finally, at last it would be safe for Pons to begin work on the new claustral buildings and church. It would be safe, if it were possible, but the sculptors and builders could not yet be released from the project at Saint-Gilles, where they were still needed.

....

161   *Authentique*, Arles, Bibliotheque Municipale, MS 1242, fol. 146–146 vo.
162   See Albanes and Chevalier, *Arles,* no. 563. On the dating of this document to ca. 1142-43, see Schneider, "Sculptures," 29–33.

Sext

Midday—sixth-hour bells

Anno Domini MCXLV

Arles, Summer 1145

All of Christendom would shudder with foreboding on learning that the Christian forces had been defeated at the Siege of Edessa in 1144. One year later much of the Holy Land was controlled by the Turks. *The Kingdom of Jerusalem, Antioch, and other crusader states were now imperiled. Four decades after the successful First Crusade, Christendom now faced the threat of losing the Holy Land; Christendom now feared the loss of the land of its birth.*

In Arles and Provence the situation was more immediately dire. The conflict between the Catalans and the House of Baux that had been simmering and escalating for over a decade had finally erupted into full, all-out, open conflict.[163] The Catalan Berenguer Ramon I, Count of Provence since 1131, had the support both of his older brother, Ramon Berenguer IV, Count of Barcelona, as well as that of the local viscounts of Carcassonne, Nîmes, and Béziers. Raymond of Baux had the support of the Count of Toulouse, the county of Foix, the Republic of Arles, and the Republic of Genoa. During an offensive against Genoa, Berenguer Ramon I died in Melgueil in 1144, leaving his young son Ramon Berenguer II to inherit both the claim to the County of Provence and the full-blown war against Raymond of Baux.

....

163   For the Baux wars, see "Baussenque Wars," *Wikipedia*, https://en.wikipedia.org/wiki/Baussenque_Wars.

War now engulfed Arles, the town that was siding with Raymond of Baux, the town that was also the capital of the Catalan Count of Provence's holdings. The House of Barcelona continued to maintain its residence here within the Cité at the Palais de la Trouille, where the Catalan men now grouped visibly in defense, while Raymond of Baux, as always, maintained his main fortress, the chateau of Trinquetaille, not far away, outside the city and just across the Rhône.[164]

Arles and its surroundings became the battleground, the locus of the conflict, with battles within and surrounding the town. Raymond of Baux and his coalition fought courageously, continuously challenging the young Catalan claimant's right to the town and the territory.

War raged in and near Arles, sometimes within the Cité not far from the doorstep of the church, sometimes in other quarters of the city, sometimes to the east or to the west across the river—always moving, always threatening, always pernicious. The towers guarding an entrance to the town came down, razed during the hostilities. Roman columns at the antique theater were toppled, one crushing several townspeople to death. An archway at the Roman arena came down, with the cascading collapse of stones crushing to death some combatants but even more innocent merchants and burghers with their families. But remarkably, the war never imperiled the cathedral grounds.

With the death of Berenger Ramon I in 1144, Raymond of Baux recognized the change in the opposing forces and the possible new weakness resulting from it. He quickly acted on his full plan to claim the County of Provence, the lands allocated to the Catalans in the division of 1125, lands for which the Baux now had a legitimate claim.

Raymond of Baux slipped out of Provence and traveled quickly to Würzburg to appeal to Conrad III, King of Burgundy, who had the legal authority to invest him with Provence because it was a fief of Burgundy. In August 1145 King Conrad responded by giving a somewhat ambiguous but nevertheless formal recognition of Raymond of Baux's claim to Provence through his marriage to Stephanie. King Conrad also granted the Baux the authority to coin money at Arles and at Trinquetaille, a lucrative grant that would help the Baux finance their war. However, King Conrad was not about to take an active role in the war himself,

---

164   See Baratier, *Histoire*, 137–139; Poly, *La Provence*, 294, 334–340; and V.-L. Bourrilly et Raoul Busquet, *La Provence au Moyen âge (1112–1481)* (Paris, Edouard Champion / Marseille, Barlatier, 1924), 311–317.

having already in 1144 formally ceded his authority and jurisdiction over the Cité, the quarter that was the heart of the old Roman castrum, to the archbishop.[165]

But in 1145, as the war in Arles was building to a bloody climax, the powerful and mighty Count of Barcelona, Ramon Berenguer IV, entered directly into the fray and charged full-strong into Provence in thunderous support of his young nephew, Ramon Berenguer II. Wielding his overwhelmingly superior and fearsome power, the mighty Count of Barcelona was certain to emerge victorious and was now winning the war against the Baux, crushing many of the viscounts and nobles of Provence. Nevertheless, Raymond of Baux steadfastly refused to surrender. Now buoyed by King Conrad's newly awarded recognition of his claim, Raymond of Baux continued in vain to fight valiantly for his rights, with Alphonse Jourdain, Count of Toulouse at his side.

As what would be the first of the Baux Wars was coming to its bloody climax around Arles, the Petrobrusian heresy continued to rage forth throughout Provence and the County of Toulouse, and especially near the town of Toulouse. There the charismatic Henry of Lausanne was actively luring the orthodox faithful into the heresy—and to their doom. The hotbed of heresy had become such a threat to the Church that Bernard of Clairvaux had been invited by Cardinal Alberic of Ostia to come to Provence to preach throughout the region, to combat the heresy, to fight the Petrobrusian demon.[166]

It was in June 1145 that Bernard of Clairvaux journeyed south, first preaching extensively in the viper's nest of heresy the Petrobrusians had spawned in the towns to the east of Bordeaux. Continuing south, Bernard finally reached Toulouse, chasing Henry of Lausanne out of the town at his approach. Bernard then boldly challenged the heretic to a public debate, but Henry was so intimidated by the eloquent and renowned Cistercian that he refused to participate or even appear.

....

165   In a bull of 1144 Emperor Conrad III formally ceded to the archbishop his authority and jurisdiction over the Cité. Conrad also accorded to the archbishop the lucrative regalian rights in Arles and confirmed the extensive holdings of the archbishop and his church, both in and surrounding Arles. The lucrative rights in Arles specifically listed control over the secular courts, the mint, the Jews, flour mills, ropes, weights, measures, deliveries by ships, saltworks, reservoirs or cisterns, marshes (and therefore rice), and the pastures of Crau. See Anibert, Memoires, vol. I, 300–340 and vol. II, 81–95. See also Albanes and Chevalier, Arles, no. 551.

166   See New World Encyclopedia, Bernard of Clairvaux, http://www.newworldencyclopedia.org/entry/Bernard_of_Clairvaux.

Having delivered such a solid and decisive blow to the heresy, Bernard could now return home to Cîteaux. To travel quickly while avoiding the circuitous return route around the Massif Central from Toulouse,[167] Bernard would follow the well-traveled pilgrimage route eastward through Saint-Gilles toward Arles, but he would leave it well before entering directly into the actual war arena and encountering the hostilities to veer northward and then follow the Rhône River Valley northward, passing Avignon, and continuing on to Lyon, leaving the Rhône there to continue on northward, following the Saône River valley, passing Mâcon, finally to arrive home at Cîteaux, south of Dijon.[168]

* * *

Canon Pons had heard that Bernard of Clairvaux would be passing through the town of Saint-Gilles, where he was expected to preach briefly to the faithful.[169] Pons keenly wanted to hear Bernard speak. He also wanted desperately not only to get away from the chaos and upheaval of the war, but also to see what progress had been made in the past three years on the abbey church at Saint-Gilles.

Hostilities at Arles were, for the present, mostly directed outside the city, far to the east, closer to Marignane, so Pons knew he would be fairly safe if he traveled up the hill, past the ruins of the old Roman theater, and past the ancient arena to exit the city from the northern ramparts. He could even use the bridge of boats stationed there at Arles to cross the Rhône River. If he were to leave that morning, immediately after celebrating *Prime*, he could certainly expect to arrive well before *Sext*.

Celebrating *Prime* with the chapter that morning, Pons found himself participating by rote, and his heart was simply not in it. His participation was automatic, without thought, because he was preoccupied with his own difficulties, with his own shortcomings, and although he was a bit embarrassed and ashamed of this, he could not stop his mind from wandering from the celebration of the office.

----

167   Bernard's return route from Toulouse via Saint-Gilles is a logical conjecture, given the geography.

168   See map, page 4.

169   If Bernard did pass through Saint-Gilles, as conjectured here, he would not have missed the opportunity to further denounce Henry of Lausanne and the Petrobrusians at the site where Peter of Bruys had been burned to death.

Vincent Van Gogh painting. Field with Irises near Arles.
Van Gogh Museum, Amsterdam (Vincent van Gogh Foundation).[170]

Nevertheless, after celebrating *Prime* he set out once again on the route toward Saint-Gilles, carefully following his chosen route out of Arles to be sure he was avoiding any new and unexpected hostilities. He crossed the boat bridge to walk west through the Camargue. It was once again a magnificently beautiful day, with gloriously beautiful azure skies, and once he had passed beyond the hostilities, all around him the fields were spotted with clusters of lavender and rosemary growing in the wild.

But Pons was too consumed with worries about his own situation to enjoy the sun-drenched landscape during his short journey. His commitment to God and to the Church had not waned, but though he was certainly aware of the real threats facing Christendom, both from heretics in Provence and from infidels in the Holy Land, Pons simply had more immediate worries and concerns constantly occupying him at Arles. The war at their doorstep. His brother's intransigence in laying claim to Provence. The delayed building campaign. And, most especially, the chapter's distress at the immediacy of the war and of the resulting temporary stopping of all building activity.

170 Photo provided and used with permission of Van Gogh Museum, Amsterdam (Vincent van Gogh Foundation).

As a result of all this, the chapter had lost faith in Pons and his plans and had removed him two years before from the position of *capud scole,* replacing him with William Garnerius.[171] Although on some level Pons recognized this as an unfair punishment of him, imposed by the chapter because of their disappointment at an external turn of events, he also somehow felt at fault for those events, despite his inability to control them.

Always the perfectionist, he had come to believe he had not worked hard enough, or long enough, or well enough to accomplish what God had commanded him to do. He had failed his brethren, and rather than becoming frustrated or angry at them for their repudiation of him, he found fault within himself. He perceived the failure as his own. He had failed his brethren. He had failed his God. God had spoken; he, Pons, had failed. What was he to do?

"Why, oh, why have I failed You so?" he sobbed aloud repeatedly as he walked along. "Please, please show me where I have gone astray," he begged again and again.

Eventually arriving at the town of Saint-Gilles and passing through its ramparts, Pons paused momentarily to look up at the several castle fortifications to gain his bearings. Now reoriented, he was suddenly startled at someone gently clasping his arm. He spun his head around to confront the person.

It was she. Beatrice!

"Augh!" he gasped audibly, incapable of voicing a word.

"Pons! I— I am . . . I am so . . . surprised, but so very happy—relieved, actually—to finally see you here," she uttered softly.

She had been so very fiercely angry at him for so long a time. It was not just that he had left her so abruptly after their one night together. That had been difficult for the young woman to accept, of course, but it was perhaps even somewhat understandable for her, considering the unusual circumstances that had thrown the young couple together. After all, had not her own mother, after being thrown out by the count, taught her how to survive when the stars altered one's fate for the worse?

No, what was much worse—if not intolerable—for her was Pons's coldhearted rejection of her when she had sought him out in Arles, when she was seeking some solace and comfort, some help, some relief, and he had commanded her to go get absolution for their "sin" from one of his brethren. That

---

171   It is Willelmus Garnerius who is listed as *capud scole* or *precentor* in documents from 1143–45. See for instance Albanes and Chevalier, *Arles,* no. 548.

rejection had been unbearable. For weeks afterwards, she had been choleric with yellow bile, livid with rage at the man she called a "damned pious pig!"

Yet she had still maintained hope of seeing him. Her situation living without her mother had become so very difficult, and she really thought she could seek his help. She really needed his help. She desperately wanted to talk with him. She had wanted this so desperately for so long that when he now almost miraculously reappeared, she simply forgot all about her anger and her frustration. She was overwhelmed with surprise and relief, completely sanguine, her liver flooding her body with blood. Here he was, in person, at last. He was still her best chance to make things better for herself, and he was here. She could confront him. She could talk with him. She could make things right.

To Pons, Beatrice was as beautiful as ever, as beautiful as he had remembered her before he had forced himself to stop remembering. Stopping short in his tracks, he took a huge gulp of air as he tried to maintain his composure. His breath then seemed to be cut off. His head was spinning inside as he closed his eyes, trying desperately to focus his attention elsewhere, anywhere else but on her. But he had not closed them quickly enough. With the touch of her hand on his arm, with the sight of her beautiful eyes and luscious mouth, it all came back to him. Everything. Every wonderfully stirring sensation. His loins tightened; his abdomen tensed; his member swelled up and straightened. Pulling away from her, rather awkwardly, only one step, his throat constricted, and he could not speak at first. He also could not stop her from speaking.

"I have tried several times to see you at Arles," she began quietly, calmly. "I do want to speak with you. No, I really do *need* to speak with you. Each time I went to Arles, to deliver goods or to purchase cloth or supplies for my trade, I tried to see you, but I could never get to you."

"Madam," he began softly, choking on the word. "You forget yourself," he continued haltingly, beginning to regain his voice. "You forget who I am."

"But do you forget who I am?" she whispered as her eyes began filling with tears.

As he regained his voice and gained control of his body, Pons started becoming angry. Very, very angry. Angry at her for provoking his weakness. Angry at himself perhaps, too, for being weak. But even as he now focused more anger on her than could possibly be called for, somewhere deep inside he was asking himself how he could possibly be taking out all of this anger on her.

"Yes, I know full well who you are—and what you are," he began very frostily, bracing himself against any possible feelings of warmth toward her. "I expect to become a canon regular at Arles. I expect to take my vow along with my chapter to follow the Rule of St. Augustine, to serve God in the church and to fully adopt the *vita apostolica* as soon as we are able to live the communal life.

"I do not fraternize with women," he continued, now very coldly. "I can no longer be friends with women outside my church duties. I no longer speak with women outside my church offices. That we may have known each other earlier, before I dedicated myself completely to God and decided to adopt the Rule, I do now regret. I have repented. You must forget me. May God have mercy on your soul," he concluded. And, ripping her hand from his arm, he turned abruptly to pull himself away.

"But you don't . . ." she cried out meekly. "But you cannot . . ." she gasped, trying to explain as he began spinning rather haughtily away from her before continuing on up the town road.

As Pons walked away, tears now welled up in his eyes

"God help me! Please help me!" he began sobbing. "I would be lost! I had to do it," he wailed. "I could not let myself speak with her. Oh, oh! Perhaps I should have. . ."

He began arguing with himself. "She seemed so innocent and needful. She seemed really to want help. Oh, I know it's not all her fault that I am not strong enough. Oh, my dear God, help me, please help me!

"No, no, I couldn't be kind to her," he retorted abruptly to himself, now putting his hand to his face and wiping his eyes. "No, I couldn't. It's . . . I'm just not strong enough."

But after sniveling about his weakness and walking aimlessly for a short time, he again began denying any guilt on his part and laying the blame wholly on her. "No. No! She is the temptress!" he eventually concluded, as his reasoning took on a bitter, sharp edge. "She is the woman. As St. Paul taught,

'Adam enim primus formatus est deinde Eva	'For Adam was first formed then Eve.
'Et Adam non est seductus mulier autem seducta in praevaricatione fuit'.	'And Adam was not seduced; but the woman, being seduced, was in the transgression.'
(*I ad Timotheum* 2:13–14)	(I Timothy 2:13–14)

"She is woman. She is the temptress who leads man to temptations of the flesh. She is the temptress who leads man to sin and hell! Yes, it is her fault I sinned! It's because of her I gave in to weakness. It's all because of her that I became weak!"

Then, after walking a bit further, he again began to recant momentarily. "Oh, it cannot be solely her fault that I am weak, that I am flawed. If I were stronger, I could have resisted her! It cannot all be her fault that I cannot resist her. Some of the fault may be mine too. . ."

"No. No!" he finally insisted blindly, adamantly, and vehemently to himself at last. "It is her fault! It must be her fault! It must be her fault! She is the temptress. She is woman. Woman is temptation. Woman is lust. Woman is evil. I can never see or talk to her again.

"I must take my vow to follow the Rule of St. Augustine. I will follow the Rule even now before taking it. This has to be for the best. Oh, God, have mercy on me! I know I am right! God, please help me! Have mercy on me!"

As for Beatrice, she was aghast, unable even to breathe at first. Here was the moment she had hoped for so desperately, had tried to make happen for so long, and it was gone. Gone! She had thought if she could just speak with him, even for just a moment . . . She wanted his help so badly. She desperately needed his help. She needed . . . him.

"If he could know how difficult it is for me now," she wailed dejectedly to herself as she began sobbing softly. "It is just so difficult to carry on, without my mother, with my mother dead, with no one to help me. Life is just so hard, so very hard."

"He was so protective that horrid day. He seemed so kind and innocent that night. I thought he truly felt something for me. I really think he does. No, I *know* he still feels something for me. I can see it. I can feel it. I know he would help if I could just explain everything to him, just tell him everything. But he wouldn't let me! Why?

"Priests everywhere take wives, take mistresses," she thought confusedly to herself, now becoming more and more perplexed. "I only want what is natural. I only hope for what is normal. Like my own mother had. Maybe to be his mistress. Maybe for him to visit me sometimes . . . and to bring nice gifts. Or even just to bring me some meat or . . . something from time to time. What is his problem? What is the matter with him? I don't care about any absurd vow he is taking.

"But he just dismissed me again!" she realized with a jolt. "He, the supposed man of God, has dismissed me, turned his back on me! Turned his back on me and walked away. God damn him! Damn him! May God damn him to hell!"

Standing motionless in the middle of the road, she first had been sobbing softly, but as the full reality of what had transpired slowly dawned on her, she became ever angrier, and eventually her tears ceased. She knew he would never help. Now livid with rage, choleric with yellow bile, she slowly wiped her eyes. She clenched her jaw and narrowed her eyes as her facial expression froze. Cold bitterness took hold as she, too, turned and slowly walked away.

As soon as Pons realized he had been walking aimlessly and was lost, he stopped to try to get his bearings again. The town of Saint-Gilles had been built up around the monastery, but it was a large town, big enough to get somewhat lost in. It was a thriving port city because of its position near the mouth of the west branch of the Rhône River. Both Genoa and Pisa, the competing maritime republics at that time, enjoyed special commercial privileges with Saint-Gilles as a safe port of call where their commercial ships could land while en route to Muslim Spain, or recover merchandise in the event of shipwreck, or continue up the Rhône River for trading. Bertrand, the Count of Toulouse had four decades earlier awarded Genoa these special commercial privileges to the town, while Ramon Berenguer III had not much later given those same rights to Pisa.[172]

After asking directions of a local burgher, Pons despondently made his way toward the monastery church, where Bernard was expected to preach, and joining the small group now gathering near the building site, he sat down dejectedly on a large, apparently rejected stray stone to wait. Unable even to look at the building structure, he lowered his head in his hands, overcome with despair.

Once again, his own difficulties consumed his thoughts, but now his earlier concerns were all overlaid, suffocated by intense guilt and anger. Guilt at having fornicated with Beatrice, even though his sin had been confessed and absolved. Anger at himself for not accepting the absolution he had received for his sin. Guilt at remembering how thoroughly he had enjoyed fornicating. Anger at himself for now wanting to fornicate again with her.

---

172   See Silvia Orvietani Busch, *Medieval Mediterranean Ports: The Catalan and Tuscan Coasts, 1100–1235*, (Leiden; Boston; Köln: BRILL, 2001) 209–210.

Guilt at pushing her away today. Guilt at fobbing all the blame onto her. Anger at her for tempting him. Anger at himself for being tempted. Anger at her for being the temptress. Anger at her, the woman.

Finally, sensing some commotion, Pons looked up. Approaching him and the now larger crowd was a tall, lean, gaunt, skeleton of a figure, a white-haired phantasm with transparent skin, dressed all in white.[173] It was Bernard of Clairvaux, and as he made his way to the front of the many faithful who were gathering outside the church, the monk caught Pons's eye for just a moment and held it, jolting the canon to attention and riveting Pons's attention on this commanding figure.

Bernard was a Cistercian, a White Monk, so-called because these monks always dressed in a habit of pure white wool, which only occasionally they would cover with a protective black scapular or apron. After early entering the monastery of Cîteaux as a young man, Bernard had soon been sent, in 1115, to found a new house for the order in a valley he named Claire Vallée, and this moniker had quickly been transformed into his own, Clairvaux.

The Cistercian Order had been founded by Robert of Molesme at Cîteaux, near Dijon, in 1098 with the goal of restoring strict adherence to the Rule of St. Benedict, by returning to the austere, simple lifestyle of St. Benedict's time and embracing the simple life of hard work, love, prayer, and self-denial. This Rule stressed manual labor and self-sufficiency, so these monks did all their own physical labor and agricultural fieldwork. This reform movement sought utter simplicity and purity in everything; it rejected as impure distraction and sinful contamination all the opulence, richness, extravagances, and lavish decoration that were to be found in other Benedictine houses, notably in those of the Order of Cluny.

After lowering his head for a brief prayer, Bernard blessed the gathering and made the sign of the cross before beginning.

"Praise be to God for permitting me to come here to speak with you today," he proclaimed in a clear, resonant voice.[174]

"My sons and daughters, it is truly difficult sometimes to find our way to salvation, to obey God. We seek in our hearts to obey Him. We ask Him what He wants of us, what He wants us to do. We try to follow what He wants of

---

173   Description is taken from Weir, *Eleanor*, 35 and Hindley, *Brief*, 72.

174   Both Bernard's appearance here and what he may have said are, of course, logical conjecture.

us. But sometimes we do not understand His answers. We earnestly try to understand; we want to understand. And in our earnest desire to hear God, we may look to others whom we desperately hope can show us the answers. And it is so very easy to be misled—misled by those who speak eloquently, who are better educated, who seem to know more, who seem to know better."

The crowd was fairly quiet, listening with respectful attention as he addressed them, and many began nodding their heads in agreement as he continued, "I, myself, Bernard, skeptical about the words of the eloquent academics, skeptical about the path they offered me, retreated to a Cistercian monastery at Claire Vallée. There we follow a strict and austere Rule. There we devote ourselves to spiritual meditation and physical labor. As I myself have written,

'Experto crede: aliquid amplius invenies in silvis, quam in libri. Ligna et lapides docebunt te, quod a magistris audire non possis.' *Bernardi, Epist.* 106[175]	'Trust one who has tried it, you will find more in woods than in books. Trees and stones will teach you what you can never learn from masters.' Bernard, Epist. 106

"There is now in this region someone who professes to hear God better, to know God's word, to know what God really wants. And some may think he should be able to hear God better, because they think he should understand better than we what God commands. Some may think we should be able to trust his teachings, because he is a former monk of Cluny and a deacon. I speak of Henry of Lausanne, who appears to be so well educated and so knowledgeable. But do not be deceived! He is a demon in disguise!" A few now put their heads together whispering, apparently expressing agreement with Bernard's description.

"Henry of Lausanne will stand before you with his stormy, dark face, with his eyes flashing fire, and he will speak to you in his powerful, deep,

---

175   Sancti Bernardi, *Epistola*, 106, "Ad Magistrum Henricum Murdach," in Migne, *Patrologia Latina*, vol. 182, col. 241–242. Also quoted and translated in "Saint Bernard of Claivaux," *Medieval Sourcebook*, http://www.fordham.edu/halsall/source/eb9-bernard.html.

thunderous voice,[176] sounding like a man who is well educated, who knows the Scriptures, who knows God's will. But do not be deceived! Henry of Lausanne is a demon in disguise!

"He will stand before you, looking like a saint, like a humble man of God—majestically tall, long-bearded, barefoot, and dressed simply in poor apparel. It would be so easy to mistake him for a saintly John the Baptist.[177] But do not be deceived! Henry of Lausanne is a false prophet! He is a demon in disguise!

"St. Paul warned us against such false prophets in his Second Letter to the Corinthians:

'nam eiusmodi pseudoapostoli operarii subdoli transfigurantes se in apostolos Christi

et non mirum ipse enim Satanas transfigurat se in angelum lucis'

(*II ad Corinthios* 11:13–14)

'For such false apostles are deceitful workmen, transforming themselves into the apostles of Christ.

And no wonder; for Satan himself transformeth himself into an angel of light.'

(II Corinthians 11:13–14)

"Henry of Lausanne may appear and sound like 'an angel of light,' like a prophet who knows the Scriptures, who hears God, who knows God's will," Bernard continued, as more began whispering quietly together, apparently surprised at the phrase, "angel of light," and Pons pressed forward a bit to be able to hear even better. "But beware: he is not a true man of God! He is a demon in disguise! He is Satan disguised as a prophet! Henry of Lausanne is a false prophet. His mentor, Peter of Bruys, was a false prophet. Demons. Servants of the devil. False prophets.

"Our Lord Jesus Christ, forewarned us about false prophets such as them, in the Gospel Book of Matthew:

....

176   See Miller, "Henricians" in *Short Papers on Church History* for the physical description.
177   See Miller, "Henricians" in *Short Papers on Church History* for the physical description.

'adtendite a falsis prophetis qui veniunt ad vos in vestimentis ovium intrinsecus autem sunt lupi rapaces,

'Beware of false prophets, who come to you in the clothing of sheep, but inwardly they are ravening wolves.

a fructibus eorum cognoscetis eos numquid colligunt de spinis uvas aut de tribulis ficus'

By their fruits you shall know them. Do men gather grapes of thorns, or figs of thistles?'

(*secundum Matthaeum* 7: 15–16)

(Matthew 7:15–16)

"Henry of Lausanne is one of the 'ravening wolves' our Lord Jesus Christ warned us about! He is a false prophet, a servant of the devil! He is a heretic who would lead you straight into hell!

"How do we know Henry to be a 'ravening wolf'? What are the 'thorns' and 'thistles' by which we can recognize this 'ravening wolf'?" Bernard asked, pointing to one man in the crowd, who called back, "Yes, how?"

"By his words!" Bernard confidently answered. "His words go against the words of our Lord Jesus Christ!

"This 'ravening wolf,' this heretic would ask you to reject the authority of our blessed Church—our blessed Church that was founded by Christ Himself! This we cannot do! As our Lord Jesus Christ told Peter and his other disciples, again in the Gospel according to St. Matthew,

'et ego dico tibi quia tu es Petrus et super hanc petram aedificabo ecclesiam meam et portae inferi non praevalebunt adversum eam.

'And I say to thee: That thou art Peter; and upon this rock I will build my church, and the gates of hell shall not prevail against it.

et tibi dabo claves regni caelorum et quodcumque ligaveris super terram erit ligatum in caelis et quodcumque solveris super terram erit solutum in caelis.'

And I will give to thee the keys of the kingdom of heaven. And whatsoever thou shalt bind upon earth, it shall be bound also in heaven; and whatever thou shalt loose on earth, it shall be loosed also in heaven'

(*secundum Matthaeum* 16:18–19)

(Matthew 16:18–19)

"Are we to listen to the words of Henry of Lausanne rather than to the words of our Lord Jesus Christ?" Bernard asked, shaking his head, as many in the crowd shook theirs, too, in response. "Only a 'ravening wolf,' a heretic would ask us to reject the authority of our blessed Church—our blessed Church that was founded by our Lord, Jesus Christ Himself!

"Henry of Lausanne is a ravening wolf! He is wrong! He is wrong in what he preaches! He lies! He is not a true man of God! He does not know God better than you or I. His words are twisted. We cannot listen to what he says. He is committing the most grievous sins against our beloved God and against our blessed Church! He is a heretic! He is a demon in disguise!

"This heretic, Henry, this 'ravening wolf' would ask you to reject the blessed sacrament of baptism for your infants. This we cannot do, for the souls of our children!" Bernard proclaimed as many women in the crowd began shaking their heads in agreement. "Our Lord Jesus Christ called the children to himself, in the Gospel Book of Mark," Bernard continued. "He instructed us not to keep them from Him:

'... sinite parvulos venire ad me et ne prohibueritis eos talium est enim regnum Dei.	'... Suffer the little children to come unto me and forbid them not: for of such is the kingdom of God.
amen dico vobis quisque non receperit regnum Dei velut parvulus non intrabit in illud.'	Amen I say to you, whosoever shall not receive the kingdom of God as a little child shall not enter into it.'
(*secundum Marcum* 10:14–15)	(Mark 10:14–15)

"Are we to close our ears to the words of Lord Jesus Christ and heed the words of Henry of Lausanne and the Petrobrusian heretics instead? No! For the sake of the souls of our beloved children! No!" Bernard repeated. Several women in the crowd immediately echoed him in shouting out "no," leading Pons to recall another woman's cry about infants during the burning of Peter of Bruys at Saint-Gilles.

"Henry of Lausanne and the heretics are already condemned to hell. Their own souls are surely lost. They would take you with them to hell. Henry of Lausanne would take you and your children with him to hell!

"They are heretics! They are demons in disguise! Henry and the heretics mock the blessed sacrament of Eucharist," Bernard bellowed, throwing out his arms as if in disbelief that anyone could so mock the sacrament, spurring Pons and several others to involuntarily clasp their own hands in prayer at such a sacrilege. "They ask you to reject the blessed sacrament of Eucharist. They ask you to reject Christ's body and blood! As you all surely know, at the Last Supper, our blessed Lord Jesus Christ Himself took the unleavened bread and gave it to His disciples, saying,

'. . . Accipite et comedite hoc est corpus meum.'	'. . . Take ye and eat. This is my body.'
(*secundum Matthaeum* 26:26)	(Matthew 26:26)

"And taking the chalice, our blessed Lord and Savior gave thanks and handed it to His disciples, saying,

'. . . Bibite ex hoc omnes	'. . . Drink ye all of this.
hic est enim sanguis meus novi testamenti qui pro multis effunditur in remissionem peccatorum'	for this is my blood of the new testament, which shall be shed for many unto remission of sins.'
(*secundum Matthaeum* 26:27–28)	(Matthew 26:27–28)

"It was our Lord Jesus Christ Himself who taught us that the bread of Eucharist is His own body and the wine of Eucharist is His own blood, His own body and blood, which He shed for our salvation! Are we to listen to Henry of Lausanne and the Petrobrusians and close our ears to our Lord and Savior?" Bernard asked, to which Pons joined the crowd in calling back a resounding, "No," almost in unison.

"Are we to question the words of our Lord Jesus Christ?" Bernard continued, "No! No! No! For the sake of our own souls. Henry of Lausanne is wrong in what he preaches! He is misguided. His words are twisted. He is a heretic! He is a demon in disguise!

"These heretics, who will surely burn forever in hellfire, would ask you to abhor the cross of Christ's crucifixion. They ask you to reject the cross on which Christ gave His life for us! They ask you to reject the cross through which Christ granted us salvation! Our blessed Lord Jesus Christ gave his life on the cross for us to be saved. Are we now to reject salvation?" Bernard challenged. "No! This we must not do, or we will be in peril of eternal hellfire!"

Bernard was making the heresy seem so obviously misguided to Pons. The issues were becoming so simple and clear as Bernard continued speaking, "Henry of Lausanne and all the followers of Peter of Bruys tell us to ignore the words of our Lord Jesus Christ. They tell us to defy what our Lord Jesus Christ instructed us to do. They tell us to refuse the body and blood of our Lord, which He gave for our redemption. They tell us to deny the cross on which our Lord gave His life for our salvation."

"We cannot listen to these heretics! Henry of Lausanne and the Petrobrusians do not know God better than you and I. They would have you condemn your soul; they would lead you to eternal hellfire! Henry of Lausanne and the Petrobrusians will themselves burn forever in hellfire! Their souls are lost forever! They are trying to take you with them straight into the flames of hell! They are trying to doom your soul to eternal damnation! Your souls! Yours and yours and yours . . ." Bernard proclaimed, pointing again and again to individuals throughout the crowd, from which loud audible gasps could now be heard.

"Henry of Lausanne is a 'ravening wolf.' He is a false prophet! He is a servant of the devil! He is a heretic! He is a demon in disguise.

"I was called here today to speak out and tell you the truth about Henry of Lausanne. I am telling you now: what the demon Henry of Lausanne preaches will lead you to hell. Straight to hell! The evil preachings of Henry of Lausanne and his predecessor Peter of Bruys are putting our souls in peril of damnation!"

Bernard was passionately fighting to save souls, and as he continued speaking, Pons began to recognize and to understand why Bernard had become so influential. It soon became evident to all when he spoke that this sincere, deeply spiritual monk passionately believed in the true word of God. He not only preached, he fought to save souls. Pons now understood why it was said that when Bernard preached, "mothers hid their sons, wives their husbands, companions their friends" for fear of losing them to his way of life through his persuasive words.[178]

---

178   See "Saint Bernard of Clairvaux,"*Medieval Sourcebook*, http://www.fordham.edu/ halsall/source/eb9-bernard.html.

Pons was beginning to understand why the house of Clairvaux was becoming the most important house in the Cistercian Order. It was because of Bernard of Clairvaux that the Cistercian Order no longer remained hidden in the shadow of the Cluniac monastic empire.[179] Even here in heresy-ridden Provence, Pons knew that three Cistercian monasteries[180] were founded as a result of Bernard's influence: Le Thoronet in the Var, Notre-Dame de Sénanque in the Vaucluse near Gordes, and Silvacane Abbey at La Roque d'Antheron.

"To mislead us, the heretic Henry of Lausanne appears to appeal to our reason," Bernard continued. "He appears to be calling for rational study, for us to use our reasoning, but his own reasoning is demented and twisted. He is wrong! Do not listen to his twisted words!

"We cannot gain divine understanding from reason, from rational study or from books written by men. It is only through our own personal faith that we can gain divine understanding. It is only by knowing God ourselves, through our own personal relationship with God, that we are saved, and it is the Virgin Mary through whom Christ came to us who intercedes for us. It is,

'... quoniam Virgo regia ipsa est via, per quam Salvator advenit ...'	'... because the Virgin herself is the royal way, by which the Savior comes to us ...'
Bernardi, Sermo II[181]	Bernard, Sermon II

"It is with the guidance of our blessed Church that our personal faith is nurtured and grows. It is through the sacraments that our personal faith is born and is renewed again and again, to grow. Through the sacrament of baptism, we are born again in Christ. Through the sacrament of Eucharist, we partake of Christ's body and blood that He gave so that we might gain eternal salvation."

As Bernard spoke, Pons could not help reflecting on how respected Bernard of Clairvaux was. His friend Nicolaus of Saint Ruf had told him that it was Bernard who had helped heal the schism that had developed within the

179   Between 1130 and 1145, at least ninety-three monasteries had either been founded or become affiliated with Clairvaux. By 1152, the year before Bernard's death, there were 333 Cistercian abbeys in Europe, mostly as a result of Bernard's influence.

180   All three were initially founded in the first half of the century, although they would only be built later, when they would be called "the three Provencal sisters."

181   Sancti Bernardi, *Operum Tomus III, Sermo II*, in Migne, *Patrologia Latina*, vol. 183, col. 43.

Church fifteen years earlier, following the death of Pope Honorius II in 1130, when two rival popes were each elected by different loyal followings. Called upon to render an opinion about which of the two claimants should occupy the throne of St. Peter, Bernard decided for Innocent II and then worked to get him accepted by the world. Nicolaus had told Pons that Bernard was able to end the schism because so many within the Church implicitly trusted his judgment and respected his decision.[182]

Nicolaus had even suggested that if Peter the Venerable might then have been the most powerful intellectual within the Church, Bernard of Clairvaux had certainly come to be one of the most respected and influential.

"Yes," Bernard admitted quietly to the crowd, "our blessed Church may, at times, be in need of some correction. Its leaders may, at times, be in need of correction. But it still remains our blessed Church, given to us by Christ Himself, founded by Christ Himself on the 'rock' of St. Peter.

"He who now sits upon the throne of St. Peter will lead this correction," and Pons immediately recalled that just before leaving Arles today, his friend William Boso had told him about the recent papal election, that a former protégé of Bernard of Clairvaux, the Cistercian Bernard of Pisa, Abbot of Three Fountains, had been elected, becoming Pope Eugenius III. Pope Innocent II had died in 1143, and for two years the Church had been without effective leadership in Rome, because during those two years there had been two successive popes who each had lived only briefly to occupy the seat. But now with this new pope came renewed hope.[183]

"His Eminence, Pope Eugenius III, has asked me to offer some guidance for carrying out this correction," Bernard continued, "and to suggest what needs to be done. By the Grace of God, I am now drafting a *Book of Consideration*[184] that will clarify what needs to be done.

"The reformation of the Church should begin at the top, with the sanctity of its leaders. Piety and meditation should guide our Church; piety and meditation should guide our Church leaders. Temporal matters of this world

182   See "Saint Bernard," *Medieval Sourcebook*, http://www.fordham.edu/halsall/source/eb9-bernard.html.

183   See "St. Bernard of Clairvaux," *New Advent Catholic Encyclopedia*, https://www.newadvent.org/cathen/02498d.htm.

184   Sancti Bernardi, *Operum Tomus Secundus, De Consideratione, Libri quinque ad Eugenium Tertium*, in Migne, *Patrologia Latina*, vol 182, col. 727–808.

should be less important; piety and meditation should take precedence. Piety and meditation are foremost."[185]

"Central to all, central to our salvation, central to our gaining divine understanding is our blessed Church. Our blessed Church! Our blessed Church that the heretics would tear down. Heretics—first, Peter of Bruys, who already burns in hellfire, and now the accursed Henry of Lausanne. We, God's people, will do battle with those who would tear down our blessed Church. We, God's people, join together to fight these heretics.

"We, God's servants, may not always appear to be in agreement. We may sometimes differ on matters of interpretation. Our Cistercian monastery was founded on the principles of simplicity: simplicity of monastic life, simplicity of monastic architecture, rejection of all opulence and adornment in any form. At the other extreme, our Cluny brethren embrace such elegant trappings as appropriate tributes to God.

"We Cistercians choose to work the fields and to worship in simple, undecorated churches, while our Cluny brethren worship in lavishly appointed buildings decorated with sumptuous art and elegant sculptures.

"So we may not always agree. But we all join together as one—as one army of the faithful to fight for our blessed Church. We all join together to do battle with those who would tear down our blessed Church!

"As a Cistercian, I come here to speak with you today. As a Cistercian I speak to you in front of the Cluniac abbey church of Saint-Gilles here. Yes, the Cluniac abbey church! And I invite you to examine the Cluniac abbey church where our blessed Church is boldly portraying in sculpture the truths that are central to our beliefs. Yes, in sculpture! In sculptural decoration from which we Cistercians usually completely abstain.

"The apostle figures you see here in front of the abbey church," he said, turning to gesture widely toward the apostles, as if introducing them, "are proclaiming the truth! That is the truth of Christ's Passion, that He willingly entered Jerusalem to suffer and die for our sins," he said, pointing toward the left portal lintel. "The truth of the Last Supper," he said, pointing toward the central portal lintel, "where He instituted the Eucharist so that we may partake of His body and blood. The truth of Christ's death on the cross and His final resurrection," he concluded, pointing toward the right portal.

185   Summary of *De Consideratione* is taken from "St. Bernard of Clairvaux," *The Catholic Encyclopedia*.

"I invite you to examine and observe carefully this church façade where our blessed Church is proclaiming the truth of the apostles, the truth related to us by the apostles. The truth is shown here for all to see! I invite you to study carefully what has already been completed of that sculpture. Study it today. Return tomorrow and study it again. And when the sculpture is finally completed, return again in the months ahead to study it yet again. Read here the truths that the Bible teaches us. Learn the truths that we have spoken about here today. Learn and take to heart those truths that will save your soul, the truths that will save you from eternal hellfire.

Saint-Gilles. Left portal. Lintel, Entry into Jerusalem; tympanum, Adoration of Magi, Dream of Joseph. (Then probably not yet completed).

Saint-Gilles. Central portal. Lintel, Christ Washing Peter's Feet, Last Supper. (Then probably not yet completed).

Saint-Gilles. Right portal. Lintel, Holy Women Buying Spices, Holy Women at Sepulchre; tympanum, Crucifixion. (Then probably not yet completed).

"I beg you to open your eyes to the truth of the apostles, to see those truths, to learn those truths, to accept those truths. I beg you to learn the words of our Lord Jesus Christ, as written in the Holy Scriptures, as shown here in sculpture on the front of the abbey church.

"I beg you to open your eyes and accept the words of our Lord Jesus Christ, as shown here. I beg you to close your ears to the twisted words of Henry of Lausanne and the Petrobrusian heretics.

"I beg you to turn your back on the heretics. I beg you to reject this damnable heresy—for the sake of your eternal soul! For the sake of all our eternal souls!

"May God show mercy upon you. May God have mercy on all of us." And, concluding his remarks, Bernard of Clairvaux again made the sign of the cross before humbly bowing and quietly slipping away from the gathering.

Deeply moved by Bernard's unaffected sincerity and true humility, Pons continued sitting a short while, as the crowd quietly dispersed. As he rose to his feet, a new realization began to dawn on him. Strangely, he began to feel personally connected somehow with this ascetic, white monk. He began to feel a new bond, a new affinity. Slowly, he arrived at the resolution of his difficulties.

"As Bernard of Clairvaux said," he thought to himself, "it is 'piety and meditation' that should be guiding what we canons do. 'Piety and meditation' are what is important. Not worrying about women. Certainly not women! They are temptresses! They are evil! Not remorse over past sins.

"'Piety and meditation' are what should guide me. Piety and meditation are what should guide the Church and me! Not the ongoing war, not what my brother wants. All such 'temporal matters' are less important. I could do nothing about those things, but they are not what I should be involved with.

"Even Bernard of Clairvaux is now, for the moment, putting aside his opposition to Cluniac sculpture, putting aside his quest for Cistercian simplicity and purity," he continued to himself. "He is here, devoting himself instead to helping fight the accursed Petrobrusian heresy. Just as I, myself, did by permitting Master Guillelmo and Master Pietro to leave their work at Arles to work on the sculptural façade of the abbey church here—the Cluniac abbey church of Saint-Gilles.

"Yes, reform of our chapter must come, and it will come," Pons now proclaimed to himself. "But how can I feel defeated in my task, ashamed that I have not yet brought communal life to the chapter when the change in plans and the temporary delay resulted from my yielding to a larger purpose? To God's larger purpose—fighting the Petrobrusian heretics?

"I am so ashamed I didn't see it before, dear God," he added, now speaking aloud directly to Him. "When will I learn to listen to Your commands, to understand Your commands, to heed Your will, to do what You want? Why is it so difficult for me to know what You want, to hear what You are telling me?"

It was with a lighter heart and a renewed sense of purpose that Pons now moved a little sideways and closer to the church, so he could get an overall view. The collapsed portion at the west end had been rebuilt. Work on the church building was proceeding remarkably well, and much of the walls had been raised. Though the sculptural friezes were still only works in progress and work on the tympana above each portal had, in fact, barely been begun, most of the sculpture on the lower part of the façade appeared finished.

"Certainly, the town here must have escaped relatively unscathed from the hostilities of my brother's war for the work on the church to have proceeded as it has," Pons admitted to himself. "Perhaps they benefited from the fact that most of the hostilities centered around our town, Arles!"

Moving closer to examine the sculptural decoration more closely, he approached it carefully, working his way through the maze of stone piles, detritus, and wooden scaffolding that marked an active stone carvers' workshop. As he examined the façade pier figures and sculpture up close, Master Guillelmo caught his eye.

"Greetings! Master Guillelmo, these pier figures are magnificent!" he cried out. "And they are so huge! They are life-size, larger than life-size![186] And they are beautiful. The carved friezes and lintels above the doors are going to be stunning when completed. And I can finally now appreciate what a huge sculptural program is being mounted—not only these huge pier figures, but the lintels, tympana, and carved friezes. It is all going to be outstandingly beautiful!"

"Canon Pons, how fortunate to see you. Yes, the sculpture here really is outstanding. My crew only worked on some of it, and the workshop really collaborates and works together. And, as you can see, the upper part of the façade is not yet finished. We are still finishing some of those friezes above. But come. Let me show you the façade and some of the work we carved or helped complete," he stated with obvious pride.

"It was Master Brunus himself who carved and signed the magnificent pier figures of the apostles Matthew and Bartholomew at the far left," Guillelmo continued as he led Pons toward the central portal. "As you know, Master Brunus had lost two sculptors before we arrived. One was a brilliant sculptor, Master Gilius, who came here from Angoulême after working on the cathedral there. Here at Saint-Gilles he had finished the two pier figures to the left of the central portal, Thomas and James the Less, and was beginning work on the central portal when the collapse occurred.

---

186   Stoddard, *Façade*, 15, gives precise measurements of all the pier figures in meters: Michael (2.0), Matthew (2.05), Bartholomew (2.01), Thomas (2.01), James the Less (2.01), John (2.03), Peter (2.03), James (1.99), Paul (2.0), Figure Central Portal Right (1.98), Central Portal Next Right (1.98), Central Portal Farther Right (1.98), Central Portal Farthest Right (1.99), Archangels (2.0).

    The average height of a man in medieval England in 1150-1200 was closer to 5 feet 7 1/2 inches or 1.71 meters. So assuming comparable average height for men from other nearby northern European cultures, such as from France and Provence, these pier figures would appear imposingly large. See Felinah Memo Hazara Khan-ad-Din, "Old Age, Height and Nutrition: Common Misconceptions About Medieval England," (2003), http://sirguillaume.com/wp-content/uploads/2012/01/Old_Age-Height-Nutrition.pdf.

"He had already carved the low-relief sculptures," he said, pointing, "on the bases or projecting pedestals below the pier figures to the left and right of the central portal—the Cain and Abel scenes and the interlocking circular rondels with a centaur hunting scene and Samson and lions. His loss was devastating to Master Brunus and the workshop.

Saint-Gilles, west façade. Far left of central portal. Pier figures, Apostles Matthew and Bartholomew, signed by Master Brunus.

Saint-Gilles, west façade. Left of central portal. Pier figures, Apostles Thomas and James the Less.

"But the other sculptor lost in the collapse was the decorative foliage sculptor. When we arrived here after the collapse, Master Brunus asked us to first start working on the foliage sculpture for him, under my supervision, of course,"[187] he added quickly and with some real pride. "We helped carve or finish several of these acanthus rinceau frieze panels over the apostles," he noted proudly, pointing to each.[188] "We also carved several of the acanthus panels on

....

187 Stoddard noted the stylistic parallels between the decorative foliage and friezes at Arles, on the northwest corner pier and on the abacus above the sacrifice of Abraham capital, and the foliage friezes at Saint-Gilles, on the bottom of the lintels and above the apostles at Saint-Gilles, but Stoddard never suggested the sculptors from Arles worked at Saint-Gilles. See Stoddard, *Façade*, 199–237, especially 233.

188 For photos, see Stoddard, *Façade*, figs.152–157.

the undersides of the lintels above the portals.[189] You will see our flower motif there, the one showing the underside of the flower with the vine stem emerging from its center, and you will see some of our five-petal cinquefoils, of course.

Saint-Gilles, west façade. Central portal, inner left splay. Pier figures, Apostles John and Peter.

Saint-Gilles, west façade. Central portal, inner right splay. Pier figures, Apostles James Major and Paul.

"We worked mostly here, on and near the central portal, Master Pietro and I, with our assistant. Both Pietro and I worked on the large apostle figures on the splays flanking the central portal and on the beautiful acanthus rinceau friezes there. I, myself, carved most of the two foliate panels above the apostles here, as well as most of the two large, vertical acanthus panels. Don't you like my little animals, birds, and figures tucked into the acanthus?"[190] he added with obvious pride.

....

189   For photos, see Stoddard, *Façade*, figs. 160–162

190   For more detailed photos, see Stoddard, *Façade*, figs. 163–165.

"They're beautiful," Pons answered. "But did you and Master Pietro carve the four large apostle pier figures on the central portal yourselves?" he gasped hopefully, wide-eyed.

"Well, let me show you. When we started working on the central portal here, only the pier figure of St. Peter was partially done. It had been blocked out by Master Gilius from Angoulême, who was buried alive in the collapse, the one who did the two other pier figures of Thomas and James the Less," he clarified, moving a few steps to the left and pointing. "The ones with the big, decorated halos here, just left of the central portal."

After moving a few steps back to the central portal, Master Guillelmo continued. "Master Brunus first assigned Master Pietro to carve the large pier figure of John here, under his supervision, of course. He worked with him, helping him finish blocking out what Master Gilius had only begun and teaching him some techniques for carving large figure sculpture. Our Master Pietro proved himself to be not only talented, but a quick learner. He learned much from Master Brunus, and vice versa, by the way. Those two are now quite the team. They get along like two peas in a pod; they both learn one from each other. They almost always have their heads together now, showing each other new techniques, how to carve better figures and drapery.

Saint-Gilles. West façade. Detail, Pier figure   *Arles. North gallery. Detail, Capital,*
Apostle Paul.   *Abraham Sacrifice of Isaac.*

"But look here," Master Guillelmo proclaimed with a huge smile, twisting quickly around to the right. "You must see this. Our Master Pietro carved this pier figure of St. Paul himself!

"Remember how talented our 'Bold One' showed himself to be when he carved your capital at Arles showing the Sacrifice of Abraham? Well, look here. Isn't it amazing? His large pier figure of St. Paul here has the same sense of physical mass, the same powerful, bulging out shoulders, the same potential for movement as do his dynamic little figures on the capital at Arles. He even has the same sharp, bony eyebrow ridges!"

"This pier figure of St. Paul is astounding! Absolutely amazing!" Pons interjected. "He looks like he's about to walk off the base! And Master Pietro carved it!"

"Didn't I tell you our 'Bold One' was talented?" Master Guillelmo responded with a huge grin. "Master Brunus developed such confidence in him that he soon asked Master Pietro to oversee all the work on the central portal, so he could begin to concentrate on the lintels and superstructure above. Pietro asked me to finish the pier figure of Peter because it still needed a lot of finishing touches. Master Pietro asked me to put some finishing touches on the pier figure of John too, so he could begin working on the Paul figure.

"The only pier figure here we did not work on," he added, pointing, "was the one of James Major. That was done by another master passing through the region whom Master Brunus asked to carve it. Working here with Master Brunus has taught us so much. We have learned a lot about handling large pier figures and about finishing details.

"But look at this. Our 'Bold One' remembers where he came from. Do you recall my showing you Master Pietro's 'signature motif,' how he liked to run a little row of foliate egg and dart decoration, foliate horseshoes, along the top and bottom moldings of his capitals for your porch? Well, here he finished the upper edge of the pier behind Paul's head with the same motif, turned upside down! And since Master Pietro supervised and oversaw all the work on the central portal, he insisted his decorative signature motif be on the capitals behind the heads of all three pier figures we worked on here at the central portal, Paul, John, and Peter."

"The entire central portal here is absolutely wonderful," Pons exclaimed with genuine admiration, laced with some hopeful expectation that work on his cloister might one day be comparably beautiful. "You should be very proud of your work here."

Now, looking up and seeing up close that much more work was underway on the superstructure, while some had only been begun there, Pons again became disheartened. It was underway but was far from completed, and he suspected these sculptors would probably not be able to leave work here for quite some time.

"When do you expect to be finished with your work here?" Pons asked hesitantly. "You must understand, I could begin construction on our cloister and communal buildings at Arles if the war hostilities all around us there were not so overwhelming, as they are now. We have not been touched at all by the war within the cathedral complex, but it would certainly be impossible for the laborers and carters to haul into Arles the huge loads of stone and supplies that will be required.

"But if, God willing, the war does not last too much longer," he added while pressing his hands together briefly in a gesture of prayer, "and if the builders were able to start work on our cloister buildings, when might you and your workshop be able to come back to do the sculptural decoration?"

"Canon Pons, I would be very willing to return as soon as the war abates," Guillelmo assured him, "and I would bring my assistant. I think our 'Bold One,' Master Pietro, would probably prefer to stay here with Master Brunus's workshop. As I said, he and Master Brunus are almost inseparable now, and Pietro is committed to the project here. But I am certain Master Brunus would be willing to let both me and our assistant go. Frankly, having two bosses puts a strain on any workshop crew. The truth is, I would prefer running my own workshop at Arles to working here under someone else."

The two agreed that when the war hostilities abated, Master Guillelmo would approach Master Brunus and the abbot for permission to return to work at Arles. Master Guillelmo then offered to take Canon Pons to meet the master masons, whom he had seen entering the church crypt. As they entered the crypt, Pons immediately identified the master builder because he was carrying the characteristic tools of his trade, the emblems of his profession: a measuring rod, a set square, and dividers.

Master Guillelmo introduced Canon Pons as the canon in charge of the building project that was to be undertaken at the cathedral church in Arles, where he and Master Pietro had first worked, adding that he hoped to be able to return there to complete his sculptural work once the project was underway again.

"Once the war hostilities around Arles have abated," Pons began, "I shall need a master stone mason with a workshop of stone masons to undertake our building campaign. We will be building a claustral complex and renovating our church."

"Then I am indeed glad you have come here to meet us," began the *magister comacinus*,[191] the master builder, speaking with a rather thick Lombard accent that was very difficult, but not impossible, for Pons to understand. "It will not be too long before we have completed our work here for the present campaign at the abbey. Probably within the year or so. And, assuming the war will have ended by then, we might be interested in undertaking your project," he offered, to Pons' excitement and delight, thinking that perhaps this was the builder who could undertake his project

"I am pleased you are here today," continued the *magister comacinus*, "because you can see what a great job we have done here with our masonry. To secure everything above, including that magnificent monumental façade, you need a really sturdy base. When we arrived, the west wall of the crypt was already here, as well as some groin-vaulted or tunnel-vaulted bays. There had been a collapse at the west wall, so we had to first shore up the vaulting in the western bay of the crypt before continuing eastward."

"You and your men have done a beautiful job!" exclaimed Pons. "I visited this crypt about ten years ago, so I can see what you've done with the vaulting. I know about the collapse at the west wall and that you were asked to strengthen the vaulting here. But how do these diagonal arches solve the problem?"

"They are supports, much like transverse arches, but they work a bit differently. As you know, we use sturdy transverse arches between regular bays of continuous, long, heavy tunnel vaulting, or, as some call it, barrel vaulting. Transverse arches define each bay and enable us to erect the continuous long stone courses of the vault from bay to bay. The transverse arches then help support the vault, but they do not carry the full weight and thrust of the vault,

---

191   The early medieval stonemasons were referred to as the Comacine masters, "*magistri comacini.*" The supposition is that the ancient Roman expertise in stonemasonry was not lost, but was retained through brotherhoods of stonemasons in Lombardy, Como, and Pavia.

because once the tunnel vault is completed, its weight and thrust are distributed evenly along the entire length of the tunnel, along each side, down to the supporting wall below.

"Here, at the western end, there was originally a heavy groin vault, a bay of two perpendicular intersecting tunnel vaults, forming four concave triangular sections of vault. Now normally this groin vault should support itself if the weight and thrust of the four equal sections of barrel push evenly against each other, balancing each other, stabilizing each other, as the weight and thrust is carried along the curved edge of each intersection down to the supporting wall or pier below.

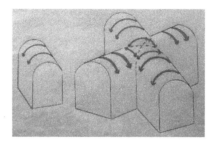

Sketches of tunnel or barrel vault, and of intersecting tunnel or barrel vaults, creating a groin vault.

"Here, let me try to draw both vaults for you on this bit of parchment. As you see, the weight and thrust of the tunnel vault continue evenly along its entire length. When two comparable tunnel vaults intersect, they create a groin vault, where the weights and thrusts of the two perpendicular tunnel vaults can counteract and balance against each other perfectly.

"But here in the crypt, the groin vault collapsed, probably because the new massive construction above added weight and thrust from one side, destabilizing the balance. So when we reconstructed it, we strengthened it by adding strong diagonal arch supports at the groins, supports called 'ribs.' This is a technique we have known how to do for some time.[192] Here, in the crypt, the ribs help carry the heavy weight and opposing thrusts that meet at the groins and travel down the rib to the support below.

....

192   The use of supporting diagonal ribs on intersecting groin vaults was known by the late eleventh and early twelfth centuries. Diagonal supporting ribs were used early in Lombardy at San Michele, Pavia, and at Sant'Ambrogio, Milan. Early rib vaults were used in Normandy at Lessay Abbey and at Caen, and in the side aisles at Durham Cathedral.

Saint-Gilles, Crypt. West wall, central bay. Corbel supporting rib at southwest corner of vault.

"In the crypt we are putting in diagonal ribs springing from the corners of the supporting piers, but here on the west wall, near the collapse, where we had to begin, there is no supporting pier, so we improvised by inserting a corbel at the level of the springing of the vault to receive the rib, and then we rebuilt the damaged portion above. Here we used strong, solid ribs, almost square in cross-section, much like what we have long used for transverse arches.[193] The supporting rib structure needs a firm footing in the corner piers. You can see how we modified the piers in the other corners to receive them.

"It all worked quite well, and we're quite pleased with the result. We were able to overcome the problem here and are now completing the vaulting of the crypt using sturdy ribs along the groins. We can be more creative now with the shape of the supporting rib, but they are all still very sturdy.

"It is unfortunate that there were such problems here," continued the master mason. "Especially the resulting two deaths. We builders all know, however, that any new building technique is experimental. We have to try something to see whether or not it will work. But you can see how solid it is now!"

The master mason led Pons along the west wall. On the west side of the west wall projection under the central portal, Pons noticed the first new epitaph:

....

193   In this central bay at the west end, the diagonal rib is almost square in cross-section, while in other bays it becomes much fancier. This bay is probably among the earliest to be rib vaulted in the crypt, where the work probably progressed generally from west to east.

hIC SEPVLTUS:
EST:GILIVSANNO
DMI:Mᵒ:C:XᵒL:Iᵒl
ORATE:PROEO

(Here is buried Gilius in
the year of our Lord MCLII
Pray for him.)

Saint-Gilles. Crypt. Epitaph of Gilius, +1142.

"Well, well," Pons noted silently to himself with a smile. "Here on Master Gilius's epitaph we again have some little 0s referencing the Arabic place number system."

And, spotting the other epitaph south of the south door on the west wall of the crypt, he noticed, "But no little 0s here."

+HICSEPV LTVS
ESTCAVSITVS:
ANNDNIM:C:XLII
ORATE PRO EO

(Here is buried Causitus
in the year of our Lord
MCLII Pray for him.)

Saint-Gilles. Crypt. Epitaph of Causitus, + 1142.

"But come with me. If you appreciate good stonemasonry, there is something you really must see," the master builder remarked, as he led Pons away and up to ground level to the upper church. As they moved toward the choir, he pointed briefly to the base of a pier, confiding, "See, we added a tiny little figure here, depicting a worker crushed by the pier, in memory of the stone workers crushed in the collapse.[194] This is dangerous work.

194   See Jean-Marie Marconot, *Saint-Gilles L'abbatiale romane* (Nîmes, France: RIRESC, 2008), 61.

"I really want to show you the stone spiral staircase we are now erecting within the north wall of the upper church next to the choir here that will give access to the upper stories. It's a real beauty! A real masterpiece!

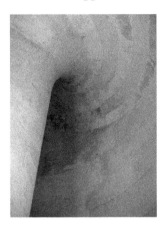

"We started with the concept of using a rampant arch for a barrel or tunnel vault. That's what let us to do it! Then we twisted the rampant arch to spiral upward, like a twisting, spiraling barrel vault. It really is an upward spiraling tunnel. And the design is quite spectacular. The monks here think it resembles a huge olive oil screw press. They call it the 'Screw of St. Gilles.'[195] We are really very, very proud of this!"

"Oh my," exclaimed Pons with a gasp upon seeing it. "I have never seen anything like this! It will be marvelous when completed!"

Saint-Gilles, remains at site of north wall of nave. Spiral stone staircase called "Screw of St. Gilles." Upward spiraling ceiling of stairs (restored).

"Well, it certainly is giving me and my tools here quite a challenge, figuring it all out! Frankly, it is even more difficult than it looks. Each voussoir stone piece overhead has to be carefully shaped, both convex and concave, to form the twisting, spiraling passageway. We are really very proud of both the design and of this stonemasonry!"

"I truly wonder what you might be able to do for us at Arles," Pons gasped, before immediately extending the *magister comacinus* a formal invitation to come to Arles to discuss the proposed project, once he had finished the work at Saint-Gilles and once the war hostilities had abated. The canon explained again that he anticipated hopefully that Master Guillelmo and his assistant would also return to Arles once the war hostilities had abated.

After spending the night at the abbey, Pons left with a light heart the next morning to walk home to Arles under the blazing Provençal sun. He could not be more pleased and excited at the new possibility of future success in his building project, and his pleasure was only heightened by what he perceived as his newfound awareness that he had participated in God's bigger plan in

---

195   The rebuilt ruins of the spiral staircase are still visible. The staircase is described in Marconot, *SaintGilles*, 59ff, and the Saint-Gilles tourist office pamphlet, *Come in the Heart of the Abbey-Church*, 9–10.

the struggle against the Petrobrusian heresy. His joy and hopefulness now completely erased from his mind any memory of the unnerving encounter with Beatrice. God truly must now be looking down favorably on him and on his project.

"Thank You, God! Thank You for showing me Your plan. Thank You for showing me the way and for blessing me and my project!"

As he continued walking, he began thinking about how beautiful the façade at the abbey church of Saint-Gilles was, and that it was associated with the Cluniac Order. This made him wonder about the new mother church of Cluny, which Peter the Venerable had described as beautifully vaulted and magnificently decorated with sculpture.

"And even though Bernard of Clairvaux rejects all sculptural decoration," Pons mused. "I do know the Cistercians build with plain stone vaulting that is also beautiful, starkly beautiful in its simplicity. Frankly, I think both Cluny and the Cistercians embrace beauty, but in different forms: one elegant and elaborate, one starkly simple.

"But we canons at Arles are not monks. We are neither Cluniac nor Cistercian. We are canons. As canons regular at Arles, we do not have to give up figural sculpture in our cloister. After all, I know firsthand how necessary the female figures on the siren and *luxuria* capitals have been to me, and now I really pray we will not have to settle for a wooden-roofed cloister."

He was certain he now understood God's plan. But why had it been so very difficult for him to recognize and to understand that plan? Seeing once again the wild horses of the Camargue off in the distance, Pons asked himself once again why his own path could not be simpler and more straightforward. Why had it always seemed to be so complicated and difficult for him? God had spoken to him, first through Peter the Venerable and now through Bernard of Clairvaux.

"God speaks to me. I have to learn to hear better," he resolved.

Upon returning to Arles, Pons found that as the ongoing hostilities of the war had escalated, centered around Arles, resentment was now building ever greater within the chapter. Moreover, because it was his brother who was waging the war, much of the resentment directed at Pons himself now intensified.

"Why can't your brother be content with what he has?" Peter Villelmus demanded angrily. "The Catalans were mostly leaving us alone, especially here in Arles. Who cares where the taxes go, who they go to? They still have to be paid!"

"It is now difficult even to get into and out of the city," Rainaldo cried.

"Why can't they move all the battles closer to your brother's holdings further away in Marignane and leave us alone?" Bernard complained.

"Can't you talk to your brother and get this resolved?" Hugues Amelius asked.

Even though Pons could not change or influence what his older brother, the imperious Lord of Baux, chose to do, the barbs pricked through any self-confidence. Most distressing was that sometimes even his friends seemed to imply that Pons was responsible somehow for the inconveniences imposed by the war.

"If your brother would only tell you where he was going, at least which direction, it would be safer for us to leave the city. We could work around his war," Jordan offered, trying to be helpful.

Yet the chapter also continued, perhaps with a bit more validity, to hold Pons responsible for the inconvenience of being surrounded by such a physical mess. Around them was what yet remained of Master Guillelmo's work there: all the not-yet-completed carved stones, the piles of stone, the mess, the rubble, and the detritus. So they complained.

"How can we carry on with our business when we cannot even enter the portal of our own chapter house to work?"

And, "You moved us from that corner of the chapter house, and now you've made me lose what I was working on! I cannot continue my work!"

Or, "You moved everything in the chapter house, and now everything is mixed up and I cannot find anything!"

"You want me to give up not only my house, but my dutiful wife and family for this God-forsaken mess you have left here."

"Do you have any idea at all where you are going with all of this?"

And they would threaten.

"You made me give up my woman for this mess? I swear sometimes I could . . . "

Or, "We canons all used to get along well, and our chapter and cathedral were thriving. Now we cannot work in our chapter house, and we are surrounded by war raging on all sides! If this is the price of adopting your absurd

Rule of St. Augustine, you can forget it! We may just reconsider the matter in chapter and decide *not* to adopt that stupid Rule."

"Brothers, brothers," Pons initially would begin in response, "let's be reasonable. These are all completely separate issues—the ongoing war, the stoppage of work on our cloister sculpture, and our adopting the Rule of St. Augustine.

"The war is between the Lord of Baux and the House of Barcelona over the County of Provence, and although the Lord of Baux is my brother, I have no influence over him. I have no involvement in the war. The war is not our concern. Such earthly, temporal matters are not important.

"The temporary cessation of work on our cloister sculpture resulted from the church's need to fight the Petrobrusian heresies of Henry of Lausanne. The stopping of work is temporary and should not be a concern. Work will resume.

"Constructing communal buildings so we can live communally was something we all agreed to. This is our concern! This is what is really important! Let's remember our sacred goal in all of this—to be able to follow the Rule of St. Augustine, to live the *vita apostolica* according to God's plan."

As the days, weeks and months passed, the never-ending whining and complaints continued, becoming ever more annoying and unnerving. The war continued; Pons continued to be blamed for it. The construction that now seemed as if it would never begin again became a source of continual aggravation.

Hope that is at first enthusiastic will eventually wane if constantly denigrated, sneeringly mocked, and attacked. Idealism, though initially buoyant, can eventually sour when continually picked at, ignorantly scorned, rudely questioned, disdainfully challenged. Bodily humors quite naturally react to such abuse.

Now alternately either choleric or melancholic, Pons swayed back and forth between the two humors as either yellow or black bile flooded and took control of his poor body. Pons's composure began fraying under the turmoil and stress. He was being blamed for things that were totally beyond his control. His responses started becoming first cuttingly impolitic, then ever more strident, ever more inflammatory, ever more inappropriate.

"Why don't you cut your damned belly-aching!"

"Keep your little children away from the stone piles. It's their own stupid fault if they get hurt!"

"Take your record books and throw 'em . . . Shove 'em up your . . . !"

"What are you complaining about? You wife can't cook worth anything, and she never has conjugal union with you anyways!"

Pons's patience and control were faring badly under the stress, his humors surging wildly. His interactions with his fellow canons were raw and becoming ever more uncivil, until finally deteriorating well beyond the point of easy recovery. Pons lost all self-control.

He knew it was he to whom God had spoken, clarifying that the chapter was to adopt the *vita apostolica*. It was he alone whom God had charged to make it so. It was he alone whom the chapter had charged with making it all possible. It was he alone who carried this heavy burden. It was now *he* alone against all of *them*.

And so it continued, week after week, month after month for the rest of the year and into the beginning of the next.

Outside the cathedral complex, the war had been going very badly for Pons's brother. The Catalan Ramon Berenguer IV had completely overwhelmed and vanquished most of the viscounts and nobles of Provence, who submitted in defeat by February 1146 to the Count of Barcelona at Tarascon. It was now only Raymond of Baux and Alphonse Jourdain, the Count of Toulouse, who were refusing to surrender and defiantly carrying on the fight against the Catalans.

Shortly after *Sext* at midday in early February 1146, Canon Pons was called to the archbishop's palace to meet with Archbishop Raymond de Monte Rotundo and his friend William Garnerius, *precentor* and chancellor.

"Canon Pons, both the archbishop and I are fully aware of all the difficulties you have been facing," William Garnerius began. "We are well aware of all the discontent and complaints you have been fielding within the chapter. The accusations and difficulties have no doubt been daunting."

"And now most of the nobles of Provence seem to have deserted your brother in his war to claim the County of Provence," the archbishop added. "This must be disheartening for you, to say the least."

"You did an excellent job," William Garnerius continued, "in bringing the chapter around to agreeing to construct communal buildings that will enable the chapter to live communally. But we both now fear you may have lost sight of what must be our ultimate goal in all of this. You are trying to build something extraordinary, both architecturally and spiritually, but to do so, you must keep the chapter on side with you.

"You know we fully support your project," William continued. "We want the chapter to adopt the *vita apostolica*, but we now fear it will not happen if the level of discord continues to rise within the chapter. You are losing your true focus. You are losing your composure. You are losing your self-control."

The canon's face flushed as his mouth opened speechlessly while his head and shoulders dropped in defeat.

"All of us in chapter are in agreement," William continued. "We strongly urge you to get away from Arles for a short respite to regain your focus. We suggest—we *strongly* suggest—that you take a trip to regain your composure."

Shifting nervously on his feet, the canon began to squirm, holding his now lowered head between both hands.

"Your *precentor* and *capud scole* William Garnerius here," the archbishop began, "has agreed to assume responsibility for keeping an eye on your project on your behalf in your absence, and the chapter has wholeheartedly endorsed this plan."

Dropping his hands to his sides, the canon now raised his flushed, distorted, emotion-wracked face to look with tearful eyes at the archbishop.

"We want you to take a trip, a trip north, to Burgundy, to Vézelay. There you can finally see the abbey church that I know you have long wanted to see," the archbishop said with a note of real kindness.

At this, Pons straightened up ever so slightly as his face began to relax.

"Why Vézelay, you might ask?" the archbishop continued. "As I'm sure you heard, Edessa fell just over a year ago. Well, Pope Eugenius II has now given his blessing to the cause of shoring up the safety of the Holy Land by defending the Crusader states, and he has urged King Louis VII of France to lead the expedition. The young king is convening an assembly at Vézelay at Easter, and the pope has asked Bernard of Clairvaux to lead the call for this Second Crusade there.[196] We want you to act on our behalf, to bear witness to Bernard's call for the Second Crusade."

After waiting a moment for Pons to take in this information, the archbishop nodded kindly and continued. "Yes, we want you to leave by next

----

196   See Hindley, *Brief*, 71–72.

week, together with your good friend, Canon Nicolaus of Saint-Ruf, and also with the visitor, Canon Gilbert, who will be returning to his home chapter up north in France near Paris.

"If you try to go west through Toulouse and then follow the Garonne River north toward Bordeaux to join up with the pilgrimage route coming from Vézelay, the trip will be longer and possibly more treacherous. So to ensure your safe and timely arrival, we suggest you follow the roads straight north, up the Rhône Valley through Avignon and Valence toward Lyon, then follow the road along the River Saône to pass near Cluny and up to Tournus, and then continue on, passing near Cîteaux to Dijon, where you can turn westward toward Autun and then on to Vézelay.[197]

"Nicolaus will be returning to his motherhouse near Avignon, but you and Gilbert will continue on from there together. Gilbert knows the route north. You will serve as our eyes and ears at Vézelay."

"And as our representative," William Garnerius continued, "you will report back on the call for the crusade and on how the crusade might be expected to affect us here at Arles. We are not now expecting to have to make any special accommodations, because even if many do take up the cross, we would expect most of them not to choose to pass through the hostilities here at Arles to take the sea route to the Holy Land, but instead choose to take the overland route through the Rhineland. After all, even if there were no hostilities around Arles, travel by sea is so very difficult. But we will want to prepare ourselves if necessary."

"Most of all, Canon Pons," the archbishop concluded, "we all pray that by the grace of God you will be able to regain your perspective by taking this journey."

And so what God had instructed Pons to do was, temporarily at least, again to be put aside. God may have spoken directly to Pons, but He was now speaking to all of Christendom, with apparently a very different message.

* * *

197   See map p 4. For a map of twelfth-century roads in this area, see the map of the histori-
      cal routes in France by René de la Coste-Messelière and Claude Petitet based on work
      from the Centre Européen des Études Compostellanes, https://www.saint-jacques.
      info/fausse-carte/faux.htm.

The route was easy to follow, for the most part, even if the journey was sometimes a bit arduous. They followed the Rhône River northward—the mighty Rhône River, the all-important waterway and trade route that in Greek and Roman times had linked the Mediterranean to east central Gaul. Beginning in the Alps, the Rhône joins at Lyon with the River Saône to turn southward, coursing toward Arles and the Mediterranean. Very soon its fierce currents might soon be delivering by boat into Arles hordes of Christians who had taken up the cross, or at least those who would dare to enter Arles to attempt to cross the sea to reach the Holy Land. But at this time it was unusually ferocious late winter winds that were now roaring down the river valley, chilling the young canons to their bones.

The trio followed alongside the Rhône on horseback to Avignon, where, as expected, after resting overnight, they left Nicolaus of Saint-Ruf behind. The pair then continued on horseback, following the river through Orange with its ancient Roman theater, then detouring only slightly to Vaison-la-Romaine, with its Roman ruins and where they found lodging at the cathedral cloister. They continued on, passing through Valence and Vienne, where they found refuge at the church of Saint-André-le-Bas. At Lyon they left the banks of the Rhône to follow northward along the River Saône and continued along through Mâcon. As traveling clerics, they always sought and found overnight lodging and respite at abbeys, priories, or churches along the way, and it was through these sojourns with newfound brethren, as well as through simply being away from the turmoil at his own chapter, that Pons's spirits began to lift, his humors regained their balance, and his composure began to return.

They were greatly relieved to able to stop for a prolonged four-day rest at the abbey of Cluny. Although the monks there had earlier suffered from a severe epidemic, they had fully recovered over a year ago, and they now received the travelers most warmly. The monks readily invited them to stay in the separate buildings reserved for guests that were included within their vast and extensive building complex that held living and working quarters both for the monks and for lay brothers.[198] Pons was hugely impressed with the extensive building complex.

....

198   George Zarnecki, *The Monastic Achievement* (New York, NY: McGraw-Hill, 1972), 63, mentions this epidemic and describes the extensive claustral complex.

He was thrilled, however, to be permitted to personally peruse the extensive library of almost 600 codices![199] He had never seen so many manuscripts, and of so wide a variety. Some were illuminated with historiated initials, enlarged alphabet letters bearing pictures of identifiable figures or scenes. Many included inhabited initials with depictions of small figures or animals. Many were magnificently beautiful, most absolutely charming. But some showed terrifying, threateningly frightening images of devouring creatures from hell. One manuscript, a Psalter, showed an absolutely terrifying image of a huge, gaping Hellmouth, with monstrous jaws holding suffering damned souls being tortured by devils and demons.[200]

Winchester Psalter, British Library. Cotton MS Nero C. IV, f.39, Hellmouth locked by an Angel.

. . . .

199   Zarnecki, *Monastic*, 123–124, cites the library as containing 570 books in the twelfth century.

200   The Cluny library would undoubtedly have held a manuscript like this, but not this particular one. This Winchester Psalter is dated around 1150. Written and illuminated at Winchester, it includes this full folio page image of a "Mouth of Hell," shown here as an angel unlocking the door of Hell. The image of the gaping mouth of a monster, full of condemned sinners, demons, and devils, first appeared earlier in Anglo-Saxon ivories and miniatures depicting the Harrowing of Hell, but by the twelfth century the image had spread and was much more widely used.

It was the enormous abbey church, however, that completely over-whelmed Pons. Even its description earlier by the Venerable Brother Peter of Montboissier, Abbot of Cluny, had not prepared him for this. Pons fell speechless in wondrous awe at the magnificence of this structure. It was truly the grandest, tallest, most breathtaking, most splendid monument ever then erected to the glory of God. An enormous five-aisled basilica, it had two transepts crossing the nave, as well as an ambulatory with radiating chapels curving around the east end, and a narthex or vestibule at the west end. There were towers above each transept's crossing of the nave and over the arms of the western transept as well. There were, in total, thirteen apses with chapels, all formally staggered in an orderly arrangement at the east end, five around the ambulatory and two at the east sides of both transepts.[201]

The entire massive structure was stone vaulted, and although the vaulting of the enormous central nave had collapsed soon after its completion in 1121, it had been successfully rebuilt for the consecration in 1130. Tunnel vaulted throughout, the nave arcade used pointed arches, one of the first such uses in the west, and above the arcade ran a small triforium passage, above which was the clerestory through which light entered.

Pons had never seen such an enormous church, whose monumentality outshone even the antique Roman remains that he knew so well at Arles. In fact, the Roman monuments seemed to be the only kind of structure with which he could compare it.

"Truly this abbey church is our Christian testament to Your power and glory, Lord God! It can only reflect Your greatness!" he cried out softly.

Nor had he ever seen such a breathtakingly beautiful, elaborately deco-rated, gloriously magnificent church. With exquisite architectural detailing, such as the pointed arches in the nave elevation, with an extraordinary use of space through its series of clustered apses, its architectural beauty was also matched by the superb elegance of its painting and sculpture.

The interior was decorated throughout with beautiful wall frescoes, and at the east end, a magnificent huge wall painting of Christ in Majesty soared over the main apse. Throughout the church, there were hundreds of beautifully carved, exquisitely detailed stone capitals, masterful in style, sophisticated in subject matter, and each as eloquently charming as it could be. Some showed

201   See Zarnecki, *Monastic,* 59–62 for a concise description of the history, architecture and sculpture of Cluny III.

biblical stories; some showed allegories, such as the Seasons and the Virtues. All were absolutely exquisite.

Musée Ochier, now Musée d'Art et d'Archéologie.
Capital from destroyed Cluny church choir. First Gregorian Tone.[202]

"Oh, my. These could not be more wonderful!" Pons exclaimed audibly while walking slowly through the ambulatory, looking closely at two capitals with eight figures suggesting the tones of the Gregorian chant.[203] "This reminds me how important music is to the Cluniac liturgy."

Having just carefully examined the carved capitals showing the tones of the Gregorian chant, he was thrilled to be invited to celebrate divine services in the church. Already exhausted from his travels, he wholeheartedly surrendered to the overwhelming majesty and beauty surrounding him. Participating in the service, he surrendered himself, opening himself to the familiar yet otherworldly

202 Photo used with permission of its author and owner, © Ricardo Muñoz Nieva - RicardMN Photography.

203 Two of the capitals still remaining from Cluny are representations of the scales (or "tones" or "modes") of the Gregorian chant. They originally showed all eight tones. One capital shows the first four tones; the other now shows only the sixth mode with the others totally or mostly destroyed. They are identified by the inscriptions, the first tone being *Hic tonus orditur modulamina musica primus.* For more on these capitals see Kathi Meyer, "The Eight Gregorian Modes on the Cluny Capitals," *The Art Bulletin* 34, no. 2 (June 1952): 75–94.

scent of incense, letting it overcome him, making him lightheaded, removing him from the outside world, and enveloping him within God's house.

The monks began to chant; the music began to swell. The music filled the huge, cavernous stone church, swelling ever more, becoming ever fuller, ever more vibrant, ever more complex, now reverberating from choir to nave to transept to aisle, and yet another transept to aisle, and from stone vault to stone vault, from one level of stone tunnel vault to another, pulsating against the magnificently painted walls, and echoing again and again and again through the transept and aisles.

Closing his eyes, Pons was transfixed by the unbelievable richness and beauty of the music, the melodious tones with their virtually unending resonances and overtones. As when he was a young boy, once again he would be transported, moved elsewhere, beyond this place, beyond this realm, moved this time by the slow, steady harmonic rhythms of the tones and their resonances. Wondrous sound overwhelmed his conscious being. He was transported into a spiritual realm, moved to an otherworldly place, a realm of pure beauty and absolute peace.

A shiver passed over his neck and back, and the hairs stood up on his scalp and forearms. "Oh, please come to me, my Lord God," he voiced silently. "I am Your humble servant . . ."

His forehead and cheeks cooled ever so slightly, and he knew he was being touched by the Spirit. He recognized the sensation. He understood what was happening. The Spirit of God was passing lightly over him, caressing his cheeks, gently touching his head and shoulders, and finally passing into and through him.

The celestial sounds were transporting him once again, as he had first been moved as a child, infusing him once again with what he knew was the Spirit of God as he had not been for . . . oh, for so long a time. God was touching him. God touched and embraced his soul through the music. And for the briefest of moments, he and God were again as one. He and God were one.

The music eventually ended. Slowly, Pons returned to the here and now. But once again, Pons had found real certainty. Once again, he knew he was right in interpreting what God had told him He wanted of him and his chapter. The abbey church of Cluny. The monastic complex. Peter the Venerable. Embracing the *vita apostolica* . . . It was all clear. It all made perfect sense to him once again.

Everything made sense. And more than that. More than that. He slowly came to realize that it was his experience of music in this stone-vaulted church that had so moved him, and if that experience could bring him so close to God, if it could make him one with God, he must now dedicate himself more fully to rebuilding the cathedral church at Arles into a magnificent stone-vaulted edifice, so the faithful there, too, might partake of this experience, might find this transformation. So they, too, might become one with God.

Until now, his sole priority had been constructing the claustral buildings, and he had been less driven, less vigorous in pursuing the rebuilding of the cathedral, even though he had known, of course, that it, too, was necessary. Now he understood that God was telling him to focus on and complete both.

But first he had to fulfill his duty and complete his mission, so he could return to his project.

And so after four days, Pons and Gilbert left Cluny to continue on their journey, still following the River Saône and passing through Tournus, where Pons marveled at the clever and unusual stone vaulting in the abbey church of St. Philibert. There the single nave was a series of short transverse tunnel vaults, lined up parallel against each other, like a row of halved wine barrels, and all flanked by the groin-vaulted aisles. The two canons continued on toward Dijon, where they sheltered overnight at the abbey of St. Bénigne. Again Pons marveled, but this time at the old sculpture, figural capitals that had been carved in the crypt over a hundred years earlier! At Dijon they finally left the River Saône to turn southwestward toward Autun.

At Autun the two canons visited the new Cathedral of Saint-Lazare. It had been built to accommodate the many pilgrims who were now stopping there to venerate the blessed relics of Lazarus, the brother of Mary and Martha whom Jesus had raised from the dead, before continuing on to Vézelay to join the pilgrimage route to Santiago de Compostela. The new cathedral at Autun had just been finished, although the relics had not yet been translated there. On arrival, the canons immediately went to the central portal,[204] where the huge, fearsome scene on the lunette tympanum above the doorway absolutely terrified them. Filled with many, many figures of various sizes, with most so

....

204   The cathedral of Saint-Lazare, Autun was begun around 1120 and mostly finished by 1146. The master sculptor, long known as Gislebertus, worked there from 1120–1135, carving both the portal sculptures and the capitals inside the cathedral. The Last Judgment tympanum is usually dated 1130–1135 or before 1135.

elongated as to be unreal, ethereal, this was a depiction of the Last Judgment, with a huge figure of Christ sitting solemnly in judgment in heaven, surrounded by a heavenly host of apostles and saints, with the resurrection of the dead below, and their tiny souls being weighed, either to be welcomed into heaven or cast to the devil and into hell.[205] Closely studying this frightening scene, Pons read the inscriptions and noticed one, "*Gislebertus hoc fecit*," which he took to identify the sculptor, beneath the feet of the imposingly judgmental figure of Christ.

Autun. Cathedral, west façade. Central portal, tympanum, Last Judgment.

Turning from this vivid, threatening imagery, Pons walked alone over to the north portal, where he was shocked to see a sculpture of a beautiful nude woman: Eve, carved on one half of the lintel directly above the north portal, where she lay in the foliage, picking an apple.[206]

....

205   On this distortion of the figures, see Beckwith, *Early*, 212–215 and fig. 202. Many of the carved capitals at Autun show this elongated distortion, but some, including the Magi capitals, show a gentle charm comparable to that of the Cluny capitals.

206   See Grivot and Zarnecki, *Gislebertus*. The lintel with the relief sculpture of the nude Eve is the only figure to have survived from the original arrangement on the north portal. It is now displayed in the Musée Rolin at Autun. The sculpture of Eve was long hidden after being confiscated in the eighteenth century for use as building material. The sculptures of the Raising of Lazarus, Adam, and the Devil are gone.

Pons let out a loud gasp. Depicted above was the Resurrection of Lazarus, appropriate for the cathedral that would receive his relics, but here, too, were figures of Adam on the other half of the lintel, and Eve, both lying languidly in foliage, and a figure of Satan.

Autun. Musée Rolin. Carved lintel originally on the north portal of the Cathedral of Saint-Lazare, Eve.

Pons was shaken. Here was the original temptress who had led Adam into sin! Pons knew she was evil. And yet here she was, lying so seductively above the church portal. And she was so beautiful, so very beautiful, so beckoning, with soft, rounded breasts . . . He could not look at her! She was evil! He immediately turned away. Why was this image here? Why was she shown as being so beautiful? Above the church portal! A sudden chill passed through his entire body. Was it fear? Was it foreboding? Visibly distressed, he immediately fought to put the image out of his mind as he quickly moved to enter the church to escape this dilemma.

Inside the cathedral, Pons was immediately calmed by the majestic formality of the design, and he recognized its derivation from Cluny. The tall nave with pointed arches had massive piers, elegantly covered with vertically fluted pilaster strips that rose to transverse arches that supported a twenty-three-meter-high broken barrel-stone vault.

But it was the many, many carved capitals with all manner of scenes that enchanted him. There were not only scenes from the Old and New Testaments, but other traditional scenes and images, such as the Virtues and Vices, and even several scenes involving the three Magi, their arrival at Herod's palace, their worship of the Christ child, the three Magi asleep and wakened by an angel, and the flight of the Holy Family into Egypt. Many of these capitals were absolutely delightful.

"How could the same sculptor, Gislebertus, have carved such absolutely delightful figures and scenes, while also carving such a frightening, judgmental Christ, as well as an immorally desirable, temptingly beautiful, nude Eve?" the naïve young canon asked himself.

But for the unnerving image of Eve, Pons would have wanted to stay on at Autun another day. The image had truly unnerved him. And they did have to continue on. So the two canons continued on northwestward toward Vézelay. They passed through the small town of Avallon, approaching the base of the steep hill on top of which was nestled the abbey of Vézelay. Near the bottom of the hill, they joined others who were also headed toward the same destination, all slowly snaking their way up the long path, working their way up the hill to the Benedictine abbey at the top. As they finally arrived at the settlement, they were astonished by the huge crowd that was now gathering on the hillside below the abbey and just outside its walls, where all were settling down, trying to claim spots they would try to hold onto for two days, either by marking them with possessions or camping there.

Everyone was eagerly awaiting the arrival of the famous Bernard of Clairvaux. His call for a crusade was expected to take place in two days, on Easter, pridie Aprilis, or II Kalends Aprilis (31 March),[207] 1146.

....

207   The Roman Julian calendar was used in the medieval era, while we now use the Gregorian calendar. In the Julian calendar, the days of each month were identified by how many days they preceded three named days: Kalends, or the first day of the month; Nones, which fell on the ninth day before Ides, counting both Nones and Ides; and Ides, which fell mid-month on the fifteenth day of the longer months and the thirteenth day of the shorter months. The days between Kalends and Nones were counted down as the sixth, the fifth, fourth, etc. before Nones; the days between Nones and Ides were counted down as the eighth, seventh, sixth, fifth, etc. before Ides; the days between Ides and Kalends of the next month were counted down as the seventeenth, sixteenth, fifteenth, etc. days before Kalends of the next month. The day before the Kalends (or Nones or Ides) was called "pridie" (or "two") Kalends. In 1146 Easter fell on Sunday, March 31, which would be the day before Kalends of April, or *pridie* of April. See "A Medieval English Calendar," *Some Notes on Medieval English Genealogy*, http://www.medievalgenealogy.org.uk/cal/medcal.shtml.

Entering the town and working their way to the doors of the Benedictine abbey, Pons and Gilbert were naïvely and perhaps foolishly hoping to find there a place to stay, knowing it had long accommodated the many pilgrims who came to venerate its relics of Ste. Mary Magdalene. After leaving their horses with an abbey stable boy, the two canons were dismayed to learn that they could not find shelter at the abbey, or anywhere at all, because King Louis and his huge entourage of nobility had taken over all available lodging space.

It was Good Friday, IV Kalends Aprilis, March 29, so the monks invited canons Pons and Gilbert to join their midday service. The abbey church of Sainte-Madeleine at Vézelay had been completed about ten years earlier, but its narthex, or vestibule, at the west end was still under construction. Being Good Friday, that day's service would, of course, be only a meditation service and not a Mass, so there would be no celebration of the Eucharist. Although Pons was relieved to be able to participate in the meditation service, he was also truly delighted to finally see this charming abbey church that was groin-vaulted throughout and built with freely intermingled stone of two different colors, giving it a lively energy.

But it was the sculpture once again that riveted his attention, captivating him. On the inner west portal were all the figures, all the imagery, that Peter the Venerable had described and explained, and Pons was so excited to be able to see it, despite the mess of the ongoing construction work in the nar-thex.[208] Here was the magnificent central portal tympanum depicting Christ giving the mission to the apostles to go and preach the Gospel. Here was the south portal showing the mysteries of the birth of Christ. Here was the north portal with the mysteries of the risen Christ, after He had risen from the dead.

Inside the church, Pons found the carved capitals along the nave and aisles to be absolutely delightful with their energetic little figures.

"Oh, look at this one," he whispered to Gilbert, pointing to a charming and strikingly beautiful symbolic capital. "I think I know what it depicts. It's the Mystic Mill!' Here's one man—that's Moses—pouring grain—that's the Old Law—into a little cross-marked mill that represents Christ through whom the grain, or Old Law, is transformed into flour—the New Law—which is received by this other man. That must be St. Paul. Oh, this capital is wonder-ful! The image conveys the complex message that it was the sacrifice of Christ

....

208   See Photos on pages 76 and 77.

that transformed the Law of Moses into the New Law, which was St. Paul's mission to distribute."

The service began, and Pons took part in the devotions. The service included readings and meditations and a beautifully sung reading of the Passion from the Gospel of John, with accompanying chanting in the sanctuary. There was also a solemn presentation of the cross.

Vézelay. Abbey Church, Ste. Madeleine, capital. The Mystic Mill.

After the service, Pons stayed quite a while to examine the church sculptures alone. He was startled to find another capital showing *luxuria*.

"It's *luxuria* as a female figure with serpents eating her breasts and abdomen," he thought to himself, "but depicted so differently from either the *luxuria* or her enticing counterpart, the siren, at Arles. And here *luxuria* is paired with a figure of despair, a demon plunging a sword into his torso. Here it is lust and despair."

Eventually Pons rejoined Gilbert, who, having lost interest in the sculptures, had returned to the stable to make arrangements for the horses. The two canons then slowly worked their way toward the field on the hillside, maneuvering carefully through the ever-growing crowd toward a wooden tribune that looked like it would be the center of attention. They could not get too close to the wooden stage with its podium that they could see had been recently

Vézelay. Abbey Church, Ste. Madeleine, capital. Luxuria (lust) and Despair.

erected especially for this event, because that area had been claimed by the nobility, who had staked out their seats with banners, colors, even some horses and carts, and although their places were empty voids, they were all guarded and tended by servants.

The hillside was a riot of people and horses, a cacophony of sound with vaguely foreign tongues and different accents all competing against each other, as everyone from near and far tried to settle themselves down for a stay of a couple of days. Pons and Gilbert were finally able to claim a tiny spot fairly close to the nobility, and they settled down, laying out their few things for the wait.

Two days passed, and Easter arrived. Many hundreds had now gathered. The surrounding air was charged. It felt like something was about to begin, something was about to burst open. All the nobility had claimed their places, filling the color-staked and banner-marked voids with glorious new splashes of richly colored garments, as if a gigantic, lavish, riotously colored patchwork quilt was now draped haphazardly over the hillside near the podium.

Pons and Gilbert were close enough to the front to see that the French King Louis VII and his Queen Eleanor of Aquitaine had now installed themselves in the front row, directly in front of the stage, only a step or two from it. They were also close enough to see several huge stacks of thin cloth strips piled high next to the stage.

A frail, gaunt figure Pons immediately recognized to be Bernard of Clairvaux slowly stepped up to the podium.[209] Pons recognized this tall, thin, white-haired skeleton of a man as much by his quiet confidence as by his appearance. Bernard calmly held up his hand and quietly waited until the surrounding noise had subsided and everyone in the crowd had acknowledged his arrival. When he finally held their rapt attention, he lowered his head, folded his hands, and prayed humbly for guidance.

He then raised his hand, saying quietly, "May God look down and bless what transpires here today."

Raising his voice, he then called out, "May God let my lips sound his apostolic trumpet!"[210]

. . . .

209   The following description of Bernard's calling the Second Crusade is taken from but greatly embellished on the description in Hindley, *Brief*, 71–74. See also Kelly, *Eleanor*, 33–35.

210   We know that Bernard began by reading the papal bull and then followed with an impassioned sermon on the threats to the Holy Land of Christ's Passion. See Hindley, *Brief*, 72–73. Kelly, *Eleanor*, 33–34, notes that Bernard said he set his lips "to the apostolic trumpet."

Bernard then pulled from the white tunic of his habit a document, and carefully opened it.

"Our most Holy and Reverend Father, Pope Eugenius III, has asked me to convey his message to you," his voice roared out, after which he read aloud the papal bull of December 1145 in which Eugenius III had appealed to all of Christendom, and to King Louis VII in particular, to take up the cross and to aid the Holy Land, with a promise of absolution of sins as the reward.

Tucking the document back into his white habit, Bernard began his impassioned sermon.

"We come together today at Easter, on this most holy day, when our beloved Lord Jesus Christ rose from the dead so that we might have the hope of eternal life. We come together today because that very land where He gave His life for us is now in grave peril. The county of Edessa, the first crusader state, has fallen, fallen in a dreadful bloody sack, fallen into the murderous hands of the evil infidels.

"The Christian souls of Edessa were murdered, raped, tortured, and slaughtered by that bloodthirsty Satan called Zangi Imad al-Din. The county of Edessa that used to provide a measure of safety along the northern frontier of our Holy Land now lies in the hands of the infidel and poses a threat instead.

"Edessa has fallen. It fell on the eve of the birth of our Lord Jesus Christ. The land of Christ's birth is now also in peril of falling to the infidels! The land where God begot his own Son to take upon Himself our sins, that land is now in grave danger. The land where Christ rose from the dead on Easter Sunday to offer us the hope of eternal life, that land is in danger of being defiled by the infidel! The Holy Land is in peril!

"On this Easter day, as we celebrate Christ's resurrection, let us commit ourselves to free the Holy Land from this threat, to chase away the infidel! Let us commit to make safe the Holy Land! Let us commit to take back the birthright of every Christian!

"And as God has given us the promise of eternal life through the death and resurrection of His son, Jesus Christ, so, too, we are today promised absolution from our sins, if we take up the Cross and go to the aid of the Holy Land. Let us go forth—under the banner of Christ, in the name of Christ, under the sign of the cross—to push back the infidels who have so cruelly murdered our brothers. Let us go forth, under the sign of the cross, to make safe the land of our Lord Jesus Christ's birth, death, and resurrection!

"God has set my lips to sound his holy trumpet!" he called out. "Who will answer the call? Who will carry the banner of Christ? Who has God chosen to step up to lead us on our mission for Christ? Who will lead us on our pilgrimage to make safe the Holy Land? Who will lead us?"

The moment Bernard had concluded his impassioned call, King Louis leaped eagerly to his feet. So visibly moved by the call to arms was the king that he appeared to be sobbing. So visibly overcome with the solemnity of his duty that he appeared to be speechless. Bending his head in penitence, the king slowly walked the few steps to the wooden stage, mounted it, and threw himself at Bernard's feet, prostrating himself on the wooden floor. The ascetic monk solemnly raised his arm high to bless him with the sign of the cross before proclaiming aloud so all could hear, "God has given us our chosen leader! *Deus vult. Deus vult.* God wills it."[211]

Bernard slowly bent down to take the king by the arm and ever so slowly helped him rise to his feet. Bernard then reached out to the king to remove briefly from his chest a cross emblem, and, holding it up high to show to the assembly, he loudly proclaimed, "This cross, this special cross emblem, has been blessed by our most Holy Reverend Father, Pope Eugenius III, to mark the cloak of him who will lead our blessed expedition, King Louis VII of France!"

After demonstratively pinning the emblem back onto the cloak of the king, Bernard turned to the crowd, raised his arms welcomingly, and cried out, "Now, in the name of our Lord Jesus Christ who will follow our chosen leader? Who will take up the cross and follow in this holy cause to make safe the land of our Lord Jesus Christ? Who will answer the call? *Deus vult! Deus vult!* God wills it! Who will take up the Cross and receive the promise of absolution from their sins? Who will take up the Cross and receive the promise of eternal grace? Who will take this sign and seal? Cursed be he who does not stain his sword with blood!"

In thunderous answer, all the barons of Gaul, all the male nobility and courtiers leaped to their feet and surged forward to take their vows, to claim their sign and seal, as had been previously arranged for this well-orchestrated event. Every noble house leaped forward as old foes temporarily put aside their rivalries and hostilities to join together to pledge to do battle under the

---

211   "*Deus vult*," or "God wills it," was the Christian motto or call to arms of the First Crusade.

French banner. Among them Pons recognized Alphonse Jourdain, Count of Toulouse. As each man took his vow, Bernard gave him two strips of white cloth taken from the nearby pile, which were then stitched onto his shoulder in the shape of a cross by assistants who had emerged from the crowd with their sewing implements at the ready.

The women of the court and ladies-in-waiting now immediately jumped up and surged forward too, led by Queen Eleanor, the most beautiful and high-spirited Queen Eleanor of Aquitaine,[212] who approached the stage. The vivacious and hot-blooded twenty-five-year-old queen now knelt piously at Bernard's feet to take the cross. After her vow, Bernard gently took her arm to raise her up, but as he handed her the two strips of white cloth that would form her cross, he took her hand and then bent forward, momentarily motionless, to speak privately into her ear so that not even those closest could hear him.

"Bless you, my child. Following our first meeting two years ago, when I reprimanded you for your flamboyant behavior, you have mended your immodest ways. You stopped stirring up the king against our Church. As I then promised you, if you would begin behaving more penitently, I prayed to God for you to give birth to a child. Praise be to God, our prayers were answered.[213] Bless you, my child, for helping orchestrate today this most important of God's missions, the calling of His Second Crusade."

As he finally made the sign of the cross to Eleanor, the other women of the court lined up before the stage, among them Sybille, Countess of Flanders, half-sister of the King of Jerusalem; Florine of Bourgogne; and Faydide of Toulouse, and they, too, knelt to take their pilgrim vows. After the ladies-in-waiting had taken their vows and received the cloth strips, Bernard again mounted the podium, held up his arms, and called out again, ever more stridently.

"Now! Who among us will take up the cross and follow our leader in this holy cause to make safe the land of our Lord Jesus Christ? Who will answer God's call? Who among us will take this pilgrimage to receive the promise of absolution from their sins? Who will receive the promise of eternal grace? Who will take this sign and seal?"

....

212   On her father's death when she was fifteen, Eleanor had inherited his vast territories in the southwest, and her guardian, King Louis the Fat, had immediately wed her to his own son, young Louis, so as to bring her vast land holdings under the French crown.

213   A daughter, Marie Capet, was born one year earlier.

The crowd, now moved to a fever pitch, roared again and again, "We will! We will! We take it up! We take it up!"

One and all thundered forward *en masse* toward the stage, led by the 300 non-noble vassals who had been recruited to the cause by Queen Eleanor herself. Any semblance of order was now burst asunder into total and utter chaos, as people clamored and fought to receive the cross, struggling to make their way to Bernard.

Surrounded by this vortex of religious fervor and enthusiasm, Pons and Gilbert first tried quite sensibly to pull back from the melee. They tried carefully to work their way toward the back of the crowd, not wanting to be trampled, not wanting to be sucked into the vortex. They could not take the pledge. They were not free to decide here to take vows to take up the cross to make this crusade. They were canons who had taken their vows and were bound to their chapters, and they were here only because they were carrying out a mission. Slowly, slowly and with great difficulty they worked their way toward the back of the melee, against the surging momentum of the crowd.

Suddenly the two canons were startled totally dumbstruck by the shocking emergence of the first rider in a spectacular troupe of mounted warrior women. Pons leaped back, gasping in panic. What immediately flashed vividly through his mind was his dream that night with Beatrice so long ago, when he had envisioned a beautiful young woman with flowing hair mounted on a white horse charge through angels battling evil human barons before changing into a demonic old hag on a black horse. Momentarily frozen, Pons could not seem to move but quickly shook his head to try to regain his bearings as Gilbert grabbed his arm, trying desperately to pull him close, to hold him tightly against his own body and out of harm's way.

Pons had narrowly escaped being trampled to death underfoot as the mounted troupe of Amazon women now burst fully upon the scene. All on horseback, they swooped past, scattering everyone in their path, terrifying anyone who was nearby. It was Queen Eleanor and her immediate entourage, who, after retiring but briefly to change their outer clothing, had reappeared with a dramatic flourish now clad flamboyantly as Amazon warriors. They cantered on horseback through the crowd, brazenly wielding drawn swords, herding forward anyone who tried to retreat away from the wooden stage.

Queen Eleanor startled and bedazzled all. An astonishing vision of fierce beauty, dressed in a stark white hauberk and gilded sandals with exotic plumes in her hair, she rode with abandon, her uncovered auburn red hair flowing wildly, wantonly, brazenly over her hauberk. As Queen of the Amazons, she led the troupe, cantering about, wielding a white shield with a central gold boss encircled with jewels. Like the queen, all the Amazon women in her wake dashed about on horses covered with white silk cloths with tinkling golden bells, their hair flying wantonly in the wind. Some brandished white shields with golden bosses and swords, others held high colorful banners and pennants. Fearlessly, the women rode through the bewildered crowd, twisting and turning aggressively on their mounts, brazenly encouraging, urging, pushing those who were not yet committed to move forward to take their pilgrimage vows.[214]

More and more people surged forward; more and more people received crosses stitched onto the shoulder of their garments. More and more demanded to be given the crosses that would bring them absolution from their sins—so many that Bernard ran out of strips of cloth. Taking off the white outer robe of his habit, he handed it to the sewing assistants, who began to rip it up into little strips to supplement the now depleted piles.

Now those who had not yet had their strips sewn onto their garment began fighting to exchange them for the pieces of the famous Bernard's robe, which they thought would be even better and more powerful in gaining eternal favor than the originals. The chaos throughout would have turned into a general brawl but for the brazen Amazon women, whose cantering horses intimidated the crowd, restrained movement, and kept the exuberant pilgrims and would-be crusaders somewhat in line.

The day wore on. Night was arriving. Exhaustion set in. All the cloth strips from the pile were gone. Almost every shoulder now bore a hastily stitched white cross. Bernard's call for the Second Crusade had been a success.

After somehow managing to pull back from the melee, Pons and Gilbert had moved far to the back of the crowd. They had managed not to be trampled by the Amazon women and not to be sucked into the vortex of crusade fervor. By the next morning they would simply be relieved to be able to finally leave the site.

....

214   This description is derived from Hindley, *Brief*, 73. The story is disputed by some historians and sometimes believed to be confused with another account of King Conrad's train of ladies during this campaign.

"I must return to Arles as quickly as possible," Pons sighed to Gilbert, "to bring the news that Bernard of Clairvaux's call for a Second Crusade was a huge success."

Christendom was going to war again to make safe the Holy Land. Once Pons had recognized Alphonse Jourdain, Count of Toulouse, among the nobility who had taken the cross, he realized that if the earlier First Crusade was any indication of what to expect, the chapter at Arles might well be affected by this Second Crusade. In the First Crusade, the first man to take the cross had been Raymond IV of Saint Gilles, Count of Toulouse, father of the current count, who then had assembled and led the third and largest contingent of fighters and non-combatant pilgrims, marching from Provence overland via Genoa and Venice, around the Adriatic, and down the Dalmation coast.[215]

"Since Alphonse Jourdain pledged himself to go on the crusade and accepted the token from Bernard," Pons continued, "the Provençal nobility can surely be expected to play an important role in this Second Crusade."

"It also means," he thought to himself, "the Count of Toulouse will no longer continue to fight alongside my brother. He will not be helping my brother claim the title Count of Provence. The war is truly over!"

Pons now wanted to hurry home to Arles with the news, to report the information he had gathered, and to begin to undertake his building project.

* * *

Bernard of Clairvaux's call for the Second Crusade through 1146 was an overwhelming success. From Vézelay Bernard traveled through northern France, Flanders, and the Rhine provinces, attracting both nobility and commoners, everywhere persuading wildly enthusiastic crowds to take up the cross. Many heeded the call in England too.[216]

As Bernard wrote to Pope Eugenius not long after the call at Vézelay, "Cities and towns are now deserted. You will barely find one man for every seven women, and everywhere there are widows to men still living."[217]

....

215   Hindley, *Brief*, 25–30.
216   See Hindley, *Brief*, 74–78.
217   "*Vacuantur urbes et castella, et pene jam non inveniunt quem apprehendant septem mulieres virum unum, adeo utique viduae vivis remanent viris.*" Bernard of Clairvaux, *Epistolae* 247. See Migne, *Patrologia Latina*, vol. 182, col. 447.

Bernard offered everyone who took up the cross the spiritual reward of the crusade, which was absolution from sin and the promise of eternal grace. He offered this to everyone—nobles, commoners, and even criminals, including the lowest ranks and the worst of sinners. Piety drove many to accept. Famine encouraged many others to accept. Many who faced the gallows were even more strongly encouraged to take up the cross, as an alternative to hanging. As Bernard noted, "God is truly merciful to offer hope of redemption to murderers, rapists, adulterers, perjurers, and other evil doers by calling them into His service."[218]

With the call such a success, no one could then have foreseen or even guessed how the Second Crusade would end.

Nor could Pons ever have suspected how directly it might eventually affect his mission.

....

218   "Quid est enim nisi exquisita prorsus et inventibilis soli Deo occasion salvationis, quod homicidas, raptores, adulteros, perjuros, eaeterisque obligatos criminibus, quasi gentem quae justitiam fecerit de servitio suo sumonere dignatur Omnipotens?" Bernard of Clairvaux, Epistolae, 363, col. 566. See Migne, Patrologia Latina, vol. 182, col. 566. Also cited in Kelly, Eleanor, 37–38.

Nones
Mid-afternoon – ninth-hour bells

Anno Domini MCXLVI

1146

––––––––––

Pons and Gilbert were preparing to leave Vézelay. Gilbert was to travel with Pons down the hill only to nearby Avallon, where they would split up, with Gilbert heading north toward Paris and Pons retracing his route back to Lyon. There Pons would continue his journey south to Arles by selling his horse and purchasing boat passage on the Rhône River.

The two canons intended to leave before celebrating *Nones,* the ninth hour after sunrise in the mid- afternoon, but they were now delayed. Gilbert's horse needed to be reshod, and although the local abbey blacksmith had promised it would be done by early afternoon, his work for the canon had been delayed when several imperious noble visitors had brought in their own horses, demanding theirs be shod immediately. So, it was *Vespers,* the end of the day, by the time the horse was ready for travel.

At last they were able to leave, and even though they would be able to travel only as far as Avallon, they returned to the stable to pack up the horses. Entering it briefly to gather up their traveling sacks, they were startled to find a slightly disheveled but otherwise well-dressed young woman cowering alone in the straw in the corner of the stable.

"Please, I beg of you, kind sirs, please take me with you," she pleaded with tears streaming down her face. "Please take me away from here."

Pons turned abruptly away from the young woman, who looked somehow vaguely familiar to him. Did she look familiar because he had seen her before? Or simply because he recognized her for what she was: a woman, the temptress, the beguiler, who would lead him to hellfire? He tried to pull his traveling companion away as well, but Gilbert turned toward the young woman with a bit more civility.

Extending his hand, he helped her rise while asking gently, "What is the problem, my lady? You are well-dressed and obviously not a poor beggar, not a wanton whore. What do you want?"

"Oh, please, please, I beg of you, take me with you."

"I asked you what your problem is, madam," Gilbert demanded a bit more gruffly as he turned his head away, revealing that although he had been polite, he had little real interest in her concerns.

"Please. My name is Lady Isabel. I need to get back to Paris immediately. I know you two are both clerics, so I would be safe with you, and I overheard you tell the stable owner that you are leaving today for Avallon, where you will split up, one traveling to Paris, the other heading south to Arles. I need to get back to Paris, and I must leave today. I cannot wait to travel with those I came here with. If you would take me with you to Paris, I would be so very grateful!"

"But who are you? And what trouble are you in?" Gilbert demanded with obvious annoyance.

"As I said, my name is Lady Isabel. I am originally from the town of Bordeaux. I have been serving as a lady-in-waiting to Queen Eleanor, who invited me to attend her at the French court in Paris, and she brought me with her here to Vézelay. But my father has sent my two brothers here to seize me, to take me back and to force me into a nunnery! I saw them in the crowd! They told me they are coming back tomorrow at dawn to take me, to take me away from the court, to steal me away before I leave for Paris, to take me home so my father can put me in the nunnery! I cannot wait here with the other ladies at court. They are not leaving for Paris for two days. My brothers are taking me captive tomorrow morning!"

Without thinking, Pons inadvertently turned directly to her once he now realized why he recognized her. She was one of the court women with Queen Eleanor's Amazon women warriors on the hillside.

"I don't understand," murmured Pons almost inaudibly, busily removing his outer garment. "You must be mistaken. Your father would not send you to a nunnery without good reason. And if your father commands you to return home, you must go."

"When my father sent me to attend Queen Eleanor at court last year, he did so only after having gone through much difficulty. He had recently remarried, taken a new wife, after the death of my mother whom he had loved so very dearly.

"My mother had the cancker, the hardening of the breast that kills. She was so sick, and he was overcome, simply distraught, at the thought of losing her. The priest's prayers were not helping at all; they were useless. My father sought everywhere for help. He heard about a German nun named Hildegard[219] who had developed a special lotion, a violet salve, to rub onto the cancker and make it go away. So he sent for some of her violet salve, hoping that because it was made by a nun it would have special power against the women's cancker. But it did not help. In desperation, he finally even sent for an Arab physician, because they are supposed to know secrets of medicine handed down by the Greeks and Romans, but he was of no help either.[220]

"My father finally gave my mother wine steeped in *Carduum benedictum*, which he was told is a treatment for cancker, and that did make her more comfortable.[221] But it didn't save her life. Nothing helped. My mother died. He was so very, very upset."

"May God have mercy on her soul," responded Pons, quickly making the sign of the cross. "I am sorry for your loss, but what does this have to do with your problem?"

"Well, my father was so distraught and, perhaps rather foolishly, he took a new wife almost immediately, without knowing much about her except that she brought a very good dowry. His new wife was young, very beautiful, and

....

219   The twelfth-century nun Hildegard of Bingen is well-known as a visionary, but she also worked with medicines and wrote both a medical encyclopedia, *Liber simplicis medicinae* (later called *Physica*), and a medical handbook, *Liber compositae medicinae* (later called *Causae et Curae*).

220   For a succinct summary of the role Arabs played in medicine, see David W. Tschanz, "The Arab Roots of European Medicine," *Saudi Aramco World* 48, no. 3 (May/June 1997): 20–31.

221   See Oswald Gabelkouer, *The Boock of Physicke* (Dorte [Dordrecht], Netherlands: Isaack Caen, 1599).

from Toulouse, and although she was not from a noble family, she did come from a very wealthy family of cloth merchants. She and I were just becoming friends when she confided to me in secrecy that she was a follower of Henry of Lausanne. That's the man who is now spreading the teachings of Peter of Bruys. She told me that many people in the area of Toulouse had been converted by Henry and were now following his teachings, and she started teaching me about him. When my father found out, he immediately arranged for me to be sent me away to serve at Queen Eleanor's court."

"So," responded Pons thoughtfully, "your father, overwrought with unbearable grief and then undoubtedly overwhelmed with distress at having unwittingly introduced a heretic into his family, was trying to keep you from being seduced by the heretics, and he sent you away to court—like any good father would do if he could! But why would he now want to send you to a nunnery?" he asked incredulously.

"I don't know," Isabel answered softly, tears welling in her eyes. "I really don't know. Maybe he fears I am now following Henry of Lausanne's teachings at the court in Paris," she murmured tremulously. "But I am not. I am not one of his followers. I know he is a heretic. My confessor at court has taught me it is heresy. I do not listen to the heresies. I am a good Christian." Biting her lip, she regained control. "I am a good Christian. I am a good woman. My confessor priest tells me every time that I am a good woman. I go to Mass. I confess my sins every week. I see my confessor every week, and he tells me I am very good, very special, that I am a very good woman.

"Please, I cannot go to a nunnery! I have to get away before my brothers find me! If I can get to Paris, I have friends who will help me, so I can stay at court. My confessor will help me. I know he will. He can convince my father that I am a good woman, so I can stay at court. Please, please take me with you!"

Poor Pons was now really torn. He wanted to leave as quickly as possible, but this young woman's plight really pricked his conscience. She seemed so innocent, and somehow, with her misfortune, she had wheedled her way into his heart by subtly plucking all the appropriate strings, touching every one of his special little sensitivities and points of vulnerability: the threat of the Petrobrusian heresies, the plight of the true believer, the naïve young virgin in need of protection. Toulouse—the county whose head was so important for his own brother's ambitions. Toulouse—the house whose head, for his own reasons, had aided Pons in undertaking God's work, the building of the cloister complex. Toulouse, whose count had first sent him Master Guillelmo and his workshop.

"Lady Isabel," Pons began with a deep sigh, "we will wait with you here, tonight, and speak with your brothers about your situation tomorrow at dawn. We cannot take you with us as a fugitive, against the wishes of your father, but neither can we in good conscience ignore your plight. After all, you are a good Christian noblewoman who has done no wrong and who has asked us for help." He shrugged his shoulders helplessly. "We will stay here tonight to speak with your brothers on your behalf, to help you convince them you are not a follower of the heretic and to ensure they will act appropriately and in good faith."

Turning to Gilbert, Pons explained, "It's already past *Vespers*, so we would only cover the ten *milles* to Avallon if we left now. We'll stay here tonight and push a bit harder once we leave tomorrow. And since the abbey is still full and in such turmoil at the moment, let's just sleep right here in the stable. I'll go arrange it with the owner. Then we can clear this up early tomorrow and quickly be on our way.

"Lady Isabel, you will prefer, I'm sure, to spend the night at the abbey with the other members of the court, where you will certainly be more comfortable. So please rest assured that we will still be here tomorrow morning at first light to attend you in speaking with your brothers."

"No, no," cried the woman softly, fearful she might somehow lose their assistance if she were to leave and that her brothers would find her before she could return. "I am so relieved and grateful! I will feel much safer if you will let me stay here near you, where I shall be quite comfortable enough."

"As you wish," Pons responded coolly as he left to speak to the stable owner. He returned, and the two canons left Lady Isabel briefly to celebrate *Compline*, night prayer before retiring, but Isabel remained with their horses to ensure she would not be deserted.

Relieved that her situation was no longer quite so desperate, Isabel now clung to the hope that the two clerics would sway her brothers from their mission, or at least gain her a temporary respite from her father's threat, so she could get back to Paris. Perhaps she could even convince them to take her away with them tomorrow and then back to Paris. When they returned from their night prayer, she carefully tried to stay out of their way as they were preparing to bed down. After each man had claimed and curled up in an opposite corner of a stall, she sat down near Pons, whom she now recognized as probably the more sympathetic of the pair to her and to her plight. She began talking to him now, trying inoffensively to befriend him, to win him over, prattling away about nothing of significance.

"I have been attending at the court now for over a year. I did miss my family ever so much at first, especially my brothers. But the young women at court were so friendly, and we had such lovely times together. Still, I was surprised Queen Eleanor chose to bring me along here with her court. I thought the journey would be exciting, and I guess it was. There was such a huge gathering to hear Bernard, but still I did not expect to see my brothers there. I think they came just to find me and take me."

She continued on and on, ever so innocently and sweetly, in a gentle, lovely cadence that began lulling the two canons into a state of easy acceptance.

"My brothers told me they are sending me to the abbey at Fontevrault," she continued. "You know the one. It's really four monastic houses but all ruled by one abbess. One's for proper nuns. The second one's called Mary Magdalene, and it's not for nuns but for lay women—normal women like me who have been at court, reformed sinners, and other women who have been put away for some reason. Another house is for lepers, and the last one is for the priests who conduct Mass and services,[222] but I'm willing to bet they probably spend most of their time at the Mary Magdalene," she added with a slight chuckle.

Isabel droned softly on and on in her gentle, sing-song cadence. Both men had early stopped paying any attention at all to what she was chattering on about but instead had now been lulled by the gentle cadence of her voice to that soft boundary that lies between wakefulness and sleep.

"Life at the court . . . so much more fun . . . ladies-in-waiting at the court . . . beautiful young women . . . wonderful parties . . . beautiful dresses . . . so very handsome . . . lovely music . . . dancing . . . Queen Eleanor herself . . . king so young and pious . . . brought up by monks . . . like a monk, she says . . . just a little boy, she says . . . no match for her . . . couldn't do it . . . but she knows . . . always others . . . such lovely parties . . . so generous . . . nice men . . . teach me . . . such nice gifts . . . generous . . . not that nasty parish priest . . . old and ugly . . . my handsome young one . . . his favorite, he says . . . says so every

---

222   On the abbey of Fontevrault, see Zarnecki, *Monastic*, 91–94.

week . . . so kind, so gentle, so friendly . . . must confess every week, or more often . . . he said so . . . special . . . men at court . . ."

And she continued as she leaned closer to Pons.

"You are so nice . . . so good and kind . . . I am so afraid . . . don't want to go . . . desperate . . . you are so nice . . . take me with you . . . to the next town . . . to Paris . . . would be so grateful . . . can't pay you . . . show you how grateful . . . know how . . . all kinds of ways . . .confessor priest . . . am very good . . . know how . . . says very, very good . . . but not everything . . . if you take me . . . with you . . . do anything for you . . . anything. . . anything . . . ." she repeated softly with emphasis.

Now leaning gently into the almost asleep Pons to turn him gently onto his back, she began stroking his thigh as he unknowingly, unwillingly presented himself to her. Finding the half-asleep canon physically responsive, Isabel slipped her nimble fingers under his chainse and into his braies where they now deftly encircled his now swelling member.

"What is this? What's going on?" Pons fumblingly demanded as he roused and tried to clear his mind. "Madam! No! Remember who you are! You are a good noble woman. You are not a whore! What is this? What you are doing? It's a sin!" Pons cried out, to the woman's obvious confusion.

But even as Pons was verbalizing his protest, he was confused, stunned at what had been happening so smoothly, but even more stunned by the rush of pleasure that was already beginning to swell up from his loins. He pulled back and tried to grab the lady's wrist to push her away.

"No!" she chided him, confidently, elegantly parrying both of his movements. "Father Henri, my confessor at the court, told me this is not a sin for a priest! This is not fornication. He said it's not even listed in his penitential.[223] This is special for priests. This is not a sin! Just lie still. It's not a sin!"

The calm, confident dignity of her response rendered him witless for a moment. Truly stunned, he was speechless. "What is she saying?" he asked himself. "Not a sin? Her confessor? Not a sin? Special for priests? What on earth had she been rambling on and on about? For normal women like her, who had been to court? Not a sin . . . for priests?"

He froze, completely paralyzed. He was simply incapable of striking a noblewoman—unable to raise his hand against her! He could not recover fast

223   The penitential handbook listed the sins a confessor priest might hear during confession with the appropriate penance that should be required of the penitent sinner.

enough. In his trance, he was not able quickly enough to forcefully push away her skillful hands or her deft fingers that were already probing and lightly stroking their obviously receptive quarry.

He was about to cry out, but she calmly, confidently put her other hand gently to his lips. Sliding over on her knees before him and pinning him down, she quickly slid down the front of his braies, removing what had covered his now exposed manhood. Pons was beside himself, at first perhaps unable but now simply unwilling to focus on anything other than her mind-piercing, disorienting words: "Not a sin. Only for priests. Not a sin."

And then he simply stopped resisting.

A kiss. A tongue. An erect member standing at attention, throbbing, seeking more. He gasped but could not exhale. His body was paralyzed but for his loins—his loins that were now the center of his entire physical being, and he could only hold onto her shoulders as he surrendered to her, pulling himself into her. And drowning him in the warmth of her mouth, she rhythmically drew him into a warm cavern of oblivion, engulfing his entire being as she drowned him in her pool of moist fire.

Traumatized at such abhorrent pleasure, Pons could not deal with it, and instead immediately escaped deep into himself. He fell into a dazed stupor. He was no longer here; he was somewhere else. Unable even to think about what had just happened, his mind simply departed, separated itself, went to another place, severed by the impossibility of what had happened, severed by what his body had recognized as such exquisite, so longed-for pleasure, but what his mind had recognized as a horrid, unforgiveable sin.

Such a deviant unnatural act for which he had no name. Such a sin against nature could not have happened! Wasting the God-given vehicle for procreation was a grievous sin for anyone! For him, a canon who had taken his vows and who would now further vow to live the *vita apostolica*, it was unthinkable! He, Pons, the self-righteous, never-do-wrong paradigm of virtue, the soon-to-be canon regular, could not have surrendered to this temptress from hell. After spending years doing penance for his encounter with Beatrice, he could not have put his soul at risk once again. Pons, who had devoted his life to obeying God, could not have succumbed to such exquisite, overwhelming sensation, such disgusting pleasure, such a grievous sin. Yet he had done so. He had stopped protesting. He had stopped resisting. He had enjoyed it.

Everything that happened had taken place smoothly and quickly, but not noiselessly. It had awakened Gilbert, who had watched it all, motionless, not knowing what to do. Strangely more aroused than he had ever been before in his life, he was desperately confused. Finally, no longer willing to restrain himself, he rose and staggered awkwardly over to the pair and, without saying a word, knelt down on the straw with them. Pons was lying motionless, as if dead, his naked loins exposed, his drooling mouth gaping open, his eyes wide with stupor. Was he aware of anything? Frankly, Gilbert did not care whether he was or not.

In a confused frenzy, Gilbert opted for Isabel, pushed her over and down under him, and violently ripped open her bodice to grab, suck, and forcefully knead her breasts. Wordlessly, he pushed up her chainse, ripped open her chemise, and began mercilessly grabbing her buttocks, devouring rather than exploring her body with his hands, ever more aggressively, ever more angrily. She was at first eagerly receptive, now hopeful she would be guaranteeing her escape and that her two new companions would want to take her with them for more of the same the next day. Finally, he took her—forcefully, hard—thrust himself into her, violently plunging again and again, harder and harder into her initially willing but now painfully bruised orifice.

Isabel's training at court had been comprehensive; she was as adept at sinning with willing men as she was at doing what her confessor had called "not sinning" with others like Pons.

After letting out several dissatisfied long grunts, Gilbert slowly turned his head toward Pons with a faint smile of recognition before giving a final thrust, spending himself while exhaling with a brutish gasp. He lay motionless for only a moment before cursing audibly and then quickly pulling back, brusquely pushing the bruised, limp woman rudely away.

Pulling himself over next to Pons, he carefully extended his arm under the limp body, tenderly encircled the young canon's shoulders, pulled him toward himself, then gently cradled Pons's head at his own shoulder.

"There, there, that's all right now," Gilbert cooed softly, patting him gently on the back. "Everything will be fine. I am here now, my lovely boy, my sweet, lovely boy," he continued. "I will take care of you now, my sweet boy, my beautiful boy, my . . . love." He gently rocked Pons's limp body slowly back and forth, back and forth, before finally kissing Pons lightly on the forehead, then on the cheek. Then, gently laying the canon back against a post, he leaned over Pons to kiss him on the ear, on the lips. And, taking his companion's limp expended member in hand, he lowered his head onto him.

Although Pons had been locked in a shocked stupor, with his mind imprisoned somewhere far, far away, this act now violently jolted him back. Women, fornication with women, may have been an unfathomable evil to him—one he could not contemplate, could not deal with, could not face giving into. But men and male advances were something else. These were an evil less unknown to him.

Although he had never engaged in such behavior, practices he believed were not only sinful but perverse as well, he had long lived within a community of men, and he certainly knew very well that this temptation existed amongst other presumably celibate clerics living communally.

Sodomites were a recognizable threat. Several times some years ago, when he was still a beautifully lithe, smooth-skinned youth, some older clerics had tried to seduce him, but after managing to evade their unwanted attentions, he had run for safety to his protector, Peter Villelmus. Pons had long been shielded from such advances, first by Peter Villelmus and then eventually by his own well-deserved reputation as a rigidly self-righteous paragon of virtue.

So although mortally horrified at Gilbert's advance on him, this behavior was at least recognizable, a more real assault that he was able to face and to defend himself against, and one he could deal with. His mind now jolted back from that distant, far-away place where it had sought refuge, and Pons leaped angrily to his feet, swinging his fists at Gilbert.

"Zounds![224] Zounds! Argggh! No! What are you doing? What on earth are you doing? Who are you?" shrieked the infuriated Pons, jumping away, almost as livid with anger at the canon's personal betrayal as he was horrified at the behavior itself.

Seeing Isabel, his face turned white as he stumbled backward and began writhing in horror as the full awareness slowly began to dawn on him about everything—everything—that had transpired.

"What...? What are we doing here? Zounds! My God! What have I done?" he now screamed in absolute horror. "Oh, my God, my God, what have I done?" Pons wailed in shame. "*Mea culpa, mea culpa, mea culpa!* My God, my God, why have I forsaken Thee?"

224   "Zounds" was a strong swear word, a vile profanity meaning "God's wounds," a reference to Christ's wounds. Pons would have to confess to having used this word.

"Satan, get thee hence! Get thee hence!" he screamed at both of them, as he leaped toward the door and grabbed his travel sack. "Get away from me! Get away from me, you devil! I'll not be with you! I will return home alone. I'll not go with Satan. Get thee hence!"

He ran blindly from the stable to the only refuge he knew. He ran back to the abbey church, angrily picking up a stick, a weapon, on the way, but it was now nighttime, and the door was locked tight. Throwing himself to the ground at the church door, amidst the debris and building materials, he first beat the floor of the porch with his stick in anger and frustration, but as his own guilt soon overtook his anger, he began flagellating himself, scourging himself with the stick again and again. Prostrated on the stone floor, he flogged himself, physically and mentally.

His immortal soul was damned. He had descended to hell, to the darkest depths of his being. He had entered his own heart of darkness. His immortal soul was doomed for all eternity.

He prayed and prayed, but to no avail. He prayed and prayed, but he knew it would probably not be until *Matins,* the night vigil, or more likely *Lauds* at dawn, that anyone would open the church to let him in or that he would finally find someone who could hear his confession.

Finally, in the very early morning someone did come, an elderly monk, an uneducated but very wise and experienced old monk, and fortunately someone much kinder, much wiser, much more understanding and compassionate, and much less rigid than Pons himself.

"Bless me, Father, for I have sinned. *Mea culpa, mea culpa*, I am damned to hell. I have most grievously sinned."

Confession. Full confession to a truly wise and compassionate confessor, who recognized it was the young canon who would be unable to forgive himself. And then penance, huge penance, more scourging, more penance, more flogging, prayer as penance, prayer to atone. But from the darkest depths of his being, Pons still could find little hope of relief, little hope of forgiveness for himself.

His soul could find no respite. His soul fell into the deepest, darkest of pits. He knew he was beyond help. He knew his soul was damned to hellfire for all eternity.

Most distressing, most damning of all to him was his ever-growing awareness of his own role in these sins. The temptress, Woman, Isabel, *luxuria*, lust may have led him astray, but he had followed, and he knew it. He knew it. He could have refused, but he had not. He had not pushed her away. He had followed, perhaps even willingly. He had willingly succumbed. If he had not succumbed to her, Gilbert would not have been so incited and might not have given in to his own mortally sinful urges. Certainly Gilbert had never before demonstrated such urges during their long travels together. Maybe Gilbert had not recognized his urges. Maybe until then he had been able to contain them. He, Pons, was at fault. He, Pons, had opened the door. He was at fault. He could no longer cling to his long-held credo from St. Paul:

"et Adam non est seductus mulier autem seducta in praevaricatione fuit."	"And Adam was not seduced; but the woman, being seduced, was in the transgression."
(*I ad Timotheum* 2:14)	(I Timothy 2:14)

No. Adam may have been led astray by Eve, but Adam had followed willingly. Adam had been a full participant in discovering this evil. Adam was himself guilty. Yes, he, Pons, had helped open the door to hell. He himself had unlocked the horrifying mouth of hell, that image in the manuscripts that had held him spellbound in fear in the library at Cluny, that image that now bound his soul in chains of torment. Doomed like the damned souls on the doorway at the cathedral of Autun.

He could not lay all the burden of this sin on Woman, the temptress, for Man had played a part. He, the man, had played a part. So the burden of sin and guilt was on Pons himself, was on him to expiate. With his deeply troubled and distressed soul, he prayed and prayed and prayed again.

"My son, ask our Lord Jesus Christ for forgiveness," his wise old confessor guided, ever so gently.

"I cannot. I am not worthy of His forgiveness," he whispered tearfully. Pons now saw himself not only as the sinner he had always recognized himself to be, with all the small human frailties, committing all the small sins and pardonable offenses he could so easily and readily confess to and receive absolution for. He now saw himself as a sinner guilty of unforgivably grievous sins, the grave sins, or sins unto death, so defined by St. Jerome[225] and other early

---

225   As described by Jerome in 393 AD in *Against Jovinian* 2:30.

church fathers. He was now a sinner unto death, a sinner whose soul was dead to God, a sinner condemned to hellfire.

He now envisioned himself as a *peccator*, sinner, branded with a letter P, a huge letter P, a full folio-page letter P full of animals, as in so many of the manuscripts he had seen at Cluny, but the letter branding him was full of writhing monsters gnawing at his flesh, like the Hellmouth image he had seen there. He was a grave sinner deserving of condemnation, a sinner who in human weakness could give in to the temptation of the flesh, a sinner who could break the strictest prohibitions of the Church—fornicating in a manner like the most deviant of sodomites, fornicating and breaking the foremost rule of celibacy he had for so long condemned his fellow clerics for breaking.

Over many, many days he flagellated himself mercilessly, mortifying his flesh, beating his bleeding, swollen body. He prayed again and again and again in penance. He returned often to the abbey church, where he repeatedly recited the daily canonical prayers that he knew so well. And eventually, as he prayed and recited, the repetitive certainty and familiarity of the words and ritual slowly began to bring a tiny bit of relief at least, if no real comfort, to his distressed soul. Confession, penance, atonement, absolution, prayers. Penance, prayers. Penance, prayers.

And as Pons returned again and again to the abbey church in penance, to expiate his sins, he would descend slowly into the crypt and kneel to pray at the little confessional that held the relics of Ste. Mary Magdalene, to whom the abbey church was dedicated. Ste. Mary Magdalene, who was receiving him, the sinner unto death, into her church. Ste. Mary Magdalene, whose monastic house at Fontevrault received fallen women like Isabel. Ste. Mary Magdalene, who did not turn her back on him now. Ste. Mary Magdalene, who now began guiding him toward accepting himself as a sinner.

Mary Magdalene, the whore. Mary Magdalene, the reformed whore. Mary Magdalene, the reformed sinner. Mary Magdalene, the reformed sinner, forgiven by Jesus. Mary Magdalene, the woman, forgiven by Jesus. Mary Magdalene, the woman, beloved by Jesus.

Kneeling before the relics, the despondent, condemned Pons slowly began to recognize some kinship with Mary Magdalene. He began to identify with her, bond with her. He began to see Mary Magdalene and himself as comparably sinful beings. She was a whore, a prostitute, the woman, the temptress, the vessel of sin, the personification of lust. But he had succumbed to the vilest temptations of the flesh. He had played a role in his full folio-page sins, illuminated with demons from hell. He was a fornicator, the worst of the sodomites, who had participated, albeit unwillingly, in a sin against nature, in a deviant, unnatural act. Which was the greater sin? Both had committed sins so grave as to be damnable for all eternity.

Of course, he had long been taught and therefore knew that as a woman, Mary Magdalene was born by nature of lower stature than man, a creature who was sinful by nature, whose nature was to be the temptress, a vessel of sin. He knew that as a man, he was a higher order of being, who could strive to rise above such yearnings of the flesh. But he had failed. He had failed grievously. He had succumbed to the flesh. And now he was a sinner unto death, condemned to the eternal flames of hell.

And as Pons knelt before the relics, his agonized soul now began to find its first bit of real comfort, its first ray of hope, because when Pons was finally able to identify with this reformed whore turned saint, he could begin to learn from her. Indeed, both of them had been grave sinners, but Mary Magdalene had repented. She was able to be forgiven. She was forgiven. She could be loved by Jesus. Could Pons, too, repent? Could he, too, be forgiven? Could he, too, ever be loved once again by God?

Mary Magdalene, whom Jesus had forgiven, whom Jesus had loved, slowly led Pons through his pain and turmoil. If he like she could repent, if he like she could be forgiven, he like she could be wrested from the consuming mouth of eternal hellfire. Slowly, Pons was able to find an ever-fuller measure of relief and comfort, until finally, at long last, his soul was able to make its peace with his God.

And at the same time, while working through his soul's intense pain and turmoil, Pons began to find some humanity. He could no longer despise Woman. Of course, for him Woman would always inherently be, by nature, a lower being, the temptress, a vessel of sin, the personification of lust. He knew Eve and Adam could never be fully equal. Created by God from Adam's rib, Eve could never be Adam's equal. But Pons now understood that despite her lower nature, Woman could repent, could turn away from her nature, could turn away from being a vessel of temptation. Both Man and Woman could turn away from sin, and be forgiven, and be saved.

At long last, Pons, the sinner, the despiser of women, could begin to reconcile himself with Woman. He could finally see both Man and Woman as inherently unequal but still comparably sinful beings, who could each repent and be forgiven by Christ. Both Man and Woman could err, could be forgiven by Christ, could be loved by Christ, could be loved by God.

Finally, he was able to accept Christ's forgiveness. Believing God had forgiven him, Pons could forgive himself. What had happened in the stable was now between him and his God. What had happened in Vézelay could stay in Vézelay.

He began his journey home alone, spending most of his time in contemplation, while traveling quickly.

* * *

A well-chastened but much wiser Pons arrived at Arles. On arrival, he immediately met with Archbishop Raymond de Monte Rotundo and William Garnerius to tell them his news about the call for a Second Crusade and about seeing Alphonse Jourdain take up the cross.

"I have news, too," the archbishop responded, "about the heretic, Henry of Lausanne. Henry has finally been seized and arrested, taken in chains before the Bishop of Toulouse, where he is now imprisoned."[226]

"Let's just hope they can keep him in chains, and maybe the heresies will abate," William Garnerius added to everyone's agreement.

As Pons resumed his duties within the chapter, the transformed canon was no longer such a prig. He still recognized that his mission from God was to bring the *vita apostolica* to his chapter, but he had now learned and accepted that everyone is human and fallible, that anyone could succumb to temptations. He recognized that he could not expect everyone to readily accept his mission. He knew he had made some fierce enemies, not only Gilbert, whom he had branded as Satan, but others, such as Peter Villelmus, the surrogate father and protector he had so grievously offended; Rainaldo, who had sent away his beloved Hildegarde; Bernard Aiguillus, and so many others, even some who had already left the chapter in protest.

Pons now recognized that he could not undo the rancor he had already caused or the hatred he had already stirred up through his priggish rigidity in asking the canons to vow to live by the Rule of St. Augustine and to give

---

226   See Miller, "Henricians" in *Short Papers on Church History,* and "Henry of Lausanne," *Encyclopedia Britannica.*

up their loving wives and families even though communal living was not yet possible. He now knew that to move forward he must more effectively bring the entire chapter on side with his goals. He now recognized that the first step was to complete the infrastructure that would enable the canons easily to live communally and in celibacy. That would encourage the chapter to want to do so, and it would help the canons to know and hear God's wishes as he did.

The war still continued, but it had changed by the time Pons had returned from Vézelay. Raymond of Baux earlier had been abandoned by most of his supporters, other than the Count of Toulouse, but was still valiantly carrying on his challenge, refusing to surrender. However, once Alphonse Jourdain turned his attention toward the Second Crusade, the writing was on the wall.

When the count finally left for the crusade in 1147, Raymond of Baux had no alternative but to give up his challenge, to agree to submit, and to come to terms with the House of Barcelona. Hostilities finally abated. Raymond of Baux left for Barcelona, where he would die before the peace treaty was finalized.

With the ravages of war now abating, the wiser and less arrogantly pious Pons regained the confidence of the chapter. By 1147 he was again named *capud scole*.[227]

"Canon Pons," William Garnerius confirmed one day. "Our chapter has now unanimously reconfirmed our decision for you to be fully in charge of overseeing construction of all the new claustral buildings we will need. We recognize that you were responsible for initiating this project, and we believe you should have the privilege of bringing it to completion.

"And," he continued, "although you will also be responsible for overseeing the reconstruction of the cathedral church, both the archbishop and the dean, Hughes Amelius, have asked me to help you by supervising that part of the project, which we have now decided will include rebuilding the nave by raising the main altar and choir—transept, crossing and apse—over the crypt, where we hope eventually to be able to house the relics of St. Trophîme, so faithful worshippers will be able to proceed eastward down the nave to either enter the crypt or mount a stairway to worship in the choir or at the main altar.[228]

....

227   See Schneider, "Sculptures," 74.

228   On the architectural modifications to the early church made in order to accommodate the translation of the relics of St. Trophîme, which then took place in 1152, see
Rouquette, *Provence*, 271–273 and 265–295.

"You will be solely responsible for the claustral buildings, however," William Garnerius repeated, "but I will help you and work with you in supervising work on the cathedral."

"But when can we begin?" Pons asked exuberantly.

"Much sooner than you may think!" answered the canon with a grin. "I have just received a message from the abbot at Saint-Gilles. Master Guillelmo, Master Pietro, and their assistant have been working full-time with Master Brunus on the sculpture there for almost five years, but it now seems that Brunus no longer needs all of them to complete the remaining sculpture on the superstructure. Master Guillelmo will be arriving here in a few days!

"Moreover, the stone masons have also just about completed their work there. I'm told that after restoring the crypt, they finished erecting the walls of the church, and have just about completed their part of the building campaign there. The master builder will be coming with Master Guillelmo to look at what we are planning and to speak with you about the project here."

Only a few days later, Master Guillelmo and a small group of stone masons arrived at the canons' portal, where they were waiting impatiently. Pons hurried to greet them and invited them into the cathedral complex, where they were quickly joined by William Garnerius.

"Welcome back, Master Guillelmo," Pons began warmly. "And greetings to you, *Magister Comacinus*," he immediately added, upon recognizing the master builder was ready to work, carrying his trademark tools. "Did you have any trouble getting here? Did you encounter any war hostilities?"

"Not really, none at all," the master builder replied in his thick accent. "We were stopped just outside of Arles by some men, supporters of the Baux, who demanded we declare who we were for, but they immediately recognized that we are Lombard masons, with no ties to Genoa, or even to Pisa, for that matter. They did not detain us further. They seemed to be impressed that we were coming here to look for work from your chapter and the archbishop."

As they walked toward the chapter house, Pons explained both his and William Garnerius's roles in the two-fold project. "It is the claustral buildings that will really be a challenge here," he continued. "What I envision is a very traditional layout of the buildings around the new cloister, with the existing chapter house here to the north and the dormitory to the east."

Turning to the *magister comacinus*, Pons then continued, "We need your guidance as a master builder. We began here with the porch to the chapter house as an expedient, and at Master Guillelmo's suggestion, intending it to become the north gallery of the cloister, but we now need additional guidance and planning from you.

"The porch, as you see, is now lovely, with beautiful carved capitals and slender piers flanked by paired colonettes. But it has a simple lean-to wooden roof. We have seen how beautiful stone-vaulted cloister galleries can be, even the undecorated plain vaulted cloisters of the Cistercians. Master builder, I have seen how clever you are at vaulting. Could you vault our cloister galleries for us?"

"But no one could erect a stone vault in this gallery without taking down what's there!" challenged William Garnerius. "I don't see how on earth this could be vaulted with a stone roof, so we would have to tear down what is already here."

"Oh, no! You must not tear down our porch with the beautiful carved capitals!" cried out Master Guillelmo, so aghast that he momentarily forgot his place and spoke out of turn.

"No, no, absolutely not," clarified Pons. "We insist on keeping everything's that there, all the beautiful sculpture we already have, including not only your charming carved capitals, but also the portal and the two carved capitals of the female siren and *luxuria* on the north façade wall."

"That's a very tall order!" began the master builder, looking to a much younger stone mason colleague, whose eyes immediately lit up encouragingly with keen interest and real enthusiasm at this demanding new challenge. "But hey, we are *magistri comacini*, the Lombard professionals!" he continued with a swagger and a huge grin. "Let us have a look. Give us some time alone, a day or two, to look at what is here and to sort out the challenges and what might be possible."

For the remainder of that day and on through the next, the master builder and the masons seemed to be poking around everywhere, always underfoot, examining the site. Surprised by these intrusive strangers, the canons quickly voiced their annoyance, and Pons was kept busy indeed, calming everyone who was being disrupted at their work or in their homes.

First the masons darted around the porch wall, into the chapter house then out again, all the while shouting short bits of information to each other in a Lombard argot the canons could not comprehend. When the master builder took out his measuring stick and began examining the wall of the chapter house more closely, other masons shouted out information to him while making comments to each other.

After quite some time, the entire group moved outside to examine the area surrounding the chapter house, to the north, to the east, and to the south, sometimes digging a bit into the ground at the foundations, occasionally digging more deeply, all the while continuing to shout out short comments in their own argot. Several masons then began wandering further, throughout the cathedral grounds, moving among the small private dwellings there and examining the overall lay of the land.

These examinations culminated in an animated, obviously heated, private, and unintelligible discussion among the group, after which they again began climbing all around the porch wall, picking at the lower stone courses, climbing up to poke at the existing stonework at the tall portal, and pacing out some approximate measurements while the master builder applied his measuring stick.

Finally, they asked to meet with Pons, William Garnerius, and Master Guillelmo, who were all beginning to despair.

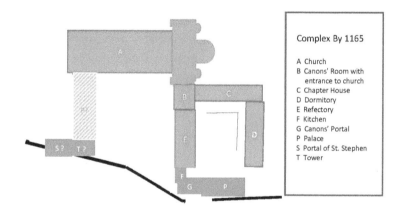

Arles. Ground plan. What the complex would become later, by 1165.
Partially completed vaulted cloister and surrounding communal buildings.[229]

229   The portal here called the canons' portal is still visible in the antique Roman *enceinte* south of the existing cloister. It has long been considered to be the Portal of St. Stephen, and the twelfth-century building next to it and directly south of the cloister was usually thought to be the original archbishop's palace. See Robert E.M. Wheeler, "The Roman Town-Walls of Arles: and a Note on Other Roman Town-Walls in Gaul and Britain," *Journal of Roman Studies* XVI (1926), 175, 186–193. See Louis Mathieu Anibert, *Mémoires Historiques et Critiques sur l'Ancienne République d'Arles* (Yverdon: 1779) vol I, 83. See also Schneider, "Sculptures," 56–58. A recent study challenges these long-held assumptions. See Vanessa Eggert, "Le Palais archiépiscopal d'Arles: D.F.S. Opération de prospection thématique," *Aix-en-Provence: SRA-PACA* (2002). Extract

"Well, we have an overall plan to deal with the slope of the ground and the area of your enclosure here," the master builder began. "First of all, we propose expanding the structure housing your existing chapter house eastward to more than double its length and adding an additional new bay to what will become the north gallery of your cloister before beginning the vaulted east gallery with the dormitory off it to the east.

"Keeping this existing façade wall of the chapter house poses the first of two real problems in vaulting your cloister galleries, but it may not be an insurmountable one. It should be possible to vault what will be the north gallery of the cloister here, if we make one side of the vault higher than the other; that is, if we erect an asymmetrical barrel vault with the curve beginning high on the existing façade wall and descending much lower on its other side, which will be open to the cloister," the master builder continued. "Stone-vaulted roofs do not necessarily have to be regular and even-sided. Even the ancient Romans occasionally built barrel-stone vaults with uneven sides or rampant vaults, if they had to, if the building required it."

"That's right!" exclaimed Pons. "I remember as a boy I used to climb around the Roman amphitheater here at Arles, and there are uneven stone vaults there—covering stairways, I think—beneath tiers of seats where the asymmetrical shape of the vault fits well under the sloped tiers of seats."[230]

....

published by Site du Patrimoine d'Arles as "Le Palais Archiépiscopal d'Arles, Histoire et Architecture," http://www.patrimoine.ville-arles.fr/document/archeveche-cite-episcopale-st-trophime-arles-eggert.pdf.

Eggert argues fairly convincingly that the Portal of St. Stephen was located further west, just outside the southwest corner of the cathedral enclosure, adjacent to a tower called the Tower of Gioffredi. She is not convincing, however, about the archbishop's palace, which she suggests was never the early twelfth-century palace structure south of the cloister, but instead was originally located between the tower and the west end of the cathedral. There is no documentary evidence to indicate the location of the archbishop's palace before the twelfth century. Using Eggert's documentary evidence, if the Tower of Gioffredi was sold in 1152, and the first mention of an act being signed in a room above the Portal of St. Stephen is in 1166, by which date the canons had adopted the Rule, is it not quite possible that in that time period the archbishop vacated his palace next to the cloister and moved, possibly to the site between the tower and the cathedral, a move which would have given the canons the entire area surrounding the cloister for communal buildings, thereby facilitating their adopting and living by the strict Rule?

230   See Schneider, "Sculptures," 149–155, especially 151.

"It's that tall portal on the chapter house that is the real challenge, more of a challenge than you probably realize," continued the master builder. "The portal opening is really very tall, even taller on the chapter house side than on the face here on the gallery side, where it is partially covered with a fairly thin archivolt. But the wall of the chapter house seems to be thick and solid enough. So if we put in a stone barrel vault with uneven sides, we believe the thick wall of the chapter house would support much of the weight and thrust of the higher side of the barrel vault here on the north side of the gallery, *if* we raise the springing of the barrel vault there above the height of the tall opening in the thick wall.[231]

"However, to build that massive stone vault, and to help support it near the tall portal opening, we're going to need strong transverse arches. And to carry each transverse arch, we're going to need new stone supports within the north wall, if we're going to keep the decorative arcade there. We suggest inserting stone corbels into the wall, so a new stone corbel will project outward to receive and support each transverse arch. That's just like what we did on the problematic part of the west wall of the crypt at Saint-Gilles, where the corbel supports the thick diagonal rib.

"But on the garden side," continued the master builder, "is another challenge. There we will need much more massive piers to support the weight and thrust of such a stone vault. If we are going to keep your colonettes with carved capitals there, we will have to modify the piers, thicken them, grow them, add mass to the piers, bulk them up with stone so we can spring the transverse arches and the barrel vault from what is here.[232]

"Remember, this will be the lower side of the uneven barrel vault, which will be very heavy, so it will be a bit tricky. We can keep your colonettes with the carved figural capitals in each bay between the piers, but to be able to bulk up the piers sufficiently to support the vault, we will have to remove the colonettes now immediately flanking each slender pier and replace them with solid stone. I'm sorry, but there's no way we can keep them.

"We will have to make the supporting piers as massive as possible, as bulky as possible, not only by replacing the flanking colonettes with solid stone, effectively making the piers wider, but by also adding tall solid stone buttresses out in the garden, making the piers deeper as well. Remember,

231   For this analysis of the vault, see Schneider, "Sculptures," 139–140.

232   For the garden side springing of the vault, see Schneider, "Sculptures," 141–142.

there's nothing else to counteract the weight and thrust of that north gallery vault pushing down and out on the garden side, so we will have to add bulky stone buttresses there. And we will add heavy impost blocks to support the transverse arches there.

"So yes, we do believe we can put an asymmetrical barrel-stone vault here, higher on the north side than on the south. But it will be tricky, and it will be a gamble! We've never done it on a long gallery before. But hey, we love challenges, and we would really like to try it! Remember what we were able to do with the rampant vault in our spiral staircase in the choir at Saint-Gilles?"

"Yes, of course," responded Pons, more hesitantly this time, thinking of how much he had vested in all this. "But how risky will it be?"

"We'll proceed cautiously," replied the master builder, "by first expanding the chapter house eastward so we have a good solid north wall at the east end of the gallery. Frankly, like all stone vaults, it will be trial and error, and some stone vaults do fall. Remember the collapse at Saint-Gilles! Remember the collapse at Cluny! We masons really don't know how tall we can build something or whether a new type of stone vault will stay up until we try it! But, heh! We really do want to try this new long uneven barrel vault here at Arles."

Pons was now both elated and very apprehensive as he burst out, "But you do think the vaulting will work?"

"Yes, we do," answered the master builder calmly and full of confidence, "but I have cautioned you that we have never done cloister galleries like these with this particular vault before."

"Well," continued Pons, "the massive new stone piers you will build will not be very attractive. Could we have carved low-relief figural decoration on the piers? Cloister piers are often decorated with low-relief carvings."

"Why low-relief figures? Why not large pier figures like those we carved at Saint-Gilles?" asked Master Guillelmo tentatively. "We already have one, a smaller one, of St. Stephen . . ."

"Oh, I don't think that would that be possible. But . . . would it?" Pons gasped loudly, hopefully, fearful he was overstepping the boundaries of possibility.

"Well . . ." began the master builder, looking at the younger mason, who immediately started mumbling unintelligibly to the architect as he was thinking. "Um, perhaps . . . Yes. Well . . . Yes! Why not?" he finally responded confidently after several moments of reflection. "The new compound piers will certainly be much larger and more complex, with more surfaces and new salient sections supporting the transverse arches. We can insert your Stephen figure into a corner. You could probably put new pier figures in all the new pier sections if you would like,[233] so long as we know ahead of time and make the piers massive enough. We will simply have to add more massive exterior buttressing on the garden side to make up for what is lost to the pier figures.

"Maybe Master Guillelmo here could carve some corbels for us for the north wall supports. There are some beautiful old Roman carved animal corbels at Nîmes,"[234] the master builder continued, speaking to the sculptor, "if you need to see what I am talking about. My masons can cut corbels, but they are not master stone carvers, and their corbels will be rather crude. Yours would be much more refined. I know how lovely your little animals are, Master Guillelmo."

"Oh, certainly! We want them," responded Canon Pons with a huge grin. "I cannot believe how beautiful this is going to be."

"We believe the vault will work, and your pier figures should work well too," offered the master builder. "The new piers with their salient imposts and buttresses will be complex and massive, but we can cover everything with simple fluting or channeling, just like we added on our work at Saint-Gilles, both on the crypt piers and on the central portal at Saint-Gilles, on the door jambs there and behind those pier figures on the right."

"They included channeling behind the new pier figures of Paul and James Major there," offered Master Guillelmo, "but not behind the Peter and John figures, because those figures were undamaged by the collapse and were already installed and partially completed."

"The decorative channeling will unify all the parts of the complex piers here. We can even continue it down the length of the north wall façade here. I believe the cloister gallery will be quite beautiful."

After conferring briefly in private with William Garnerius, Pons then invited the masons to descend to the cathedral, where William Garnerius explained his vision for the nave, that it was to be reconstructed with a raised choir and crypt at the crossing and vaulted as well. Pons and Master Guillelmo remained behind to confirm the terms of their arrangement. Master Guillelmo agreed to begin work as soon as possible and immediately began foraging

---

233   The large pier figures were not envisioned in the original design but were added later when the decision to vault the gallery was made. See Schneider, "Sculptures," 155–162.

234   See Schneider, "Sculptures," 153.

through the endless heaps of stone, wood, and refuse materials piled around the chapter house to see what could be salvaged. When the master builder then returned, confirming his interest in the project, Pons pulled him aside to discuss the financial terms of their arrangement. Pons then enthusiastically offered to have contracts drawn up so the masters of both workshops could begin work as soon as possible.

The next day, Pons quickly met with Archbishop Raymond de Monte Rotundo to tell him about the exciting new plans.

"The master builder is going to try to cover the cloister gallery with a stone vault, but because we want to keep the sculptural decoration there, he is going to put up an uneven barrel vault, like those I first saw as a young lad exploring the stairways in the Roman amphitheater here," Pons began.

"Yes, of course!" burst out the archbishop. "I grew up in the city of Nîmes before taking my vows,[235] and I explored its Roman monuments there, too, as a boy, just as you did here in Arles. In the amphitheater of Nîmes, too, the Romans used asymmetrical rampant stone vaults when they needed to cover stairways beneath tiers of seats.[236] Why not use an uneven barrel vault?"

"The master builder is going to mount the uneven vault on transverse arches that on the north wall will rest on large corbels inserted in the wall, and on the south side they will rest on imposts they will add to bigger, bulked-up piers," added Pons. "If it works, we will be able to keep our decorative arcade on the chapter house there with the siren and lust capitals, as well as our beautiful carved capitals with biblical stories on the garden side."

"But, of course, it should work!" interjected Archbishop Raimundus. "Has your master builder seen the corbels at the Roman amphitheater at Nîmes?"

"Indeed he has," responded Pons. "But what impresses me most about him is his cleverness, his willingness to try something new. His work at Saint-Gilles on the vaults in the crypt certainly demonstrates how clever he can be with supporting arches or ribs.[237] And his spiral staircase in the north wall of

---

235   Peter the Venerable provided biographical information about Raimundus de Monte Rotundo and described him as an ardently loyal Nîmois, who was born in the diocese of Nîmes, offered as a young boy to the church at Nîmes, and raised to become a canon at the church of Nîmes before being made Bishop of Agde and then Archbishop at Arles. See Albanes and Chevalier, *Arles*, no. 541. See also Schneider, "Sculptures," 154.

236   See Schneider, "Sculptures," 149–155, especially 151.

237   For the similarities between the Arles vaulting and the vaulting of the crypt at Saint-Gilles, see Schneider, "Sculptures," 180ff.

the upper church is essentially a rampant barrel vault spiraling upwards. Both are incredibly clever and absolutely outstanding!"

"Good! Let's pray his inventiveness is successful here for us," concluded the archbishop with a smile of genuine affection toward the canon. "Who knows? We may start a new trend, a new style. This new asymmetrical barrel vault may become the new standard for cloisters here. But don't forget he is reconstructing the church nave too!" the archbishop added with a chuckle.

Work on the north gallery of the cloister was begun again fairly quickly, within days for the sculptors and within weeks for the masons. Master Guillelmo and his assistant could begin anew on the foliate capitals almost immediately by first using stone leftover from their earlier work. It was very simple and straightforward for the masons to begin procuring the building materials, stone and wood, for the new project, because they just continued using the same sources that had served them well at Saint-Gilles. They also reused some of the wood from Saint-Gilles, hauling it to Arles by teams of horses. Because Arles was situated at the other mouth of the Rhône River, transport to Arles by water was as convenient as it had been to Saint-Gilles, and teams of horses simply helped cart the heavy stone and building materials to the cathedral site.

Now that war hostilities had abated, it was also easy for the two masters to begin moving their workshops from Saint-Gilles to Arles. Master Guillelmo returned immediately with his one assistant. The *magister comacinus* first returned with only three of the masons who had accompanied him here earlier and who were his most skilled workers.

The *magister comacinus* and his masons began their project by poking around the upper courses of masonry on the north façade wall, to verify once again that it was solid enough for erecting a stone vault. He then met with Canon Pons.

"So on this north wall, we're going to have to tear down some of the existing façade wall above the decorative arcade, so we can run at least one good solid course of masonry beneath the corbel supports. Don't worry; we will keep the carved capitals and colonettes below.[238] Are you agreed? Can we proceed?"

---

238   On the tearing down of the top of the north façade wall and the running of one good new course of stone, see Schneider, "Sculptures," 142–143.

"Certainly," responded Pons. "Go ahead if it is what we need for a stone vault."

Using his measuring stick and dividers, the *magister comacinus* now began his work, carefully measuring again and again the height of the north wall and the width of the gallery, transposing these measurements onto a piece of parchment and drawing several possible arcs across the width above using his dividers. Eventually he addressed Pons.

"On the courtyard side I am not sure how tall we should make the buttresses, so we'll be conservative. We will make them as tall as they would be if they were supporting a regular, even barrel vault and raise them all the way up to the height of the springing of the vault on the north wall, that is, to the level where the arc of the barrel leaves the north wall.[239]

"We'll use nice solid transverse arches, like those first ribs we used near the collapse at the west end of the crypt at Saint-Gilles," the master builder continued. "We're going to have to build solid supports for the transverse arches on the garden side, by adding stone to carry the weight of the transverse arches all the way from the vault to the ground, adding impost blocks at the top, with the impost blocks sitting on new stone sections below. Are you agreed? Can we proceed?"

"Yes, of course, of course. Go ahead, if that is what you need to do," answered Pons, with just a hint of bewilderment.

"Well then, as we now envision the expanded new piers," continued the master builder, "you will be able to include sets of three large figures on each pier, with two at the corners flanking a central one set either into the salient angle of the corner piers or under the new impost block of the intermediate piers facing into the gallery."

"Wonderful!" responded Pons more animatedly, as he called to Master Guillelmo to begin discussing the pier figures and sculptural decoration. "Now, for the pier figures, we certainly want the four apostles Peter, Paul, James Major, and John, our models for the *vita apostolica*."

"I can try to do them like the four pier figures on the central portal at Saint-Gilles," offered Master Guillelmo. "Will you now want a Last Supper scene? At Saint-Gilles they are including all the scenes from Christ's Passion, including the Last Supper, the Crucifixion, everything—even Christ's appearances

....

239   On the height of the buttresses, see Schneider, "Sculptures," 139–140.

after the Resurrection. I had to leave room for a scene of Christ meeting the disciples on the road to Emmaus, at the end of the rinceau panel above the two pier figures at the far right of the central portal."[240]

"No!" retorted Canon Pons, brusquely and a bit too harshly. "As I told you long ago, we do not need to address the Petrobrusian heresy in our cloister decoration. Our decoration here will speak to other issues of special meaning for us canons living the *vita apostolica* in the cloister here. Besides, we already have our three capitals that more subtly allude to the Annunciation, Birth, Sacrifice, and Resurrection of our Lord."

"I'm sorry. I'm not as learned as you, so I don't know the difference," Master Guillelmo admitted sheepishly with obvious chagrin.

"But you are a master stone carver, Master Guillelmo, and you will carve beautiful images in stone to inspire our faith," responded Pons, trying to smooth over and undo the unfortunate insult he had inadvertently given the surprisingly sensitive artisan.

"In our cloister," Pons then said, having decided to try to explain the rationale, "our chapter wants images of the apostles because they will remind us of the *vita apostolica* we will have adopted. But we also want images of the resurrected Christ, who appeared to the apostles. You see, depictions of the resurrected Christ and His triumph over death are especially appropriate for cloisters where they have special significance. In a monastery, the hallowed ground of the cloister garden often serves as the burial site for the abbey, and images of the risen Christ suggest the triumph over death for the true Christian. Of course, our own chapter still enjoys the privilege of interment at the most venerable site of Les Alyscamps, but our chapter still wants images of the resurrected Christ in our cloister too.

"You know, we have all heard about beautiful depictions of the resurrected Christ in other renowned cloisters, such as the old cloister at Santo Domingo de Silos, off the route to Compostela, south of Burgos. We know that the relief sculptures there depict not only Christ's Entombment and Resurrection, but the appearances of the risen Christ to the Disciples on the Road to Emmaus

---

240   For photos, see Stoddard, *Façade*, figs. 157 and 159 for this foliate panel and figs. 105, 106, and 134 for the Emmaus figures. (*N.B.*, fig. 134 is mislabeled as LPL.) The Emmaus sculpture is largely hidden by the column capital in front of it. It is overshadowed by the figure of Christ from the "Noli me tangere" scene. For photos of this, see Stoddard, *Façade*, figs. 107, 108, 123, and 104.

and to Doubting Thomas, in addition to His Ascension. Our chapter wants sculptures like those here too.

"Look," Pons continued kindly, "you mentioned the scene of Christ meeting the Disciples on the Road to Emmaus on the frieze at Saint-Gilles. Could you do large pier figures for us of Christ and the two Disciples on the Road to Emmaus?"

"We would be pleased to do so," admitted Guillelmo gratefully.

"You know that story, of course," Pons continued. "The two pilgrims walking to Emmaus met someone they did not recognize as Christ our Lord until they later sat down to break bread together.

"The theme of the disciples journeying to Emmaus is also now seen as suggesting the journey of faith taken by pilgrims who make the pilgrimage to Compostela. That's another reason why that scene is shown in low relief on piers in many cloisters on the pilgrimage routes, as so many pilgrims have described to us. And that theme is especially appropriate for us," Pons concluded, "because Arles is a starting point on the *Via Tolosana*, the pilgrimage route to Santiago de Compostela that passes through Toulouse."

"We will be most pleased to carve the Pilgrims to Emmaus!" the carver responded proudly and again full of confidence.

"Thank you! That would be wonderful!" Pons responded, relieved that the artisan had recovered. "Could you also do pier figures of Doubting Thomas touching the wounds of Christ? I don't know if that is included anywhere at Saint-Gilles,[241] but we do want it here. That scene, too, is shown in low relief on piers in many cloisters on the pilgrimage routes.

"You remember the story. The Apostle Thomas, doubting at first that Christ had been resurrected from the dead, insisted on touching the wounds in Christ's side, but after doing so[242] accepted and believed He was the resurrected Christ."

"Yes, we will be pleased to try," responded Master Guillelmo, a bit less confidently, wondering whether he would be able to portray a wounded nude

241   This scene is not included at Saint-Gilles.

242   The event is described only in John 20:24–29. The Bible does not clarify whether Thomas actually proceeded to touch the wounds. In the twelfth century it was believed that Thomas did touch the wounds, and most depictions show him doing so. See, for example, the relief of Doubting Thomas in the cloister at Santo Domingo de Silos. It was only later, with the Protestant Reformation, that the belief became widespread that Thomas did not proceed to actually touch them.

torso and wishing he had helped more with the nude figures of Adam and Eve when they were working with Master Niccolo on the Creation scenes at San Zeno, Verona.

"The corner piers are going to have to be very bulky," the master builder interjected as he rejoined them. "I'll have to work closely with Master Guillelmo here on the configuration of your large pier figures, because some of them will have to help support the heavy vault by receiving the thrust of the supporting arches."

"Yes, yes, certainly, go ahead and do so," Pons answered, rather shortly.

"Also, on the north wall," the master builder continued brusquely, "we will first need a couple of those new corbels so we can spring the supporting arches from them. If you cannot produce them quickly enough, my men can cut some simple animal heads, but they won't be very elegant. Master Guillelmo should carve them soon."

"Fine! Master Guillelmo will carve them. Now, go ahead and proceed with whatever is necessary," added Canon Pons a bit too curtly, and because he was beginning to tire of dealing with so many minor details without yet having seen any results, he ended the conversation.

Although the *magister comacinus* had first arrived with only six master masons, his workshop now began swelling into an ever-growing host of scores upon scores of men, who now began to arrive along with the building materials. First there came the carpenters, along with unskilled laborers, the carters, who hauled the lumber that would be fashioned into scaffolding, movable ladders, and lifting devices, such as cranes with counterweights or double pulleys, or even treadmills. As the seemingly endless supply of stones began arriving, hauled again by unskilled laborers, there came the stonecutters, who would dress the stones with precision. At the same time came the blacksmiths who would make, sharpen, and temper the specialized tools and hammers for shaping the stone. Then came more masons, who would lay the stones, along with all the other minor craftsmen, who were also important, such as the men who mixed the mortar. The cathedral enclosure soon teemed with strangers, many speaking indecipherable argots.[243]

....

243 For a description of the medieval building sites, see Alain Erlande-Brandenburg, *The Cathedral Builders of the Middle Ages* (London, UK: Thames and Hudson, 1995), 89–123.

As all these craftsmen and apprentices began arriving, Pons had to help in finding some sort of rude accommodations. All these men were needed for the construction campaign, and most of them needed somewhere to sleep and eat to be able to work. Although the carters and unskilled laborers could be hired very cheaply from among the local population in or near Arles, all of the skilled strangers—that is, all the craftsmen—needed some sort of accommodations. Some of the canons offered up space in their own lodgings for this, but Pons could offer accommodation within the cathedral complex only to those highest and most respected within the workshop hierarchy. The cathedral complex was soon bursting at its seams, with every possible available room, bed, or pallet taken by the strangers. All the other strangers had to be accommodated nearby, and they soon began filling up any available lodging, room, bed, or pallet, anywhere in the surrounding neighborhood, anywhere around the old Roman arena, and then anywhere in Arles.

The master builder's workshop started by removing and retaining for reuse the twin colonettes flanking the piers, and Master Guillelmo began carving the large pier figures. The masons then began what would become a long process of bulking up the piers on the garden side. As soon as they began replacing the twin colonettes with solid stone blocks, the master mason again met with both Canon Pons and Master Guillelmo.

"Master Guillelmo's pier figures are going to be beautiful," the master mason began, "but they are cut very deeply, very skillfully, in very high relief—more deeply than we had expected him capable of, quite frankly. His figures will reduce the total mass of the piers more than we had anticipated, and we are going to have to make up for the loss of mass by making the new buttresses even bulkier. On each corner pier we will add a heavy solid stone buttress, square in cross-section, setting it into what would have been an open angle at the corner facing into the garden. That should suffice at the corners. But the two intermediate piers will be even trickier and need a lot more bulk. There's nothing else to counteract the thrust of that north gallery vault there, so we want to add an additional tall piece to the intermediate pier buttresses that will protrude into the garden, making those piers T-shaped in cross-section.[244] So we will need more stone than we had originally contracted for, and there will be an additional cost. Are you agreed? Can we proceed?"

....

244   For the changes to the piers, see Schneider, "Sculptures," 135–136, 161ff.

"Yes, yes, yes, of course. Please do whatever you need to do," responded Pons, who was now beginning to lose patience. "I need to know when there will be increases in cost, but I don't want to have to approve every single construction detail."

In addition to dealing with such details, equally vexing for Pons was his always having to be so very careful when interacting with the sculptor and the master builder. Pons early recognized that while Master Guillelmo could appear confident, he often needed praise and stroking to reassure him about the quality of his sculpture, while the master builder, who was so full of blustery confidence, could be brutally cruel to anyone showing the slightest lack of confidence and sometimes needed to be gently toned down. Pons worried that the interactions between these two artist types could become so explosively destructive that no work would be completed at all.

"Could these two really have interacted collaboratively together on the façade at Saint-Gilles?" Pons asked himself after one of their small clashes. "I think I now understand what Master Brunus must have gone through over there, why he was willing to let these sculptors go, and why Master Pietro wanted to stay there when the others left to come here."

With the beginning of construction had come the incessant noise and inevitable chaos and turmoil of renovation and creation. The construction progressed ever so slowly, but the chaos and turmoil were constant and ever growing, as constant and ever growing as the inevitable whining and complaining of anyone and everyone who was ever even temporarily inconvenienced.

"Canon Pons! If we had known what kind of hell you were going to put us through to build your confounded communal buildings," they would all begin again, just as they had done five years earlier, "we would never have agreed to this! We cannot tolerate this infernal noise," or "this hellish racket," or "this horrid cacophony," or "this utter chaos," or "this impossible mess."

"We have God's work to do," they would whine. "How can you expect us to work in such a place?" Or "We have church business to attend to," or "We have an important donor coming in. Can't you keep those infernal carvers and masons quiet?"

While construction was in progress, the canons still needed to carry on with the chapter's business and activities, and all the tradesmen had to work around the canons and their activities. The chapter house almost immediately became unusable once construction had begun, and Pons needed to arrange to move the canons' workplace elsewhere. Optimistically, he first approached Peter Villelmus, who rebuffed him soundly.

"No! You have some nerve," Peter Villelmus spat at Pons, "asking me to move my family out of the home I took you into! You're asking me to help you bring about your damned scheme that will force me to give up my loving wife and to send my own sons and daughters away! Well, it may eventually come to that, I guess, because you got the chapter to agree to your scheme, *if* you can get these buildings built. It may well come to that, but until it does, I swear I will keep my family as close to me as I can, for as long as I possibly can! Go get someone else to help you, you ass."

In fact, no one whose private home was nearby but outside the proposed building complex would volunteer to disrupt their living arrangement completely and move out to permit the chapter to take over use of their home for business. Certainly no one would agree to leave the walled cathedral complex, where they had known safe refuge from the war outside. So Pons was forced to arrange a series of moves into temporary locations in canons' homes that were on or very near the proposed building complex and that were available only because each was scheduled in turn soon to be demolished as construction progressed.

"Of course, I will move out immediately so the chapter can use my large room for a while." Canon Jordan offered. "Pons, I am your friend! Besides, unlike most of the others, I have no wife, no mistress, and no family to worry about. More importantly, I believe in what you are trying to do, and I will do what I can to help you make it happen."

First the chapter moved their work temporarily into Canon Jordan's room, very near the cathedral but not immediately within the initial building site. This would become the first of a series of temporary locations in a series of moves to keep one step ahead of the construction work.

As soon as the chapter was moved to the new temporary location, however, the whining simply morphed into other complaints.

"We went along with your moving us because you told us this move would help, but it's still too damned noisy! How do you expect us to get anything done?" Or "You accursed . . . ! You expect me to give up my house, too, and my dutiful wife and family, for this God-forsaken mess you are making here!"

As the construction progressed, the never-ending whining and complaints continued, becoming ever more annoying and threatening. The construction that had seemed at first as if it would never begin, and then seemed doomed to a false start and eternal delay, now became a source of seemingly interminable aggravation and incessant strife. Nevertheless, with his renewed spirit, the chastened Pons was now able to throw himself wholeheartedly into his project, and somehow, this time, the project became more manageable.

Arles. North gallery. Corbel, northwest corner. Ram.

Once work on the north gallery of the cloister really began, it progressed well and at a good pace. Inspired by what they had learned from helping with the large pier figure of St. Paul at Saint-Gilles, Master Guillelmo and his assistant completed the pier figure of St. Peter for the Arles cloister and were beginning the companion pier figure of St. Paul. Well-known for his animals and rinceaux, Master Guillelmo had also completed a beautifully carved ram corbel that would eventually be inserted into the north wall at the northwest corner to support the diagonal arch there.

The master builder and his masons were working closely with the master sculptor, bulking up both the northwest corner pier and the western intermediate pier sufficiently for them to receive the supporting arches and the thrust of the uneven barrel vault. The master builder was also expanding the original chapter house, extending it eastward with a thick, solid south wall that would support the thrust of the uneven barrel vault to be erected in the north gallery while also continuing the line of the older, thinner decorative façade of the original chapter house.

The three canons overseeing construction, Pons, William Garnerius, and Dean Hughes Amelius, eventually met with the two master craftsmen.

Arles, cloister, north gallery. Pier figure. St. Peter

Arles, cloister, north gallery. Pier figure. St. Peter, detail.

"Your pier figure of St. Peter is absolutely wonderful!" exclaimed Pons in genuine admiration. "All the wonderful little details! Look at this delightful detail of sandals with crossed ropes."

"Oh, I had earlier done sandals with crossed ropes on two figures on my capital of the Raising of Lazarus. Master Pietro, our 'Bold One,' liked the motif so much he used it at Saint-Gilles on his figure of St. Paul on the central portal, where the other visiting master also then copied it on his figure of St. James Major there."

"And the pilaster behind your St. Peter is so elegant, with a capital with foliage and rosettes!" Pons continued.

"Well, it's certainly more decorative than what Master Brunus carved behind his large pier figures at Saint-Gilles!" retorted Master Guillelmo. "Remember, what we really excel at is decorative work, rinceau vine scrolls, foliage, animals and decorative motifs. At Saint-Gilles I could only carve the foliate work Master Brunus wanted. On the pier figures there they only wanted me to finish the decorative detail and drapery folds on the pier figures that had already been conceived and blocked out, on St. Peter and St. John. Here, where I am Master, I can use my decorative skill more effectively. What I now want to carve are some panels with rinceau scrolls to flank the pier figures here, like those we did at Saint-Gilles to flank the figures of St. Paul and St. John."

"Well, that would be beautiful! And your ram corbel is exquisite." responded Pons.

"Now all of you can see the form that the piers will finally take," interjected the master builder, a bit peeved that Pons kept focusing solely on the sculptures, "so you can better visualize what I was proposing for the corner piers. Large salient pier figures, like the Peter figure here, will support the impost blocks and transverse arches. On the corner, this large salient block with a niche will support the diagonal arch and its impost. You can see that we could accommodate a much taller figure than the Stephen figure here in each corner niche."

"Yes, Master Pietro carved this shorter figure of St. Stephen earlier before leaving to work with Master Brunus. If only we could move the pier figure of St. Stephen," added Hughes Amelius, wistfully.

"Do you want to do so?" asked the master builder, turning to Canon Pons.

"Well, yes, if it was possible," Pons responded. "We originally asked for a pier figure of St. Stephen, and this shorter figure was carved, but things have changed since then. You see, our church has long been dedicated to St. Stephen, but for a time it was also dedicated to St. Trophîme, whose relics we once held, but we are now developing plans to bring back the relics and rededicate our church and our entire claustral complex solely to St. Trophîme."[245]

"In fact, that's the rationale for rebuilding the nave of the church with a raised choir above the crypt, so we will display the relics of St. Trophîme here," added Hughes Amelius.

"Well, of course, we can easily move the St. Stephen figure into another corner pier with little difficulty," the master builder retorted triumphantly. "The pier figure is carved out of a separate block of stone, as are most of the other decorative parts. Remember, this corner compound pier has been built up, given added mass, to be able to support the new uneven barrel vault, but

....

245   See Rouquette, *Provence*, 271-273.

we have not yet erected this section of the vault over the transverse arches. So yes, we can easily move the Stephen figure.

Arles, cloister, north gallery.
Northeast corner. Pier figure.
St. Stephen.

"In fact," he bragged, "we could even move it after the vault is in place, but it would be a bit more difficult and a little bit riskier. We do know how to change and replace supports in a structure without disturbing everything above, you know."[246]

"Yes, let's move it, then!" said Pons. "So, Master Guillelmo, we'll move the figure of St. Stephen to the northeast corner pier. Right here at the northwest corner of the cloister, near the entrance to the church where St. Trophîme's relics will be, we would like to have a figure of St. Trophîme, the first bishop of Arles in the third century, who is going to be named the sole patron saint of our church and cloister. And this new figure of St. Trophîme can be taller, comparable in height to the Peter figure here, as our master builder suggests."

"And you can even add low-relief sculptures on two faces of each corner pier," offered the master builder, with obvious pride that his opinion on the sculptural decoration was being taken seriously.

Speaking directly to William Garnerius and Hughes Amelius and ignoring the tradesmen, Pons began cautiously, "During my recent journey back from Vézelay, I thought a great deal about what we should depict here if we could. Our chapter has asked for images of the apostles and of the risen Christ, like those we have heard about at other renowned cloisters, like the old cloister at Santo Domingo de Silos. Master Guillelmo has already agreed to carve large pier figures of the two Disciples with Christ on the Road to Emmaus and the Doubting Thomas with Christ.

"We should also portray Christ's Entombment and Resurrection in the low-relief sculptures on the piers," proposed Pons boldly and confidently. "And to do this," he added, now a bit more hesitantly, "we should include scenes showing the three Holy Women and the empty tomb. Remember,

246   Erlande-Brandenburg, *Cathedral*, 99 suggests that medieval builders could and did do this.

the story, taken from the Gospel of Mark in the Bible,[247] says that Mary Magdalene, Mary the mother of James, and Salome bought spices so that they could anoint Christ after his death. But when they entered the sepulchre, an angel told them the crucified Christ had been resurrected from the dead."

"But surely you of all people are not proposing to draw attention to figures of women in the cloister," blustered Hughes Amelius in a huff.

"After all, this is not Saint-Gilles" added William Garnerius. "Here in our cloister we do not need to refute the Petrobrusians by visually proclaiming that the Crucifixion is not disgraceful because it represents triumph over sin and death."[248]

"Woman may be the beautiful siren that lures man into temptations of the flesh," Pons responded quietly, directly facing Hughes Amelius and William Garnerius. "Woman may be lust, the vessel of man's downfall into pleasures of the flesh, into sin, damnation, and hellfire. We have representations of both at the door of our chapter house. But Woman can also repent. Woman can be the repentant sinner, the forgiven and beloved repentant sinner.

"The preeminence of the abbey of Vézelay, dedicated to Ste. Mary Magdalene, the reformed sinner, the repentant sinner beloved by Christ, suggests it would not be inappropriate to include the scene of the three Holy Women, one of whom was Mary Magdalene," Pons continued in retort. "The abbey of Vézelay, for which Peter the Venerable designed the inner west portal tympanum showing Christ's Ascension combined with His Mission to the Apostles. The abbey of Vézelay, where Bernard of Clairvaux chose to call for the Second Crusade.

"So yes," Pons declared confidently, "I propose we include low-relief scenes of the three Holy Women buying spices and going to the Holy Sepulchre, where they find the tomb empty and Christ already resurrected. Remember, those two themes will directly call to mind the Passion plays, the liturgical plays that are now becoming such important components of our Easter celebrations. We now enact a short liturgical drama of the Three Women Buying Spices along with the longer *Visitatio Sepulcri* liturgical drama for Easter morning *Matins*, immediately following the *Dum transisset Sabbatum*,

247 Mark 16:1–7.

248 On this interpretation of the Resurrection scenes at Saint-Gilles, see Colish, "Peter," 458, and Stoddard, *Façade*, 143f.

the third and last liturgical responsory of Easter *Matins* in which the Holy Women buying spices is mentioned."[249]

"Well, that's true," sighed Hughes Amelius.

"And certainly our own local legends suggest that after Christ's resurrection, the three Holy Women, including Mary Magdalene and Martha, and their brother Lazarus arrived miraculously here by boat and were received by Trophîme when they disembarked in the Camargue," added Pons.[250] "So it would be very appropriate to include them here, after all. They could go here, at the northwest corner, as low-relief sculptures on the corner pier with St. Trophîme and next to the capital showing the Raising of Lazarus."

"Still, I have never heard of any other cloister sculptures of the three Holy Women buying spices," objected William Garnerius.

"If I may suggest," Master Guillelmo interjected rather boldly, "at Saint-Gilles we helped with some of the decorative details near the right portal lintel. And on that lintel they show three women buying spices from two merchants and an angel at Christ's tomb with the soldiers asleep,"[251] he clarified, gently trying to defuse what he recognized could easily escalate into an unresolvable conflict between the two canons, who were both now his bosses.

"Well, so be it," submitted William Garnerius. "I do now remember hearing that the lintels and frieze on the façade of Saint-Gilles include those scenes with the three Holy Women, as well as several scenes with Mary Magdalene, such as the *Noli me tangere*.[252] So you will have to gain the chapter's approval for the scenes, of course, but I will support your proposal to them to include a scene with the three chaste Holy Women in our cloister," he concluded, with Hughes Amelius now nodding his assent as well.

"Yes! Thank you!" sighed the grateful Pons.

....

249   Émile Mâle first recognized the direct influence of liturgical drama on the two reliefs at Arles of the Three Holy Women buying perfume and the Holy Sepulchre. See Émile Mâle, *L'Art Religieux du XIIe Siècle en France* (Paris, France: Librairie Armand Colin, 1924), 133–136. For a fuller discussion of the influence of the Passion plays on this iconography at Arles, see Schneider, "Sculptures," 508–531.

250   Mâle first drew attention to the relevance of this Provencal legend, in Mâle, *L'Art*, 213–215. For further discussion, see Schneider, "Sculptures," 503ff and 512ff.

251   On the Holy Women buying Spices on the lintel at Saint-Gilles, see Stoddard, *Façade*, 75f, 143f, 145f.

252   On the sculpture of the superstructure at Saint-Gilles, see Stoddard, *Façade*, 63–107.

"And thank You, dear God," Pons voiced silently to himself, now confident that he would gain approval. "The scene of the three Holy Women will bring the reformed sinner, Mary Magdalene, into our sculptural program, an embodiment of repentance and of Your forgiveness."

Work was now progressing at a faster pace on the entire construction project, with Pons supervising the claustral project and William Garnerius helping supervise the rebuilding of the church. Both components now received focus and attention.

To Pons, however, construction of the new cloister vault and renovation of the chapter house seemed to be moving much too slowly. What seemed to Pons like it should take several moments often continued until the bell of the next hour. What seemed to him like it ought to go on only until the next hour often continued several days. What seemed to him like it should take a day or two often took several weeks. The slow speed of progress was unsettling to him. The delays were devastatingly unnerving.

"Was ever a reconstruction or renovation as slow as this?" Pons asked himself.

To hasten progress on the north gallery of the cloister, Pons finally decided to forego adding too many additional historiated capitals carved with figural scenes and agreed to settle for mostly foliate capitals carved with acanthus or palmette leaves. These Master Guillelmo could delegate almost entirely to the assistant. Master Guillelmo could then concentrate his efforts on the piers, pier figures, relief sculpture, and the rinceau foliate panels.

Pons did ask chapter for permission to include two more historiated capitals for the north gallery, however: one showing the Old Law and one the New Law. Without much questioning, chapter had readily agreed. Calling both his friend Hughes Amelius and Master Guillelmo over to him one day, he instructed the sculptor.

"We have agreed on two more historiated, figural capitals in this north gallery. One will show the Old Testament story from Exodus of Moses receiving the tablets of the law, the Ten Commandments.[253] That is the Old Law.

---

253   Exodus 20: 1–17.

The other capital will depict the *Traditio Legis*, Christ as lawgiver, giving His New Law, a scroll, to St. Peter and St. Paul."[254]

Arles. Cloister, north gallery capital. Moses Receives Tablets of the Law.   *Arles. Cloister, north gallery capital. Traditio Legis, Giving of the Law.*

Turning to the sculptor, he explained more fully his reasoning for this pairing of themes. "The Old Law contains truth but in an incomplete, unrefined, or obscured form. The New Law, taught to us by St. Paul, is derived from the Old Law but has been refined and transformed by divine inspiration.

....

254   Although long described as depicting "St. Paul Before the Areopagites" (see Stoddard, *Façade*, 222, 226), this capital has now been correctly identified as showing the *Traditio Legis*, the Giving of the Law, which traditionally shows Christ handing a scroll or manuscript to St. Peter in the presence of St. Paul. This interpretation, first proposed by A. Hartmann-Virnich, has been accepted and promoted by Geraldine Martin Orrit. See Geraldine M. Orrit, "Le Cloître de la Cathédrale Saint-Trophime d'Arles: Étude du Décor Sculpté," *Lettre d'Information, Patrimoine en Paca – DRAC/MET*, no. 30 (January 2016), 5–6, http://www.infos-patrimoinespaca.org/articles/articles_pdf/article_332.pdf. See also A. Hartmann-Virnich, "Les galeries romanes du cloître de Saint-Trophime d'Arles: études sur un chantier de prestige," in P.K. Klein, ed., *Der mittelalterliche Kreuzgang – The Medieval Cloister – Le cloître au Moyen Age. Architektur, Funktion und Programm* (Regensburg: Schnell & Steiner, 2004), 301.

The central figure bears a lightly inscribed cross on his nimbus, which certainly identifies him as Christ, if the inscribed cross is original, which it appears to be. Moreover, he is flanked by two figures, one receiving something from him, one holding a manuscript.

It includes Christ's Mission to the Apostles to go out into the world to convert the heathen, to preach to the unbelievers.[255]

"In the abbey church at Vézelay I saw a beautiful capital in the nave that shows this theme symbolically as a Mystic Mill, where Moses pours unrefined grain, representing the Old Law, into a mill from which St. Paul collects the refined, transformed flour." Turning then to Hughes Amelius, he continued, "But we should have the two Laws portrayed separately on capitals here because for us canons, the two Laws might suggest another additional implied layer of meaning. God gave the Old Law, the Ten Commandments, as rules to govern how all men live. St. Paul interpreted the New Law after his miraculous conversion. But we clerics, as church canons, must meet even higher standards if we are to fulfill our mission. God gave us clerics the model of the *vita apostolica* in the New Testament as the way we canons should live our lives."

"You are preaching to the converted, Pons my friend. It is our other fellow canons you must bring and keep on side," responded Hughes Amelius. "But erecting the buildings for communal sleeping and eating will go a long way toward accomplishing it."

Progress on the north gallery continued steadily. At last the masons had expanded the chapter house and prepared the north wall. The master builder was now ready to begin erecting the uneven barrel vault. He knew well that traditional barrel vaults gained stability from the even distribution of their thrust and weight along the length of the supporting wall structure below. Here, however, the skilled master builder recognized that because of the large opening of the large portal, the north wall would be relatively unstable at this point, so the uneven barrel vault would be least secure at the large portal. Here, at the large portal, the uneven barrel vault would not provide the same stability for itself as a traditional barrel vault. Here it would need the strong transverse arches for skeletal support to carry some of the thrust of the vault to the side of the large arch opening and then down the side of the portal.

The master builder boldly decided to face the challenge head-on and begin the vaulting with the western bay directly in front of the large chapter house

255   On the evolving interpretation of the *Traditio Legis* image in medieval art, see Armin F. Bergmeier, "The *Traditio Legis* in Late Antiquity and Its Afterlives in the Middle Ages," *Gesta* 56, no. 1, (Spring 2017), https://www.journals.uchicago.edu/doi/10.1086/689968

portal. The wooden scaffolding had already been built and was now put in place immediately east of the portal. The master builder would begin here, with the transverse arch immediately adjacent to the tall chapter house portal. Once the transverse arch held here, nearest what was the weakest part of the north wall, and was deemed secure, he would then erect the next transverse arch to the west.

With the two transverse arches across the span of the north gallery, the stone masons would then lay the stone barrel vault on top of them in front of the large portal. If this section held—or rather *when*, God willing, this section held—adding the more stable sections to the west and east would lend additional stability and strength. So the master builder would then move as quickly as possible to complete each remaining supporting transverse arch and continue the tunnel vault both into the northwest corner and eastward along the length of the gallery.

The stonecutters had meticulously cut and shaped the stones that would comprise the first transverse arch. Being a bit wary about this transverse arch holding at the large portal, while also being afraid to tempt fate and the stars, the master builder had given the stone cutters a wooden template with a very simple profile to use as their model to cut the stones for this transverse arch,[256] a profile that was a simplified version of the one he had previously used for repairing the collapse at the west wall of the crypt at Saint-Gilles. It was very conservative in cross-section profile: flat along the top, with two gently incised rolls following the two edges, and some simple, shallow detailing along the sides.

"Better to use the simple profile that held in Saint-Gilles rather than spending too much time cutting and shaping a fancier one," he thought privately to himself, "in case it does collapse and we have to redo the whole damned thing!"

The strong wooden falsework that would support the stone arch as it was being erected across the span of the gallery had been constructed and was now in place.

At the north façade wall, a corbel depicting an acrobat had already been inserted and above it, a carved impost supporting block decorated with acanthus foliage. At the south there had been erected another impost block where

....

256   On templates and rib profiles, see Erlande-Brandenburg, *Cathedral*, 80ff.

the transverse arch would be received by the massive pier, above the spot where the figure of Christ would be later be positioned between the two pilgrims to Emmaus.

Beginning at the lower south side, the laborers now used a small crane to hoist up the first stone of the arch, which the masons then guided carefully onto the impost block there, carefully positioning it immediately against the supporting wooden falsework. Then a second stone was hoisted up and painstakingly set onto the first, carefully aligning it. Then, slowly, a third. As the fitted stones rose upward and began leaning toward the center of the arch, they curved inward to follow the arc along their supporting curved wooden falsework.

Arles. Cloister, north gallery. Corbel on north wall. Acrobat. (With foliate impost and transverse arch above.)

As soon as the stones reached the height of the springing of the vault on the opposite north wall, above the acrobat corbel and impost, other masons and laborers positioned at the north wall began their own work there, the laborers using another small crane to slowly raise the lowest stone of the arch for the masons to carefully set into place there. Each of the two teams of laborers now continued hoisting up their next stone for the masons to set into place, and, alternating between north and south, the two ends of the transverse arch were slowly incremented almost simultaneously. Ever more carefully now, each additional stone was added, each time carefully following the curve of the falsework arch, thereby ensuring the two arcs of the curve were directed toward each other. Slowly, the two sides of the arch were nearing each other. Only three stones remained.

"Stonecutters! Quickly! And I mean now!" bellowed the master builder from below the scaffolding in sudden panic. "The falsework is compressing unevenly so the alignment of the stones will not quite be true! It could shift and twist. It could collapse! Stonecutters! On the next north stone to be put in place, shave back the east side of the face that will join up with what's already erected there. Do it now! *Now!* Reduce the stone face by just a little, less than half a little finger's width near the edge, tapering to no more than a hair's breadth or two near the middle. Just a few hairs' breadths at the middle, mind you! But don't touch the other sides! Shave off the stone carefully and keep the face absolutely flat! Now! Hop to it! Quickly! Now!"

When the stonecutters seemed to have been successful, the master builder calmly commanded again, "Good. Now quickly do the same thing to its south counterpart, the next stone, but on the west side of the face to be joined with what's there. You men should understand what I am calling for! If you don't see it, I'll . . . The stones have to line up perfectly!"

It was not long before the two stones, ever so slightly altered, were painstakingly hoisted up and carefully set in place. It had worked. The two sides now appeared to be perfectly aligned.

Finally, the keystone, the last and topmost stone, was hoisted up by the laborers to the masons, who perched on the scaffolding above the arch. Receiving the stone, they ever so carefully and painstakingly maneuvered it into place above the single remaining hole in the arch and then very slowly, ever so gently and carefully, eased it down into place. This was the keystone, the critical joint, the lock, the final fitted stone that would lock the two arcs of fitted stones into one strong, stable, sturdy, continuous arch.

Everyone held their breath. Nothing moved. Nothing budged. The masons then cautiously descended from the wooden scaffolding, all the while keeping themselves well clear of the stonework above—just in case—and scurried away. They would leave the wooden falsework here temporarily to provide some stability. The carpenters were already building more wooden falsework to support the next transverse arch that would be erected just to the west on the other side of the large portal.

The transverse arch of fitted stones now had to hold itself up. Soon it would also have to help support the weight of the section of the stone barrel vault they would lay above it.

Everyone continued holding their breath. Still nothing moved. Still nothing budged. The central keystone lock held. The arch was firm and true.

"It is good and solid!" proclaimed the master builder heartily at last and with some evident relief. "We'll give it a few days to settle well, while we're continuing with the next transverse arch. But the alignment is tricky, probably because of the unevenness of the barrel vault. And much too tricky with rolls inscribed along the two edges.

"For the remaining transverse arches, I want to keep it even simpler. I'll give you stonecutters a new wooden template with an even simpler profile—with only one simple roll incised down the middle of the arch. That will make it easier to adjust the edges, if necessary. Or rather *when* necessary!"

Progress on the vault and gallery continued steadily now, but at a somewhat slower pace because of the canons' curiosity. Pons still struggled to transition the chapter's workplace to the series of temporary locations nearby, but the excitement of the vaulting process added a new dimension to the curiosity and fear of the canons. They all wanted to see what had been erected and walked to and from their temporary chapter house location via the construction site. But, fearful of a collapse, they would sneak their peek at the work only by walking close to the tradesmen whom they assumed knew where it was safe to walk. So all the tradesmen—the master builder, the masons, the stonecutters, the carpenters, everyone—now had to work with a stream of curious canons quite literally underfoot.

Of course, the chapter still had to endure the unbearably loud noise of active workshops of busy sculptors, stonecutters, carpenters, masons, and even a blacksmith along with their clutter, debris, scaffolding, stone piles, wood piles, fires, dirt, and filth. On top of that, the chapter now also had to learn to tolerate the danger posed by the construction. But this time Pons threw himself full-time into the task of cajoling the tradesmen while smoothing the ruffled feathers of the canons. Having learned his lesson from the earlier breakdown in relations, Pons now focused on conveying what the canons would be gaining as well as the logic of the course of construction.

"Remember, one day we will have a huge, spacious, stone-vaulted dormitory. It will be so pleasantly cool during the summer, when our Provençal sun beats down so mercilessly," he would begin, "but also cozily protected and warm during the winters, when the bone-chilling cold winds rampage down the Rhône River.

"Once the chapter house is completed with a vaulted north gallery of the cloister," he would continue diplomatically, "this will form the north edge of our claustral complex, from which we can erect our spacious, vaulted dormitory southward at the east edge, in tandem with a vaulted east gallery of the cloister. With the refectory along the west, we canons can then live very comfortably and communally around the cloister in a completely enclosed community. Yet we will still have direct access to the church at the west end of the chapter house as well as our own direct access to the city through the canons' portal to the south."

Under his calm leadership that held up through the almost unbearable chaos and seemingly endless turmoil of the months ahead, work progressed steadily, albeit painfully slowly, on the construction in the cloister and on the nave of the church. Indeed, progress was to continue steadily over the next few years.

At the same time, the Second Crusade was also being played out, but all the more painfully. And though it seemed so far removed from Arles, its outcome was destined to affect Pons's cloister in ways no one could ever have predicted.

Within a few months, by early 1148, one of the canons, Bernardo, found two straggling crusaders wandering around the old Roman arena. Astonished to learn they were Norman barons from England, Bernardo led them through the canons' portal to the cathedral complex to bring their news to the canons. Canon Jordan immediately invited them into the rooms that were now being used as the chapter house.

"Please give us news of the Holy Land!" Jordan urged.

"That would be difficult for us," one of the Norman barons answered, "because we are only now making our way there. Many of us answered the blessed Bernard's call in England and took up the cross, but as we were sailing with the Flemish crusaders around Brittany heading for the Mediterranean in June ..."

"Bad weather forced all of us to take refuge at Oporto on the Portuguese coast, and there the Bishop of Oporto offered us a better option," interrupted the second crusader.[257]

"Yes," continued the first. "He told us that we could serve God and fulfill our pilgrimage vows right there in Iberia by joining up with Count Alfonso Henriques and fighting the local infidels. You see, the count wanted to expand the kingdom of Portugal to the south by taking Moorish Lisbon. So we all sailed on to Lisbon and helped him take it—by October!"

"Oh, we took Lisbon," the second Norman added proudly. "We took good plunder as well. Really good plunder. All the plunder the count had promised us. And we all got our absolution from our sins, too—the absolution that is awarded to all crusaders!"

....

257   The account of the Norman participation is taken from Hindley, *Brief*, 76–78, and from Malcolm Barber, *The Two Cities: Medieval Europe, 1050–1320*, (Abingdon-on-Thames, UK: Routledge, 2004), 323–324.

"So none of you went to the Holy Land?" asked Jordan incredulously.

"Oh, a few of us may now continue on to the Holy Land, but most were satisfied with getting rich on all the booty in Lisbon," the first baron explained. "But you see, things really went awry in Lisbon. Crusaders were tearing things apart, hurting the citizens. They even slit the throat of the Mozarabic Bishop of Lisbon—the Christian Bishop. Murdered him . . ."

"We couldn't decide what to do, so we are walking back in this direction on the pilgrimage route while we decide where to go," explained the second.

"Well, we certainly welcome you to bed down here in the adjoining room if you want to spend a night here before continuing on," offered Hughes Amelius, rather disappointed but unwilling to offend these men who had fought the infidel so violently and bravely, albeit in Lisbon rather than in the Holy Land.

Months later, some isolated small groups of returning crusaders began passing through town, or occasionally some individual stragglers. Some were homeward bound and seeking to follow the Rhône River to the north. Some were trying to find any way back home overland after refusing to sail again on the treacherous open seas. Those returning were welcomed by the chapter, expectantly hopeful at first for news of Christian gains in the Holy Land, and then later wishing for any signs that all those earlier reports had been mistaken.

It was Rainaldo who encountered the first small group of returning crusaders talking with the local carpenter at the ancient arena, and he invited them all to visit. They accepted, and even Archbishop Raymond joined them to hear the news from the Holy Land. With the help of one of the carpenters in the workshop, Frederick, who was from the north and could understand their dialect, the canons were surprised to find the returning men were assorted peasant Germans who were making their way homeward overland.

"When the call went out for the crusade at home, there was a lot of confusion at first," one of the crusaders began, with Frederick's help in translation. "You see, a man named Raoul arrived first, saying he was Bernard's disciple. Raoul called for anyone who wanted to take up the cross to first annihilate German Jews, because, he told us, German Jews are Christ's enemies at home. So we did as he said, and we all slaughtered Jews until Bernard arrived and ordered us to stop. Bernard told us all that it was wrong to kill Jews, and that anyone who killed a Jew was hurting Jesus, because Christ Himself was a Jew.

So that's when most of us took up the cross, hundreds of us. It seemed a good thing to do since the crops had failed, too, and most of us were starving."[258]

"So did you join up with the French King Louis's forces?" Pons asked.

"No. Well, at least not at first," another crusader answered, again with Frederick's help. "We all assembled at Metz and then set out under our German king, Conrad III of Hohenstaufen. We were so proud at first because Conrad had taken up the cross, at Bernard's urging, at Speyer on Christmas Day, 1146, but later we all heard a rumor that the king had taken the vow only because he was hoping to get something from the pope."

"Conrad has long held the title King of Burgundy or Arles," Archbishop Raymond explained to the chapter, "but he is still officially only 'King of the Romans.' He undoubtedly now wants to be recognized and crowned 'Holy Roman Emperor' by the pope. But he has several rivals for that title."

"Well, anyway, we set out as a huge army last year through the Danube Valley under King Conrad," continued another crusader. "The king led us overland to the east, to Byzantium, and we reached Constantinople, where we were supposed to meet up with the French king's army. But from then on, everything just went terribly wrong. Our own troops met with terrible hardships. We really don't understand why, but somehow it seemed as if we were doomed. The two armies never got along, maybe because the two leaders didn't seem to get along."

"The two kings couldn't get along? The two leaders couldn't cooperate? So you suffered from split leadership?" Pons asked incredulously.

"Oh, I don't understand what happened. But King Conrad decided to move us out quickly, without waiting for the French. We were told that the Byzantine Emperor Manuel had advised him about the routes and supplied guides, but ignoring that advice, King Conrad chose the ancient caravan route from Byzantium to Tarsus and Edessa—that's the more direct overland camel route southeast through Anatolia. But we could not find any supplies at all along the way. We ran out of food and water; we were dying of thirst and famine. We finally reached Dorylaeum, but most of our troops were massacred there in a battle. Nine out of every ten of our soldiers were killed or captured by the Seljuk armies. We were among the few who survived."[259]

....

258   The entire account related the German participation is taken mostly from Hindley, *Brief*, 74–76, 78–80, and from Kelly, *Eleanor*, 36–37.

259   Account is taken from Hindley, *Brief*, 78–80, and Kelly, *Eleanor*, 41, 45–46.

"Only one out of every ten survived! Yet you were still en route and had not even reached the Holy Land?" cried Rainaldo.

"Yes, I am sorry to say. The few of us who could continue on eventually joined up with the French. King Conrad became ill at Ephesus, but Emperor Manuel took him back to Constantinople to recover, and eventually he was able to continue on by ship to Acre, where he rejoined us for the final campaign at Damascus."

"And at Damascus . . . ?" asked Pons, tremulously inquiring further.

"Damascus was a disaster—a total disaster. We were defeated. Destroyed," the German murmured quietly in reply. "We are all so ashamed. We can say nothing more about it," he concluded.

No one could respond to this. No one could offer any solace.

After accepting the canons' offer of overnight lodging, the Germans continued on their way the next day. Several weeks went by. Pons, Jordan, Rainaldo, everyone in the chapter was simply refusing to believe that the tale told by the returning German crusaders had been accurate. Perhaps they did not know the entire story. They had left Damascus downhearted. Perhaps events had taken a different turn after they had left.

Pons had gone to inspect the progress on the vaulting of the cloister gallery. Looking up, he burst into a huge smile and ran toward the canons' portal. There he had seen his good friend, Nicolaus of Saint-Ruf, casually entering.

"Nicolaus," Pons called out with real pleasure at seeing his friend. "How wonderful to see you."

"And I am truly pleased to see both you and your magnificent claustral buildings in the making," Nicolaus called back. "I want to see all the progress you have made here in the cloister and in the church!"

"But of course," answered Pons. "Let me show you." He took his friend along the stone and wood-filled north gallery before entering the chapter house and then descending the stairs to the church.

After proudly showing Nicolaus all the progress on the construction, Pons finally calmed down enough to ask his friend, "Tell me. Do you have any news of the Second Crusade?"

"Most certainly, I do. Nothing recent though," he explained, as the two sat down outside the chapter house.

"Last year I was sent up to Paris on some business for my abbot. There I learned that King Louis VII was going to leave for the Crusade, but first he wanted to be blessed at the abbey church of Saint-Denis. You see, the abbey of Saint-Denis holds special meaning for the French monarchy. The abbey not only holds the royal insignia and the royal banner of the French monarchy, the *oriflamme*, but it has long been the pantheon and burial place of the kings of France. And now the front of the abbey church has been adorned with figures of royalty, Old Testament kings and queens. King Louis's taking up the crusade cross was to be a truly momentous event, so he wanted first to be blessed in the abbey church. The ceremony took place in June.

"The abbey church is now absolutely magnificent. Unbelievably beautiful! Abbot Suger had recently completed the rebuilding of the west and east ends of the church in a remarkable new style, and the new church had just been dedicated three years earlier in the presence of King Louis. It was in this magnificent new church that King Louis wanted to receive his special blessing before leaving for the Crusade."

"Did you attend the ceremony? Tell me everything you know and saw," Pons begged his friend.

"Yes, I managed to slip into the back of the church," Nicolaus began. "It was all unbelievably beautiful and magnificent. King Louis VII solemnly entered the central portal of the church, with its new west front so magnificently decorated with the new figure sculptures attached to columns, figures from the Old Testament, kings and queens as well as patriarchs and prophets. So King Louis solemnly passed by these Old Testament kings and queens as he entered the church to receive his special blessing before leaving to make safe the Holy Land of those same Old Testament kings and prophets.

"The inside of the church was wondrous, lit up with thousands of candles and strung with banners for the special event.[260] The King, dressed humbly in a black pilgrim's tunic decorated only with a red cross, walked very slowly all the way down the candle-lit nave toward the abbey's glorious, light-filled new choir.

"I cannot describe how beautiful the new choir is, with chapels radiating out from the ambulatory. Some call it Abbot Suger's new vision of light and space. Well, it is a vision of light and space, with windows of stained glass filling the walls and lighting up the interior with its pointed arches, unusual ribbed vaulting, and clustered columns. It is unbelievably beautiful!

....

260   The account of the ceremony is taken from Hindley, *Brief*, 78.

"At the choir, King Louis knelt before Pope Eugenius. The king solemnly declared that Abbot Suger would be the regent of France during his absence in the Second Crusade, committing the care of the Kingdom to the abbot. Pope Eugenius bestowed his solemn blessing on the king, and everyone cried out in joyous cheers when the pope ceremoniously handed the king the traditional emblems of the pilgrim: a staff and wallet decorated with the cockleshell of St. James. Oh, it was a glorious ceremony, an absolutely magnificent sendoff for King Louis to leave on his crusade with the pope's blessing.

"But as for what happened after he left, and how successful they were in the campaign, I have no recent news and cannot say anything," Nicoluas ended.

Pons related this description to the chapter, and they all now regained some small hope that the earlier reports from the small band of German crusaders may have been misleading. Perhaps they had been ashamed of their own performance and had been overly negative about the outcome. But within another week or so, French crusaders began showing up at the arena in Arles. This time it was William Garnerius who encountered the returning crusaders and urgently invited them to come dine with the canons at his own house, an invitation that was gratefully accepted by the hungry men.

"Please tell us everything that has happened since you set out," William Garnerius urged them. "We are as hungry for news of the crusade as you are for this good meal."

"Well, we set out so confidently in 1147, a huge army under King Louis," the crusader began. "King Louis led us overland to the east, and we moved at a good pace—ten to twenty *milles* each day. At Constantinople, we were supposed to join up with the German King Conrad's large army, but the German king had decided to lead his troops out over the more direct overland route. It was not a good decision, because we later learned that at Dorylaeum they were massacred by the Seljuk armies."[261]

"We have already heard that as many as nine out of every ten of the German soldiers were killed or captured there," Pons added.

"Yes," the crusader confirmed, "most of the German troops were lost.

"King Louis had already decided to lead us out of Byzantium on what seemed the safer route past Nicea. It was only after we were en route that

....

261   The entire account of French participation is taken mostly from Hindley, *Brief*, 78–83; Kelly, *Eleanor*, 47–51, 61–68; and "St. Bernard of Clairvaux," *Medieval Sourcebook*, https://sourcebooks.fordham.edu/source/eb9-bernard.asp.

King Conrad's nephew, Frederick Barbarossa, arrived with the news about the Germans. King Louis sent some of our troops to the desert to rescue the survivors, and King Conrad and most of his few survivors ended up joining us at Ephesus. King Louis had resolved not to take the treacherous route through Cappadocia, so he led us westward toward Demetria.

"We had been following not far from the coast for months," the crusader continued, "and finally, just before Christmas, we reached a lovely valley with a stream, and we camped there to celebrate the feast day. But while we were celebrating Christmas *Lauds*, the sky burst open with a violent downpour of rain, with gale winds, and the swollen river swept away our men, our horses, and our gear. Most of the German barons were so downhearted they fled back to Byzantium, but some even renounced their crusader vows and returned home, despite the papal interdicts on anyone returning without fulfilling their vows."

"You see," interjected another crusader as the interpreter turned to assist him, "until then most of us were blaming the difficulties on the treachery of the Greeks, but this now seemed to be an act of God. A flood! With gale winds! Many of us thought God was telling us to turn around."

"Yet we did go on," the first crusader continued, "but we turned inland toward Laodicea in the mountains. The mountain territory we had to pass through was so difficult and dangerous that we had to carry Queen Eleanor and her entourage in litters."

"Queen Eleanor and her court had to be carried in litters?" Pons asked with disbelief, remembering vividly the fearless Amazon warriors who had brazenly ridden across the field at Vézelay.

"Yes," the crusader replied with more than a bit of annoyance at the memory. "But then, in those mountains of Paphlagonia, we, too, were attacked by Seljuk Turks, losing so many knights and hundreds of men-at-arms."

"But many of us put the blame for that loss on the queen's vassal, Geoffrey de Rancon, because of his own stupidity and breach of conduct," the second crusader broke in.

"Regardless, we finally made it to the Greek port of Satalia on the southern coast," the first crusader continued. "From there King Louis wanted to continue on to Antioch by sea, but he couldn't find enough ships—only enough ships for himself, his household, and some cavalry. So the King took those ships and left us, after delegating two other leaders to find more ships. But when they, too, could not find more ships, they, too, set sail in their own ship and left us troops stranded. At least 7,000 of us infantry were stranded, left to fend for ourselves. Then a plague broke out, and finally those of us who survived the plague had no alternative but to continue on to Antioch by the dangerous overland route. Eventually we arrived by foot at Antioch.

"We waited around for what seemed a very long time in Antioch, until suddenly King Louis moved us out, leading us to Jerusalem. There was a war council at Acre, where they decided not to move on Edessa, but to take Damascus instead!

"So we all assembled at Tiberius: our French King Louis with us crusaders; the German King Conrad with his men; and Baldwin III, King of Jerusalem, with his men. We marched out to Damascus. We tried to take the city, but we had no water, and it was total confusion. It was a disaster! We had to retreat in defeat. We simply do not know why we were so humiliated and defeated. We simply do not understand it. We failed. We failed miserably."

The entire chapter was rendered speechless at this admission. Although they should have been braced for this terrible news by the earlier German reports, they could not understand why God would have deserted the Second Crusade and its army. The crusaders reporting the miserable news could not have known what had transpired to shape these events and could only report on the outcome. Subsequent returning crusaders could only confirm what was already known.

It was not until the next year, late in 1149, that the chapter would get more informative news. It was just after midday, and Dean Hugues Amelius was standing at the canons' portal, having just come from celebrating *Nones*, when someone called out to him.

"Hello there! Are you entering the cathedral precinct? Lend me a hand!"

Turning around, Hugues spied a man dismounting from his horse and quickly lashing it to a post. Hugues quickly recognized him to be a Knight Templar because he was wearing the characteristic white mantle with a red cross.

"I need to see the archbishop here, Raymond of Monte Rotundo, I believe. I am on urgent business on behalf of the King of France."

"Yes, of course, as you wish," responded Hughes politely, as he waited at the portal to assist the Templar. "I'll take you to him. He's in the archbishop's palace."

"But perhaps I can help you. I am Hughes Amelius, dean of the canons here, and am authorized to speak for the chapter. May I ask what the nature of your urgent business is with the archbishop? Is it something I or the chapter can help you with?"

"Well, yes, quite possibly. I am Thierry Galeran, of the Order of the Temple, sent by their Royal Highnesses King Louis of France and Queen Eleanor to arrange their return to France.[262] They will be passing through Arles on their way to Saint-Gilles, where they want to worship at the renowned abbey church. Bernard of Clairvaux has told them about some remarkable sculptures on the façade there, and the king is very keen to see them. They will want to stay overnight here before continuing on to Saint-Gilles, and they will need appropriate and secure accommodations for themselves and their entourage."

"We can certainly help you make arrangements. But first, do give us some news. Did you take part in the crusade to reclaim Edessa? We have heard distressing reports from returning crusaders, stragglers, and the news was not good," Hughes added hesitantly. "Do you know what happened? Can you tell us?"

"Yes, I do indeed know," the Templar answered wearily, "and frankly, the story needs to be told."

"Let me gather some of the other canons so you can tell all of us and the archbishop your story," Hughes responded, as he quickly called to several fellow canons and urged them to round up everyone they could find to meet in the archbishop's palace to hear the story.

When a group began to gather, the Templar began speaking, not bothering to pause as other stragglers drifted in.

"When our blessed King Louis left to go on the crusade, he took several of us with him. He took Odo of Duilio, a monk from Saint-Denis, as his chaplain and secretary, to chronicle the crusade and to sleep near the royal tent at night at the king's request. I am Thierry Galeran, of the Order of the Temple. Our order had established a house in Paris less than a decade ago, and King Louis wanted to take me with him to manage his treasury as well as to keep away those who would pester him.[263] We Knights Templar are well-known as skilled combatants, of course, but we have also developed a well-deserved reputation for cleverness in managing finances and handling wealth.

"Together, Odo and I, we got a clear view of most of what happened. Our Order of the Temple is independent and not beholden to any ruling monarch. So what is not improper to relate, I will tell you.[264]

262   Kelly, *Eleanor*, 36, 59, 66 mentions Thierry Galeran.

263   Kelly, *Eleanor*, 36.

264   All the events related by Thierry of the French participation and the parts played by King Louis and Queen Eleanor are taken from accounts in Kelly, *Eleanor*, 52–71, and Hindley, *Brief*, 80–84.

"Apparently you have already heard about some of the many misfortunes. Much of the long trek, much of the earlier part of the crusade was really rough, but we believe it was much closer to the goal, at Antioch, where everything really fell apart. On our arrival by ships at Antioch, Prince Raymond of Antioch graciously welcomed King Louis, who as King of France is the lord of the Franks of Outremer. He welcomed the cavalry troops, but he also most enthusiastically welcomed the beautiful Queen Eleanor, who is his niece and member of his family, and whom he was clearly delighted to receive.

"Queen Eleanor adored Antioch, which has long been one of the main commercial centers of the world. Quite frankly, she seemed to blossom there. She reveled in its luxuriousness, its wealth of riches from both east and west. She enjoyed the city's many layers of cultures, its remnants of Greek and Roman deities, its intermingling of pagan temples and Christian churches. She was fascinated by its multicultural intermingling of Greeks, Saracens, and Christians, and especially by their exotic offspring of intermarriage called the 'Pullani, with their exotic dress and languages.[265]

"King Louis, on the other hand, found Antioch morally offensive. He had expected it to be a pillar of purity, a city still worthy of habitation by St. Paul himself, but instead he found it desecrated, contaminated by pagan cultures and religions. For King Louis, it was offensive and simply degenerate."

"How would you know all this?" William Garnerius asked rather timidly.

"I managed the purse, and the queen was always asking for more silver coins to enjoy those riches. And remember, Odo of Duilio slept outside the royal tent and could hear them talk. He was always discrete, but even he would sometimes talk about something that suggested how uncomfortable the king was in Antioch.

"So Queen Eleanor and her ladies were thoroughly enjoying the luxurious hospitality offered by her cousin Raymond and his Antioch court. At the same time, King Louis was uncomfortably conflicted, paralyzed with indecision.

"You see, once the king had arrived, Prince Raymond proposed a new plan, which was for the French crusaders not to simply reclaim Edessa, but instead to join with him to go against the most powerful threat, Nur al-Din of Aleppo to the east, thereby challenging Islam both to the east and to the north of Antioch. He insisted this would shore up the security of Antioch's

---

265   Kelly, *Eleanor*, 52–58.

borders while also securing Edessa. Raymond recognized that the fall of Edessa into infidel Muslim hands had not only weakened the Latin Kingdom of Jerusalem, but also posed an immediate threat to the frontiers of his own Principality of Antioch.

"King Louis simply could not decide what to do: whether to agree to Raymond's new request or to respond to the pleas of the other local Frankish rulers to simply recover Edessa. Remember, recovering Edessa was the original goal of the crusade. But Raymond kept insisting that Edessa had been lost largely because of poor and ineffectual, if not corrupt, mismanagement by Joscelin, the Count of Edessa, who is a Capet and King Louis's nephew. You can imagine how that opinion was received by the king!

"Then Prince Raymond suggested that although all of Christendom may have been called upon to reclaim Edessa, it was King Louis Capet who had now arrived to rescue his nephew's domain. In addition, many of the barons the king was leading were vassals of Queen Eleanor, whose house of Poitou would now be able to gain control of the Latin Kingdom of Jerusalem. Raymond recognized that his proposed new plan would benefit both houses, Capet and Poitou, while also shoring up the safety of his own principality. Of course, when all the other French barons also recognized this, they became suspicious about the motivation and self-interest—not only of Raymond, but of the Poitevans too.

"King Louis and Queen Eleanor argued violently about what to do," Thierry continued. "Eventually they were arguing openly. Everyone knew it! Queen Eleanor argued for aiding Prince Raymond to go up against Aleppo, but the king insisted this was not the goal of the crusade."[266]

....

266   Even Thierry may not have grasped all the underpinnings of King Louis and Queen Eleanor arguing so vehemently about this. Queen Eleanor had helped choreograph the call for this Second Crusade, and she must have believed the mission was as much hers as it was the king's. Eleanor argued for helping Prince Raymond fight Aleppo, possibly out of self-interest, but more likely simply because she was both brighter and clever enough to recognize the real strategic military benefit to be gained by a decisive strike against Nur al-Din, who was the real great power in Muslim Syria, and the son and heir of the now deceased Zangi Imad al-Din who had sacked Edessa in 1144. (See Hindley, *Brief*, 80–81; Kelly, *Eleanor*, 59.)

Queen Eleanor was more educated in the ways of the world than her husband. Raised by an enlightened and cultured ducal family, she had not only received a formal education from tutors but had gained broad experience by travelling from castle to castle throughout her family's vast lands. (See Kelly, *Eleanor*, 2–7.) In contrast, King Louis

"Frankly," Thierry continued with a sneer, "we all knew the queen was biased toward Prince Raymond. He was lavishing her with gifts, and she relished all the luxuries of his court, but it was more than that. She was his niece, and they spoke the same language, the *langue d'oc* dialect, and they shared a common background, common customs.

"They were together so frequently, so often—too often. And they were just *too* familiar, much too familiar. On many a day they sat comfortably with their heads together in long, friendly conversations in the gardens, conversations they kept private. They would smile and chuckle together. They obviously really enjoyed each other very much."[267]

"Are you implying Queen Eleanor was indiscrete—that she may have been unfaithful and broken her marriage vows . . . in an incestuous relationship?" a horrified Pons asked incredulously, and flushing deeply as his mind, awash with memories of Isabel and her tales, pulled him back again to Vézelay. Several of the other canons shuffled their feet nervously in distress.

"No, it is certainly not my place to accuse her of that," Thierry replied reluctantly after a long pause.[268] "But as one the king's closest counselors, I can say that the pair certainly worried Odo and me, because they so disquieted the king. Odo and I became very nervous about them, even though Odo kept strict vigil just outside the royal chamber every night, and I kept a tight grip on the coffers to restrict what the queen could do every day.

was the second son of Louis VI, called Louis the Fat, and as the second, "spare" son, Louis had been raised in the sheltered cloister at Notre Dame, was educated under the direction of Abbot Suger, and was destined to life as a cleric. It was only after an untimely accident, when a boar startled the horse of the older brother, taking the life of Philip the heir apparent, that the ill-prepared youth was thrust into the role of heir and successor.

267   Kelly, *Eleanor*, 58–59.

268   What Thierry undoubtedly suspected may have been correct. Beautiful, impetuous, hot-blooded Eleanor was simply more than the pious, virtuous, "monkish" young Louis could handle. She herself is said to have proclaimed, "I thought to have married a king, but find I have wed a monk." (See Kelly, *Eleanor*, 77.) She was undoubtedly biased toward Prince Raymond and his wishes, in large part because she was so thoroughly enjoying her visit to the lavish Antioch court. Suspicions of her having an incestuous affair with her suave, handsome, dark, sophisticated, older uncle certainly followed her for the rest of her life, but it is unknown whether these suspicions arose from her own misbehavior, or from the need of contemporary historians to relieve Louis of blame for any misjudgments about the crusade. (For the relationships, see Hindley, *Brief*, 80–81, and Kelly, *Eleanor*, 62–63.)

"I will say that Queen Eleanor and Prince Raymond could be very cruel. They would laugh scornfully that the king was in good company with the monk and eunuch he isolated himself with as counselors."[269]

"But that's so disrespectful of the king, and . . ." Canon Jordan called out.

"Yes! But they often amused themselves in deriding Odo Duilio and me. Queen Eleanor especially liked to ridicule me. You see, I am a eunuch. But that is one good reason I am trusted to be near the king's wife and still keep a tight grip on the coffers. Frankly, I think Queen Eleanor and Prince Raymond resented us for keeping so close an eye on them."

"God bless our beloved King Louis," the Templar continued. "He firmly believed he was bound by his crusader's vow to head to the Holy Sepulchre and Jerusalem. He had no interest in demeaning the goal of his holy crusade and would not be deterred from his goal on any account.

"When Prince Raymond called a war council of the barons," the Templar continued, "to make military plans, carefully outlining his proposed strategy and very eloquently explaining why it was the most capable plan for preserving our Latin Kingdom of Jerusalem, King Louis simply declared that he had vowed and taken up the cross to go to the Holy Sepulchre, and only after he had fulfilled his vow and pilgrimage would he listen to other advice from the Prince of Antioch or other barons at a general council.[270]

"Prince Raymond was furious, absolutely livid. He lashed out in one of his typical rages at the assembly, swearing by the saints that he would be avenged on them for dashing his hopes and opening the Latin Kingdom to the Saracens.

"So the crusaders were now to exit Antioch and move forward, and King Louis was marshaling his men, making arrangements for the exodus and moving forward. Queen Eleanor chose this moment—this very moment," Thierry stressed, "to confront her husband, the king. She told him she wanted to separate from him. She would not continue on the crusade with him but would stay in Antioch. She wanted to return to being Duchess of Aquitaine."

"She asked for a divorce?" Archbishop Raymond de Monte Rotundo choked aloud in shock before making the sign of the cross on his chest. "But . . . but . . ."

"Yes," Thierry answered simply, "on the grounds of consanguinity. She reminded Louis that they were fourth cousins, that this degree of

269   Kelly, *Eleanor*, 590.

270   See the quote in Kelly, *Eleanor*, 60. See also Hindley, *Brief*, 80–81.

consanguinity was forbidden by the church, and therefore, if he would not release her from their sinful marriage, Louis was putting both of their souls in mortal danger of damnation and hell."[271]

Wide-eyed and gasping, the canons and archbishop all shifted nervously.

"King Louis cherishes Queen Eleanor," Thierry continued quietly, with resignation. "He adores her. He was distraught not only at her request for a divorce, but even more at the issue of consanguinity. He sought advice from his council. I finally counseled the king to take Queen Eleanor captive and keep her in custody, at any cost, and to leave Antioch immediately."

"You advised him to take the queen captive?" William Garnerius gasped in disbelief.

"Yes," the Templar responded very coolly and calmly. "The barons all panicked at the council, but they were more worried about the possible results of such a separation on the political side of things than about the religious issue of divorce. If Eleanor and the king should separate, what would become of Eleanor and her vast, valuable lands? The Duchess of Aquitaine would not long remain unmarried, and her lands would not long remain unclaimed. What evil scheme might Prince Raymond, her uncle, hatch to change the current balance of competing powers by bestowing her and her valuable lands on another husband? And how was King Louis to lead the Christian forces to make safe the Latin Kingdom of Jerusalem if he could not even control and keep his queen and her vast lands within his own kingdom?

"So the king had Queen Eleanor fetched, seized, and dragged from her uncle's palace, and he and his troops marched on toward Jerusalem with Eleanor in tow.[272]

. . . .

271   Eleanor's pressing for a separation is taken from Kelly, *Eleanor*, 59–61.
       Here again Thierry may not have fully understood what had transpired. The vivacious Eleanor had already recognized she was not content to be Queen of France to this king. When she pressed Louis, she told him she wanted to separate herself from him and his crown. She wanted to leave the crusade and to stay in Antioch with Raymond. She wanted a divorce, so she could return to being Duchess of Aquitaine. Very cleverly, she made use of the training in dialectics and use of syllogism she had mastered less than a decade earlier among the scholars of Paris soon after she and Louis were married (See Kelly, *Eleanor*, 13–14) to argue the necessity of divorce on the grounds of consanguinity.
272   Hindley, *Brief*, 80–81. See also Kelly, *Eleanor*, 61–62.

"On arriving in Jerusalem,[273] King Louis immediately visited the Holy Sepulchre, where he placed on that most holy of altars, Christ's tomb, the royal banner, the *oriflamme* that he had carried from the abbey of Saint-Denis. He spent the rest of that first day visiting all the other shrines in the city.

"I was so pleased to be able to show him the headquarters of our Order of the Temple. It's on the Temple Mount. You do know that we took our full name, 'Poor Knights of Christ and the Temple of Solomon' from that site because the Temple Mount rests on the ruins of the Temple of Solomon. King Baldwin II of Jerusalem first granted us that space in a wing of the royal palace, which earlier had been the al-Aqsa Mosque before the First Crusaders recaptured Jerusalem in 1099."

"Your order was created to protect pilgrims to the Holy Land, was it not?" asked Pons deferentially. "Several of us here do hope one day to be able to make that pilgrimage and to worship at the Holy Sepulchre."

"So you shall, if, God willing, the Holy Land is still safe for pilgrims," the Templar retorted.

"The very next day," the Templar continued, "King Louis met with all the French and German barons, and, after finding their new counsels in Jerusalem to be less motivated by self-interest, they decided to hold a war council at Acre.

"This war council at Acre was presided over by Queen Melisende and her seventeen-year-old son, King Baldwin III. It included King Louis and his nobles, King Conrad and what remained of his barons, and the leading prelates of Jerusalem. The rebuffed and angered Prince Raymond refused to participate. Neither Count Raymond of Tripoli nor Count Joscelin of Edessa were present. There was no representation whatsoever from Edessa.

"They decided to attack Damascus, and we did, joined by the knights of Jerusalem. We were having some success attacking the walls when somehow the commanders received word that another angle of the wall would be better for attack. So we moved there, but then we had no water and were overcome with the summer's heat. Everything collapsed in confusion. We were forced to retreat in defeat," the Templar admitted with shame. "It was a complete failure, a total disaster."[274]

....

273   For King Louis in Jerusalem, see Kelly, *Eleanor,* 64–66.

274   For the war council, their decision and the disastrous outcome, see Hindley, *Brief,* 81–83; Kelly, *Eleanor,* 64–68. The war council was comprised of great men, but mostly foreigners from afar, who simply could not grasp the subtleties of local politics. The

"But what of Alphonse Jourdain, the Count of Toulouse?" William Garnarius inquired. "We know he took up the cross at Vézelay, but none of returning crusaders have made any mention of him."

"Did he arrive too late?" Pons asked. "We know he left for the Holy Land a bit later than most of the other crusaders, because he was engaged here in supporting my brother, Raymond of Baux, in his war. I'm aware that Alphonse Jourdain did leave, however, and the war then quickly turned in favor of the Count of Barcelona. And after my brother's other allies submitted at Tarascon, he, too, had to submit and then left for Barcelona to try to negotiate terms."

"Well, let me tell you," the Templar began. "The Count of Toulouse did arrive by sea at Acre in time, by 1148, accompanied by his wife and children. We had all anticipated he might follow in the footsteps of his father, Raymond of Toulouse, and play a major role in this crusade. After all, Alphonse Jourdain was born in the Holy Land while his father was establishing the county of Tripoli during the First Crusade, and he was baptized in the Jordan River. That's how he got his name.

"But Alphonse Jourdain's arrival at Acre unnerved Count Raymond of Tripoli, who, as the grandson of Raymond of Toulouse's bastard son, Bernard, had claimed Tripoli. You see, Alphonse Jourdain started talking about reclaiming Tripoli for himself. Then, only a few days after arriving in good health in Acre, Alphonse Jourdain died suddenly in Caesarea."[275]

"He died in Caesarea?" interrupted William Boso, looking briefly at his friend, Pons. "After fighting so fiercely with Raymond of Baux for lands here in Provence, he died in Caesarea?"

"So we had to endure all the horrors of that war here at Arles, and all the disruptions here at chapter for nothing," Bernard Aiguillus grumbled. "They lose the war. Your brother then dies in Barcelona and Alphonse Jourdain dies in Caesarea. Too bad they didn't die earlier . . . would have saved all of us a lot of trouble."

"Now, now, that's not something you should think, much less talk about," Hugues Amelius chided the ill-tempered canon. "But how did Alphonse Jourdain die, if not in battle?"

....

council foolishly decided to attack Damascus, even though the Emir of Damascus was friendly to the Christians. The Emir, recognizing that "the enemy of my enemy is my friend," appealed for and received support for his heroic army of Damascus from the great Nur al-Din. Outmaneuvered by the locals who diverted the water, and outflanked by the enemy armies, the Christian army was quickly humiliated and retreated in defeat. With this debacle, the Second Crusade ended in 1148 as an abysmal failure.

275   See "Alphonse I," *Encyclopaedia Britannica* 11th edition, 1911.

"Some think it was poisoning," the Templar responded. "Many people were suspicious of Count Raymond of Tripoli, and he became angry and indignant and refused to participate in the crusade.

"But even if Alphonse Jourdain was poisoned, we all know he had other enemies, including Queen Eleanor of Aquitaine and Queen Melisende of Jerusalem, both of whom were also nearby."[276]

"Yes, and as the Count of Toulouse, Alphonse Jourdain had made many other enemies as well," William Aicardi Rufus suggested knowingly.

"Yes, we know all too well he made many enemies as count while fighting to hold onto Toulouse and Provence," Pons began with a sigh, "and Eleanor of Aquitaine was among them. Her father had early taken Toulouse from him, but even when he regained part of the lands, he then had to fight the claims of the Catalan house. But Eleanor of Aquitaine continued to claim Toulouse, and King Louis even once tried unsuccessfully to besiege Toulouse on her behalf."[277]

"Whatever. I still prefer to think the death was an accident," the Templar retorted quickly. "It was just unfortunate that neither Alphonse Jourdain nor Count Raymond of Tripoli participated in the war council or the battle of Damascus," the Templar continued. "The Count of Toulouse would have brought skill and cunning as a combatant of well-deserved renown, and the Count of Tripoli could have brought some keen insight into local politics.

"But alas, King Louis's Crusade simply ended in total failure over a year ago," the Templar concluded.

"Do you lay the blame for the failure on Queen Eleanor?" Pons asked timidly.

"Well . . . No," the Templar finally admitted quietly, "although some would blame her. But after all, regardless of what happened in Antioch, Queen Eleanor played no active role at all in what happened in Jerusalem and

....

276   See Marion Meade, *Eleanor of Aquitaine: A Biography* (New York, NY: Penguin, 1991).

277   Alphonse Jourdain had succeeded to the county of Toulouse and marquisate of Provence on the death of his brother Bertrand in 1112. But within two years Toulouse was taken from him by Eleanor's father, William IX, count of Poitier, who claimed it through his wife Philippa of Toulouse, the daughter of William IV of Toulouse. Alphonse Jourdain regained part of the lands in 1119 but then had to fight the claims of the Catalan Raymond Berenger III until 1125. Eleanor of Aquitaine, as granddaughter of Philippa, also claimed Toulouse, and in 1141, King Louis tried unsuccessfully to reclaim it for her by siege.

Damascus. At first we all thought some malice of the devil had taken over at Damascus, to counsel the command to move from what appeared then to be a promising siege into the new location that turned out to be a doomed site, but we don't know where that advice came from. Some thought Raymond of Antioch betrayed us; some thought other barons with grudges made private side deals in self-interest. Some blamed the entire failure on the treachery of the Greeks. Even Bernard of Clairvaux at first blamed the Byzantines.[278]

"But we now know from Bernard of Clairvaux that it was a judgment from God," the Templar said quietly, as he made the sign of the cross on his chest, forming a moving echo of the red cross on his mantle. "Bernard of Clairvaux had a visitation. God spoke to him about the disaster while he was writing his *De Consideratione*. In that volume, he related,

'Non ita est; sed incidimus, ut ipse nosti, in tempus grave, quod et ipsi pene vivendi usui videbatur indicere cessationem, nedum studiis; cum scilicet Dominus provocatus peccatis nostris, ante tempus quodammodo visus sit judicasse orbem terrae, in aequitate quidem, sed misericordiae suae oblitus . . . .

Et quidem judicia Domini vera; quis nesciat? At judicium hoc abyssus tanta, ut videar mihi non immerito pronantiare beatum, qui non fuerit scandalizatus in eo.'

Sancti Bernardi, De Consideratione, II, ch. 1.

'As you know, we have fallen upon grave times, which seemed (as though) . . . the Lord, provoked by our sins, gave the appearance of having judged the world prematurely, with justice, indeed, but forgetful of his mercy . . . .

The judgments of the Lord are true indeed. Who does not know that? This judgment, however, "is a great deep," so much so, that it seems to me not unwarranted to call him blessed who is not scandalized thereat.'[279]

---

278   See Kelly, *Eleanor,* 68, and Hindley, *Brief,* 84.

279   See Migne, *Patrologia Latina,* vol. 182, cols. 741–743. The translation is from James Brundage, *The Crusades: A Documentary History* (Milwaukee: Marquette University Press, 1962), 115–121.
       Bernard began writing his *De Consideratione* probably about 1147.

The entire group was speechless for several moments, each lost in thought, each thinking silently to himself very similar thoughts. Pons thought to himself, "All God's works are just and true. All God's judgments are just and true. But it is so difficult to understand this judgment. Are we, like the biblical Job, being punished, even though we try to live righteously? If so, why? To what purpose? To teach us to despise the things of this world? To look only to the eternal hereafter? To what purpose is this judgment of God?"

Eventually it was the archbishop who first regained his awareness of the here and now, who first returned to the task at hand. "So why are you here only now, a year later, a year after the crusade failed?" Archbishop Raymond asked quizzically.

"When the crusade ended," the Templar began, "King Louis would not return home by ship immediately but stayed in the Holy Land over the winter through the spring of 1149. Having suffered such a punishing loss at the hand of God, he devoutly insisted on staying in the Holy Land to celebrate Easter, the holiest and most important day of the church year, the Resurrection of Christ. He stayed in the Holy Land even though Abbot Suger had written him, pleading with him not to stay overseas, entreating him to return to his estates.[280]

"After Easter the king and Queen Eleanor finally set sail from Acre, but on separate ships, the king with his men, including me, on one, the queen with her ladies on the other. We were making good progress at sea when disaster struck yet again, and both ships were swept up in hostilities between Sicily and Byzantium, two of King Louis's allies! The two ships were separated. Ours was seized, even though King Louis had quickly run up the French flag. The queen's was captured and taken toward Greece by Emperor Manuel of Byzantium's forces.

"It was a terrible two-month ordeal. King Louis's ship was finally able to land in Calabria, where Roger of Sicily informed him that the Sicilian fleet had rescued Eleanor, who had also finally reached safety in Palermo, Sicily."[281]

"I pray to God they are both safe now!" exclaimed William Boso.

"Yes, but I cannot tell you how trying those two months were. Oh, the hardships we endured! King Louis says he will never again travel by sea if he can avoid it!

---

280   Kelly, *Eleanor*, 68–69, quotes Suger's letter.
281   Kelly, *Eleanor*, 69–70.

"We continued on homeward by the land route. King Louis and Queen Eleanor were received in October 1149 by Pope Eugenius in Tusculum, near Rome. Queen Eleanor is with child. King Louis desperately hopes it will be a ... 'legitimate' male heir!"

"Let us all pray for such an outcome," the archbishop added quickly.

"But Queen Eleanor was furious at being abducted from Antioch. And she is still furious about it! Queen Eleanor pressed her case to the pope for an annulment of the marriage. The pope refused to agree and forbade either of them to utter the word 'consanguinity.'

"The pope then tried to orchestrate a reconciliation between the royal pair by sending them to an elegant 'love nest,' with a spacious bed in luxurious surroundings. But Eleanor could not be dissuaded. She made it very clear to all the ladies in her court that the king's efforts there were unsuccessful, and that ... nothing was achieved," the Templar added with a sneer. "So there was no reconciliation.[282]

"The king and queen continued on to Rome, where they toured all the apostolic shrines before continuing on northward by land routes, passing through Aqua Pendente on the *Via Francigena*. They will soon be arriving here by way of the pilgrimage route on land.[283] The king sent me ahead in the advance guard to announce his visit and to prepare for his return here.

"So you can expect King Louis and Queen Eleanor to be coming through Arles shortly," the Templar continued with a businesslike air, as he took the archbishop's arm and led him aside. "The king and queen will require appropriate lodgings for themselves and for their entourage for the night—separate lodgings, mind you, as I hope you now understand—and I trust you will also understand why both of them must be accommodated in every way possible.

. . . .

282   See Hindley, *Brief*, 84, and Kelly, *Eleanor*, 70–71.

283   See Kelly, *Eleanor*, 71 and Weir, *Eleanor*, 75, who both suggest the sovereigns took the land route from Aqua Pendente north and through the Jural Alpine pass to eventually reach Auxerre. However, because the sovereigns are known to have visited Saint-Gilles, they undoubtedly followed the alternate routing of the *Via Francigena* which turned westward near Piacenza and Pavia, continuing on through the pass near Torino and Suse, which would join them with the pilgrimage route to Santiago de Compostela, taking them through Arles to Saint-Gilles. In either case, because Saint-Gilles is just west of Arles on the pilgrimage route, which would be the safest and most direct land route, the sovereigns must have passed through Arles while en route to and/or from Saint-Gilles.

"Now, if I could speak with you privately," he continued quietly, leaning his head closely toward that of the archbishop, "The king and queen—separately—in your palace . . ." And the knight and the cleric left the room in step with each other to begin their discussion, parrying back and forth and sideways for good advantage in this social game.

* * *

The king and queen finally arrived in Provence by the land route, and it is documented that they visited Saint-Gilles because in October 1149, King Louis wrote to Abbot Suger from the town of Saint-Gilles:

"We be hastening unto you safe and sound, and we command you not to defer paying us a visit, on a given day and before all our other friends. Many rumors reach us touching our kingdom, and, knowing naught for certain, we be desirous to learn from you how we should bear ourselves or hold our peace, in every case. And let none but yourself know what I say to you at this present writing."[284]

At the town of Saint-Gilles, the devout King Louis would certainly have visited the renowned abbey church.[285] Work on the façade of the abbey church was very far along, although not yet completed, but the façade would have been truly impressive. Its extraordinary pier figures of apostles and angels would have been completed. Its equally extraordinary sculptural scenes running along the lintels and friezes above the pier figures, and the tympana, would have been at least mostly, if not entirely, completed.

To reach Saint-Gilles, King Louis and Queen Eleanor took the well-traveled pilgrimage routes that led first north from Rome, the Via Francigena, *and then west from Arles, the* Via Tolosana, *on which Saint-Gilles is a major early stop after Arles. Their visit to Arles is not formally documented, but they may have stopped in Arles only briefly for a short visit. By late 1149 work on the claustral buildings and on the cathedral restoration at Arles would have been in full progress. In the north gallery of the cloister, the western bay of the uneven barrel vault in front of the chapter house would certainly have been vaulted, if not at least some of the other bays as well, and most of the large pier figures, as well as most of the historiated carved capitals, would have been completed. Work was progressing on the*

....

284   Guizot, *History*, vol. I, 429.

285   Guizot dates the visit of Louis VII to Saint-Gilles October 1149. Hindley's timeline suggests the visit on his return home was in 1149 (Hindley, *Brief*, 83–84).

architectural renovation of the church, but certainly nothing had yet been begun on the sculptural façade of the church.

*　　*　　*

Although it had been only a few days earlier that the Templar Thierry Galeran had arrived at Arles, Canon Pons was startled to look up from his inspection of progress on the cloister, not long after celebrating *Nones* in mid-afternoon, to see a fairly large, varied group of travelers being led through the canons' portal by several of the archbishop's servants. Some of the group immediately jumped down from their horses, handed the reins to the servants, and quickly scurried off toward the latrine. Several others also immediately dismounted, and from their clothing—short, coarse, gray or bluish-gray woolen tunics over heavy knitted stockings—Pons could see they, too, were servants traveling with the group.

Other men in the group descended more calmly from their mounts, handing the reins to their own servants while talking with one another. Several of the travelers were mounted crusader knights bearing swords and shields and wearing their protective fighting garb: hooded chainmail tunics with chainmail leggings, metal helmets, and surcoats displaying the coat of arms identifying the knight. This group was very well protected while traveling. Pons realized it must most certainly be King Louis of France and his entourage.

Some removed their dust-covered mantles and surcoats and handed them to their servants, revealing that a couple of them wore long bliauds of brilliantly colored fine wool with long sleeves and long beige-colored linen chainses beneath. Together they formed a variegated patchwork of brilliant blues, rich shades of brown, and intense emerald green. One of the group wore a most beautifully detailed bliaud of fine wool in deep purple, with broad swaths of multi-colored needlework at the ends of the sleeves and at the hem. Most of the other travelers clustered around him, like bees around a hive, or, rather, like moths around a light, and Pons realized this must be King Louis himself.

Others hovered around an expensive horse-drawn carriage, trying to assist the occupants in getting out. Three noble women, all with head veils and very elegantly dressed in fine mantles over long bliauds, in shades of glowing red, a stunning orange, and a vibrant leaf green, cautiously descended then turned to assist the last. Finally, the most elegant of all the women appeared, dressed in a deep crimson-colored mantle, which she pushed quickly aside to adjust her head veil held by a wide gold circlet, revealing an exquisitely detailed bliaud, dark burgundy in color, embellished with a wide border of rose and wine-colored needlework edging the neckline and sleeves. She stepped out slowly, carefully, hesitantly onto the ground. Even from a distance, Pons could see she was pregnant, already heavy with child, and obviously very uncomfortable from traveling. She was also strikingly beautiful. She must be Queen Eleanor.

The group was ushered respectfully toward the archbishop's palace.

The next morning Pons was called by William Garnerius to join him in the north gallery outside the entrance to the chapter house just after *Terce*, explaining they would also be joined by the archbishop and the King of France.

"Greetings, Canon Pons. Listen, quickly! I have some important news for you." William began. "King Louis of France arrived yesterday, as you undoubt-edly noticed, and he and his entourage will be staying only one night here in the archbishop's palace, because the queen is uncomfortable and dissatisfied with her accommodations. Although the king wants to leave very soon for Saint-Gilles, well before *Sext*, he has asked to see the work being done on our cathedral church, which the archbishop has already told him so much about. So the archbishop asks us both to help him guide the king through the work here."

Very soon thereafter the archbishop approached with the king, and Pons saw that the king's garments were even finer than he had perceived from afar the previous day. The king wore a brilliant deep blue mantle of the finest wool Pons had ever seen. Tied at the shoulder, it bore along its bottom edge a wide band of darker blue, purple, crimson and gold-colored needlework. His deep purple bliaud, also of the finest wool, reached almost to his feet, but ended just above his chainse, which was also of the finest wool. The bliaud had very long sleeves, apparently to keep his hands warm. At the ends of the long sleeves and around the hem was a wide band of needlework in deep, rich colors of blue, crimson and gold, that blended with those on his mantle.

"Your most gracious Highness, King Louis Capet," the archbishop began, "may I present to you the two canons who will be honored to show you our construction work here and to answer any questions you may have. Canon Pons de Baucio, our *capud scole*, will first show you the work here in the clois-ter, and Canon William Garnerius, who is *precentor*, will then lead us to the church to show you the work there."

"Your most gracious Highness," each of the canons responded, bowing low.

Arles. North gallery. Rampant barrel vault.

"If it please Your Highness, may we begin here in the northwest corner of what will be the cloister?" suggested Pons meekly, deferentially, and a bit nervously, after glancing quickly at the archbishop. After explaining some of the difficulties they had overcome in the construction, he gestured expansively down the gallery, saying, "From here you can see our pier figures: St. Peter here with St. Trophîme at this corner, St. Paul with St. Stephen at the far other corner, and in between, Christ and the Pilgrims to Emmaus, and Christ with Doubting Thomas."

Arles. Cloister, Northwest corner pier. North side. Pier figure of St. Peter; relief of Christ's Empty Tomb.

Arles. Cloister, Northwest corner pier. West side. Pier figure of St. Trophime; relief of Holy Women Buying Spices.

"But this is magnificent!" the king burst out. "It is absolutely wonderful!

"Especially these large figure sculptures on the piers," he added enthusiastically. "They are almost like the figures on the front of Abbot Suger's abbey church of Saint-Denis. But . . . No! They are so different! So very different.

"At Saint-Denis the figures are smaller and on slender columns; here they are larger and on heavy piers. But no, it is much more than that," he continued quickly to himself, as he began thinking slowly out loud. "At Saint-Denis the jamb figures . . . hover. They float—yes—they float on the columns. They are not just slender, but ethereal. They are weightless.

"Here, these figures are large. They do not hover, do not float. They are heavy; they have weight. They have firm substance—solidity. They are part of the pier. They support what is above them.

"I think the figures on Abbot Suger's new façade—those wonderful, ethereal, weightless column figures—are much better suited to adorn the entrance to a church, the house of God. Such heavenly figures belong there. But these—these solid, sturdy, heavy figures—may be more appropriate here to adorn . . . No, rather, to support—to hold up—a cloister!

"Oh, I cannot wait to tell Abbot Suger about these figures. He now wants to build a cloister, and he will be so excited about such an idea. But what are these scenes carved here on this corner pier? This must be our Lord's empty tomb at His Resurrection! But what are these women? I do not recognize this scene. Tell me," the king demanded imperiously.

"These are the three Holy Women, Your Highness: Mary Magdalene, Mary the mother of James, and Salome. The three Holy Women who bought spices from the merchants to anoint the body of Christ at His tomb. But when the women arrived at the tomb, Christ had already arisen," Pons answered meekly.

"Oh! Oh, yes! Easter! The Holy Women at the Holy Sepulchre. The death and resurrection of our Lord!" the king gasped aloud. "I visited the Holy Sepulchre in Jerusalem. I placed the royal *oriflamme* on the altar there. And, after our . . . defeat, our punishment, we delayed our departure from the Holy Land," he continued in a whisper, speaking to himself rather than to the clerics, while closing his eyes in thought.

"I wanted to celebrate Easter there. I wanted to remain where my Lord and Savior had carried his burden and walked to his Crucifixion, for us. I had to . . . share my heavy burden, to repent my failure—my punishment," he continued inaudibly to himself.

After several moments of silence, the king opened his now tearful eyes, took in a deep breath, and spun quickly around, without taking a step, to face the north wall and the chapter house. "What supports this unusual vault on the other higher side?" the king asked perceptively.

Pons then proceeded to explain how the builder had inserted corbels to support transverse arches. "Here's one corbel with a supporting figure struggling under the weight, and over there, on the other side of the portal another with an acrobat, and in the northwest corner, one showing a ram."

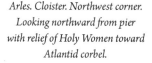

Arles. Cloister. Northwest corner. Looking northward from pier with relief of Holy Women toward Atlantid corbel.

Arles. Cloister. Northwest corner. Corbel on north wall. Atlantid (supporting figure).

"Who carved this 'supporting figure and block,' as you call it, opposite the Easter scene of our Lord's empty tomb?" the king demanded imperiously.

"Why, our Master Guillelmo," answered the canon nervously but very politely. "He excels at decorative foliage work, but he has become very skillful with large figures as well. It was he who also carved the large pier figures, including St. Peter here and St. Trophîme."

"Well, oh, ah . . . That erect flowering stem on the block above the supporting figure there. . . It almost reminds me of . . . Well, no, not really. Maybe only a little, but . . . Well, actually, yes—though with many more petals, of course, but . . . Yes! It does. It recalls for me the French lily, the *fleur de lis,* that symbol of purity and saintliness that goes all the way back to the baptismal lily at the anointing and coronation of King Clovis, and that I have adopted as my emblem," the king noted.

"And here it is, this flowering stem. Like an elaborate *fleur de lis* . . . Like my emblem. In this cloister. Here. Right near the three Holy Women and the risen Christ's empty sepulchre. The Easter images! Yes, the Easter images! Oh, bless me, dear Lord God," he gasped, holding up his hand to stop the clerics from speaking, or moving. "Bless me, dear Lord God. What are You telling me? What are You saying?" He whispered almost inaudibly.

"Speak to me, please! What am I to do?" he prayed, enigmatically pursing his lips and closing his eyes for several moments. He mumbled to himself before finally opening his eyes, lowering his hand, and acknowledging the clerics, permitting them to speak at last.

"Shall we move on to look at the work in the church," the archbishop offered diplomatically, slowly moving through the door toward the church. "Thank you, Canon Pons, for showing us all of this."

As the king, accompanied by the archbishop and William Garnerius, descended into the church, Pons thought for a few moments about the "erect flowering stem." He was certain it was a simplification of a fairly standard ancient floral motif that he had seen many times on ancient Roman friezes elsewhere. Shrugging his shoulders, he then left the enclosure and took a short walk up the hill where he could sit quietly and relax amid the remains of the ancient theater.

Late in the afternoon the next day, Pons was asked by William Garnerius to accompany him to the archbishop's palace to meet with Archbishop Raymond de Monte Rotundo and Hughes Amelius.

"Canon Pons, my dear friend," began the archbishop. "I am very sorry. I am afraid I have some unpleasant news for you. As you know, when King Louis was visiting, he admired the work in the cloister. The king was quite taken by Master Guillelmo's pier figures in the cloister, especially the ones of St. Peter and St. Trophîme, but all the others too. King Louis has decided he wants to take Master Guillelmo with him back to the Île-de-France after he visits Saint-Gilles."

"Oh! No!" gasped Pons. "But why?"

"As you know, King Louis is very close to Abbot Suger at Saint-Denis. Abbot Suger is his mentor, whom he put in charge of the French kingdom when he left for the crusade. He knows his mentor is very keen on new artistic and architectural possibilities. Abbot Suger has already rebuilt the abbey church in a striking new style, with column figures on the west portals and a new choir filled with light and space. Well . . ." the archbishop broke off, struggling to deliver the bad news.

"Apparently Abbot Suger now intends to erect a new cloister for the abbey there," Hughes Amielus continued for the archbishop, who was now shaking his lowered head. "King Louis wants the abbot to be able to have large solid pier figures in his cloister, like those we have here in Provence at Arles and at Saint-Gilles."

"But . . . but . . . Oh, no," Pons sputtered.

"King Louis knows that Abbot Suger already has stone carvers who can carve elegant, ethereal column figures like those on his church portal, but it is the sturdy solidity of the large pier figures in the cloister here that impressed him," Hughes Amielus explained. "Suger does not have stone carvers who do that kind of work in that style."

"Look. I suspect what is really going on here," the archbishop finally interjected, "is that King Louis is afraid, desperately afraid, for his soul. He wants to do something to appease God. The Second Crusade he led was a total disaster, a disaster apparently wrought by God. The king's marriage has become a serious problem that weighs heavily on his soul. He is desperately afraid of the 'consanguinity' issue while still hoping for a son and heir. King Louis is a very pious man! He truly fears for his eternal soul. He wants to appease God! I think he's hoping to help Abbot Suger create something special, to create a remarkable cloister to the glory of God, to appease and to gain forgiveness and some favor from God."

"But surely the king would rather take Master Brunus or someone working at Saint-Gilles," Pons protested.

"Unfortunately for us," William interrupted, "King Louis also took it as a sign from God that one of Guillelmo's floral motifs looks just a bit like an elaborate version of the French *fleur de lis*. After visiting our church with William Garnerius and just before leaving here, the king demanded to return to look again at the cloister, and apparently he found two more of those floral motifs there: another one near the empty tomb relief, on the impost block above the pair of capitals next to St. Peter on the garden side and a much simpler one on the capital of Moses receiving the Law, on Moses's staff where he is tending the sheep."

"But I am sure that was derived from a common ancient decorative motif," Pons sputtered, "that appears on many Roman friezes, on many ruins!"

"Yes, perhaps. But King Louis doesn't seem to care about that!" the archbishop retorted brusquely. "And even if he does, he found the motif here in your cloister, near the sculptures of the Holy Women and the empty tomb of Christ's Resurrection, which he had just seen with his own eyes, and it all reminded him that he had stayed in the Holy Land to celebrate Easter as a penance after being punished by God with the debacle of the crusade. He took what he saw as a sign from God! And, quite frankly, he may not even know the floral motif is a simplified version of a common ancient motif.

"Remember," the archbishop continued more gently, "the king was raised and educated by Abbot Suger at Notre Dame in Paris. Paris! Long only a backwater! The king may have seen little Roman sculpture there. Paris may once originally have been a Roman colony, but it was 'muddy Lutetia,' an island linked by wooden bridges to its two banks and surrounded by a wooden stockade.[286] Yes, it undoubtedly certainly once had Roman sculpture, but with all the invasions, the stone has long since been mostly carried away, used to build protective walls around the city, or destroyed.

"And until the king's father arrived and worked with Abbot Suger to start turning things around," he continued, "Paris was an unimpressive city in a tiny state, surrounded by its much more prosperous and powerful vassal states. Paris is now thriving; it has become prosperous. It even now has a famous

....

286   Lutetia was long believed to have been protected merely by being surrounded by a wooden palisade dating from Roman times, so that it was its position on the river, along with its ever-reconstructed wooden stockade, that offered protection against invaders. It was long held that it was Louis VII's son, Philippe Auguste, who first at the end of the twelfth century erected a great stone wall around the city to protect it and extended the protective wall beyond the Île de la Cité to include first the right bank and then the left bank. See Alistair Horne, *Seven Ages of Paris* (New York, NY: Vintage, 2004), 28–33.

It is now proposed, however, that by the late third century AD, invasions forced inhabitants to abandon the left bank, where most of the city was, including the Roman forum and amphitheater, and dismantle the monuments so they could reuse the stone to build the first city wall around the Île de la Cité. See Thierry Sarmant, *Histoire de Paris: Politique, Urbanisme, Civilization* (Quintin, France: Éditions Jean-Paul Gisserot, 2012), 12–14.

academic center. But as a boy the young king may not have seen much antique decorative Roman sculpture in Paris![287]

"Regardless, even if the king recognizes the source of the flowering stem, he is interpreting its simplified appearance here as a sign from God. The unfortunate fact is that King Louis has decided he wants to take Master Guillelmo with him to Abbot Suger," the archbishop now concluded, "to work on Suger's cloister if the abbot wants him. The king has already sent the Templar, Thierry Galeran, to speak with Master Guillelmo, and the sculptor has agreed to go."

"But who will complete the work here?" Pons cried out. "The master builder is now busy working on the nave of the church, but he is preparing to vault the easternmost bay of the north gallery here in the cloister. Thank goodness most of the large pier figures have been completed, but some of the foliate capitals, impost blocks, and foliate panels are not yet complete or have not yet been begun!"

"King Louis wants only Master Guillelmo," Hughes Amielus responded quietly, "and only Master Guillelmo will be going. His assistant will be staying here to continue the work and to complete the cloister sculpture. And the master builder has someone in his workshop who can help a bit by carving the last corbel for the east corner."

Pons was truly distraught, completely downhearted at this turn of events, but there seemed to be no alternative. At least the pier figures were almost all completed and much of the foliate decoration had been begun if not completed.

"Well, the assistant has developed quite a bit and become fairly skillful, so he will just have to complete the last pier figure and the rest of the foliate capitals for the north gallery himself, with some help from the builder's man," Pons concluded. "We will have to find another master sculptor to take charge of work on the east gallery whenever the construction gets to that point and the dormitory is finally under construction."

* * *

King Louis's decision to take the Provençal sculptor of pier figures north with him was not without consequence. By or before 1151 the abbey of Saint-Denis had a cloister with fairly large column figures, the earliest such cloister there. Its large,

---

287   For Paris as a backwater until the arrival of Louis le Gros and the importance of Abbot Suger, see Horne, *Seven*, 1–12.

solid figures were once all believed to have been destroyed and were known to us only through drawings, but one column figure has now been identified as one of the three figures in the drawings.[288] As shown in the drawing, all three column figures that once stood firmly in Abbot Suger's cloister show the solidity and substance of Provençal style, but it is the two destroyed figures that show the most marked stylistic resemblances to the Provençal work. These two figures convey the sense of a physical form beneath the drapery with its heavy folds, a physical form that is capable of supporting something of weight, capable of physical movement.

Saint-Denis. Drawings of column figures from Cloister of Saint-Denis.[289] Bibliothèque nationale de France

Metropolitan Museum of Art, New York. Column statue of a king, identified as one of the column figures (left figure in the drawing) from Cloister of Saint-Denis.

....

288   Vera K. Ostoia, "A Statue from Saint-Denis," *The Metropolitan Museum of Art Bulletin* 13, no. 10 (June 1955), 298–304. See also Sumner McKnight Crosby et al., *The Royal Abbey of Saint Denis in the Time of Abbot Suger (1122–1151)* (New York, NY: Metropolitan Museum of Art, 1981, especially Charles T. Little, "Monumental Sculpture at Saint-Denis Under the Patronage of Abbot Suger: The West Façade and the Cloister," 25–60, esp. 29–33 and 44–49.

289   The drawings made by Antoine Benoit and included as engravings in Dom Bernard de Montfaucon, *Les Monumens de la Monarchie Françoise*, (Paris, France: 1729), vol. I, pl. X were long believed to be the only visual record of the column figures from Abbot Suger's cloister.

Only a very limited amount of direct influence of Provençal style can be found elsewhere in the north. Acanthus foliage sculpture with undeniably close resemblance to the Provençal work can still be seen at Bourges Cathedral on the north portal lintel, probably from around 1160, which prominently displays both the five-petal cinquefoil with its stem emerging from its center, and a thin row of foliage, like elaborate horseshoes, along its lower edge, both motifs found at Arles.[290]

The Provençal pier figure would come to subtly influence the evolution of early Gothic style, but Abbot Suger's column figures were to reign supreme over Provençal pier figures in the development of French Gothic church façades. The Gothic column figures soon became larger, more solid, more integrally involved as the supporting member, but they were still column figures.

On the other hand, the failed Second Crusade would have consequences that would long be keenly felt throughout Christendom. Within the Holy Land itself, the crusaders' miserable defeat at Damascus sparked continuing reverberations, because the embarrassing debacle stoked and consolidated enthusiasm for the jihad in the Muslim world. Indeed, the heroic tale of the people of Damascus stopping the once feared but now ridiculed Christian warriors would long be celebrated.[291]

Moreover, the open split between King Louis and Queen Eleanor that erupted at Antioch would eventually come to spur the Capetian Plantagenet rivalry, with consequences that would long affect the history and map of Europe.[292] Eleanor did not back away from her demand for a divorce. Pope Eugenius knew his attempt to reconcile the couple in October 1149 had failed.

After the couple arrived back in Paris in November 1149, the unhappy Eleanor found the unsophisticated Île-de-France stifling. When she gave birth that winter to her second daughter, not having produced a male Capet heir in fifteen years of marriage, her argument of consanguinity began to be heard.[293]

In August 1151, Henry, Duke of Normandy, accompanied his father, the Count of Anjou, to Paris to pay due homage to King Louis, their feudal overlord, and

---

Photo: Montfaucon, *Les Monumens*, vol. I, plate X. Used here with permission of BnF or Bibliothèque nationale de France. (Figure here shown at the right has been moved up from its location on the original page to align the figures.)

290   See Willibald Sauerländer, *Gothic Sculpture in France 1140–1270* (London, UK: Thames and Hudson, 1972), 399-400 for the dating, and plates 34 and 35 for photos of the north portal sculpture at Bourges cathedral.

291   Hindley, *Brief*, 83

292   Hindley, *Brief*, 81.

293   Kelly, *Eleanor*, 73–74.

Eleanor was at court. Henry was a princely prize: heir through his father to the counties of Maine and Anjou, and, more importantly, through his mother, Matilda Empress, heir to Normandy and pretender to the throne of England. He was well educated, mature for his eighteen years of age, striking in appearance, bred to be a king. Eleanor, though almost thirty years of age, was charming, sophisticated, very attractive, with a lively mind, and held the vast territories of Aquitaine in her own name—a real prize fit for a prince who would be king. The next year, in March 1152, Eleanor received the annulment of her marriage, and within two months married the future King Henry II of England, Count of Anjou and Maine and Duke of Normandy.[294]

Eleanor fared far better than the vast majority of women in her time, better even than many other women born to wealthy families of privilege. Eleanor held the vast territorial holdings in the southwest in her own name. Women in Aquitaine could legally inherit and hold property at that time,[295] *and when her father, Guillaume, Count of Poitou and Duke of Aquitaine, died in 1137, leaving only two daughters as his heirs, he specified in his will that the duchy Eleanor was to inherit was not to be absorbed into her future husband's royal holdings but instead was to be held separately and inherited solely by Eleanor and her heirs. So even though King Louis VI, her feudal lord, had immediately arranged Eleanor's marriage to his sixteen-year-old son to double the Capetian realm, Eleanor continued to hold the Duchy of Aquitaine and the County of Poitou in her own name. When Eleanor obtained the dissolution of her marriage to King Louis VII and then married Henry in 1152, she took with her the vast territories she had inherited in the southwest. And when two years later Henry II became King of England, Eleanor's territories in Aquitaine became linked with the Angevin empire to be inherited by Eleanor's children with Henry.*[296]

....

294   Hindley, *Brief*, 81, 84, and Kelly, *Eleanor*, 73–81.

295   Aquitania had inherited the Visigothic Law and Roman Law, and the *Liber Judiciorum*, under which women had more rights than many of their contemporaries. Visigothic women of Spain and the Aquitaine could not only inherit land and title, but manage their property independent of their husbands, dispose of their property in legal wills if they had no heirs, as well as represent themselves in court.

296   Hindley, *Brief*, 81, and Kelly, *Eleanor*, 73–81.

Vespers
Evening—bells at sunset

Anno Domini MCLII
Arles, late September 1152

I t was to the greater glory of God, and in celebration of His grace to the cathedral and cloister at Arles, that the canons were now planning a wondrous and very special ceremony that would take place in one week: the translation of the relics of St. Trophîme from the church of Saint-Honorat in Les Alyscamps to the cathedral church at Arles.

The ceremony with a procession would celebrate the ongoing rebuilding of the cathedral and its claustral complex. Work had progressed well, in spite of the loss of Master Guillelmo. The new chapter house and the north gallery of the cloister were completed. The old refectory was almost refurbished. Work was expected to begin sometime soon on the dormitory and east gallery of the cloister. Although work on the cathedral nave was also coming along nicely, it was far from complete, even though the choir and high altar could certainly be used. In fact, it was in large part because work on decorating the west portal of the cathedral had not yet been begun that the decision had been taken to lead the grand procession first past the beautiful sculptures in the vaulted north gallery of the cloister and then on into the church through its south transept.

Pons had just this year been named *precentor*,[297] or cantor, putting him in charge of the musical portion of the services to direct the choral services, the choir, the processions, and the minor clergy. So it was Pons who was in charge of organizing the grand solemn procession.

"Have you checked on the progress the new seamstress is making on the preparation of the new bishop's chasuble to replace that horrible, ugly one done by that other incompetent woman?" demanded Dean Hughes Amelius, seated in the new chapter house. "As we both know, the archbishop is very fussy and has insisted he will not consecrate and wear such an ugly vestment." During his nine-year tenure as dean, Hughes Amelius[298] had learned that anything that could go wrong would go wrong, if given the opportunity.

"Yes, yes, yes," responded Pons with a wry smile. "I have not chased down the seamstress myself but instead delegated the task to that keen young novice, Pons Rebolli— the one who came here as a child about ten years ago while I was away. It was he who recommended that seamstress. But I approved the new design, and the archbishop will be pleased with this one. I am keeping track of it. In fact, I just received a report from the young man. He has seen the garment and applauds the beautiful needlework on it. The garment will be delivered by the end of the day, so we will have everything in plenty of time for the procession and ceremony next week. Now, let's briefly review the processional route once more." Pons was eager for the event to go well, and just a bit apprehensive that he may have overlooked some tiny detail.

"We will begin, of course, at the church of Saint-Honorat, in Les Alyscamps, the ancient and hallowed burial ground our cathedral chapter still uses for interment of our own faithful canons. Perhaps we should remind everyone again . . . No, rather, we must insist that the entire chapter must participate. After all, even though Les Alyscamps is located outside the old Roman city walls, it's really only a short walking distance southeast of the cathedral. I am certain the walk will not be too much of an effort for any of us, even for the oldest or most infirm, or even for the most overweight and rotund of us, even for 'Big Peter.' We'll cross over the little rivulet and enter the city south of the cathedral but then come up and enter the cathedral grounds through the canons' portal.

....

297   See Schneider, "Sculptures," 74–75, which cites the document Albanes and Chevalier, *Arles,* no. 563.

298   Albanes and Chevalier, *Arles,* lists Hugues Amiel as "*doyen*" 1143–1152.

"By the way, has the full chapter been informed that everyone, absolutely everyone, will participate?"

"Yes, yes, just this afternoon at *Nones*," retorted Hughes Amelius.

"Good. We will head directly to the northeast corner of the new claustral complex," Pons continued, "purposefully avoiding the ghastly construction site still spread all along the east side."

Piles of stone, haphazardly sorted into various sizes, vied for space with smaller awkward piles of timbers, some relatively unused, tall, and straight, but mostly former scaffolding and joists that had been only partially disassembled by the masons and builders. The tradesmen had been forced to leave them there after they were pressured to instead focus on the more immediately compelling project: to complete as much of the rebuilding of the cathedral nave as possible before the translation ceremony.

"Oh, I do wish we could get some of that awful mess cleaned up for our procession. There's so much stone and debris. Most of all, I do hope we can begin construction sometime soon on the east gallery and dormitory!" Pons added, with just a bit of exasperation.

"Now, now," Hughes Amelius began very calmly. "Remember, we began rebuilding the church along with the claustral complex, and when we did so, we knew such a large project would take much longer. We accepted the delay in completion of the claustral buildings in large part because of the additional cost for doing the church. But moving the blessed saint's relics here will help pay for it, at least for the reconstruction of the church."

"Yes, yes, I know," Pons responded meekly and a bit embarrassed at his outburst. "I do remember we figured all that out before beginning work on the church. And frankly, when I once discussed this with Jordan, he suggested that it might even be more profitable in the long run to leave all the construction mess around. The pilgrims, who will now start coming here to venerate the relics, will make their donation to secure the benevolence of the saint, providing a continuous and ongoing stream of revenue, but they may feel compelled to contribute to the rebuilding program as well."

"So," Pons continued, returning to the plan, "we will walk quickly past the construction mess to the northeast corner. The north gallery of the cloister is completed, so we can proceed from the pier figure of St. Stephen at the east corner, cross over the north gallery, and end at the pier figure of St. Trophîme at the western corner, before descending the stairs to the church.

"I suggest we start the Gregorian chant once we are within the claustral complex, at the east end of the gallery. It will help show off and call attention to our very special and unusual vaulted cloister gallery, and with a large procession I believe we will get some good resonance there, even though the gallery is open on the garden side. I really would like to have a glorious event.

"From the figure of St. Trophîme at the western corner we will pass through and descend the stairs west of the chapter house to enter the cathedral at the transept and then proceed to the altar. There the new vestments will be waiting, to be sanctified with incense and holy water, and after donning the consecrated vestments, the archbishop and assisting clergy will receive the venerated relics."

"It will all work out just fine, praise be to God," responded Hughes Amelius to Pon's unposed question. "Even though our processional will not pass through the west portal of the church, where work hasn't even been begun yet, it will still be a splendid event. Always keep in mind that our main goal in translating the relics in such a spectacular ceremony is to raise support for the building project—both financial support and pledges of loyalty from outside benefactors and donors—and perhaps also, in part, to win more tolerance and acceptance by members of chapter for enduring all the unavoidable inconveniences of the building campaign."

"I think you're telling me that we can't go wrong. The procession will be a huge success if we just bring the relics safely back into the church for everyone to venerate here, including my nephew!" concluded Pons with a smile.

Pons had recognized that the Baux clan were becoming dissatisfied again, and that if another war were to erupt, it was not at all certain that Hugh, the new Lord of Baux would continue to honor his father's pledge to honor and defend the church and *claustrum* at Arles. Raymond of Baux had died before signing the peace treaty in Barcelona, and although Hugh and his brothers did sign a peace treaty at Arles in 1150, after agreeing to its terms, relinquishing their rights to the counties claimed through their grandmother, and accepting compensation for them, it was clear that neither they, nor their mother, were going to accept the outcome. Pons had used the translation of the relics as the pretext for approaching Hugh and suggesting that if he as the new Lord of Baux were to confirm the pledge originally made by his father, ensuring their safety, the chapter could then ceremoniously move those most venerated relics back into the cathedral.

"Indeed," Hughes Amelius responded, "and as he requested, your nephew, the Lord of Baux, has a spot reserved for him right at the new steps near the transept of the church here where he not only can watch the procession but can touch the holy relics, which certainly won't hurt him, especially now that he is starting to stir things up again about his territorial claims. After all, he has confirmed his pledge of support for the church and its *claustrum*."[299]

"Yes, and he pledged more financial support for my claustral project, too!" Pons added with delight.

Just then there was a small commotion at the canons' portal, and a young novice came to call Pons to attend there. As Pons approached, he could see the figure of a woman carrying a bundle, and he realized this must be the seamstress who had promised to deliver the newly made bishop's chasuble today. He quickened his steps and, with an expectant smile on his face, greeted her.

"Greetings! I hope you are delivering the new chasuble?" he said with relief, now glancing impersonally at the woman as she pushed back the hood of her cape to reveal her face. It was she! A more mature, now matronly, but still very beautiful Beatrice bowed slightly and formally presented herself to him. Looking directly into his eyes, with her lips pressed tightly together— was there the slightest trace of a smile, or was that a sneer?—she handed him the bundle without saying a word. Pons carefully untied the string and opened the protective coarse muslin cloth to see the beautiful, magnificently embroidered and finely finished vestment, carefully folded to reveal its exquisitely detailed needlework and meticulously carried out artistry.

"It's very beautiful," Pons managed to say throatily, with a bit of a cough.

"It's as promised, and what you have paid for," Beatrice answered calmly, confidently.

Closing his eyes for a moment, Pons swallowed with difficulty. Beatrice's quiet formality, her lack of affect, her businesslike politeness all pierced his heart, cutting him to the quick and shredding his resolve. He was not prepared

....

299   See Albanes and Chevalier, *Arles,* no. 563. This is actually two documents, as clarified
       in Schneider, "Sculptures," 29–33. The first records the pledge of Raimundus de Baltio;
       the second records the pledge of his son, Ugo de Baltio, reconfirming his father's
       pledge. Raimundus de Baltio's pledge in the first half of this document can be dated
       to ca.1142–43, and it would have been after the death of his father in 1150 that Ugo
       of Baux, the new Lord of Baux, would have confirmed his intent to honor his father's
       earlier pledge, and the later document is firmly dated in the text to 1152.

for this. What could he say to her, this woman he now knew he had wronged so terribly for so long? What could he possibly say to her?

After carefully closing the bundle and handing it to the young novice, whom he instructed to deliver it directly to Dean Hughes Amelius, he motioned to Beatrice, inviting her to walk with him.

"We have only a few minutes, but would you be willing to take a short walk with me up the hill to the ancient theater remains . . . to talk privately?" he asked tentatively.

"I have the time, if you are permitted and are willing to . . . walk and talk with me," she responded evenly and very coolly.

They turned through the portal, leaving the compound, and walked next to each other but completely separate, some distance apart, not touching, not speaking. At the top of the hill, Pons gestured to Beatrice to sit on one of the stone seats of the ancient theater, and he sat down next to her.

There was a long, long period of silence.

"How have you been?" he began, very awkwardly.

"As well as could be expected," she responded rather coldly.

"Have you married?" he asked expectantly.

"No, I have not," she answered curtly.

He was not at all sure what to say. His mind was in turmoil. All he could think was, "How do you ask forgiveness from someone for what you did, when you also know that what you did was right?" In denying Beatrice, Pons knew he had been following God's plan. God had spoken to Pons. God had shown Pons His plan for him, and Pons knew that what he had done was right.

But Pons had laid all the blame on Beatrice for his own lapse, for his temporary digression from God's plan, and he now recognized and understood how wrong that had been. His blaming Beatrice was wrong. His hatred of her because she was a woman was wrong. He now knew Beatrice was not evil; she was not Satan. She was but a woman, a mere woman, destined by nature to be a lowly vessel of sins of the flesh. As a man, he should have been able to rise above those temptations of the flesh, so he was as much a sinner—perhaps even more a sinner—than she. How do you ask forgiveness from someone for having mistakenly thought she was Satan?

He hesitantly and very gently reached toward her, to take her hand in his. Not knowing what to make of this gesture, and cowed by the improbability of it occurring, she hesitated but did not pull her hand away. When he saw she did not seem repulsed, he gently, innocently, naïvely held her hand, her roughened, weathered, and well-used hand. He wished with all his heart he could as easily ask for her forgiveness.

"I am sorry, so very sorry," he began haltingly, continuing after a very long pause. Dumbstruck, Beatrice listened carefully, her mind quickening as her heart began to race.

"I am so sorry. I've long done you a terrible injustice. I blamed you for what I shouldn't have," he began.

"What is he saying? What is this about? Where is this going? What does he want?" Beatrice asked herself incredulously, without speaking a word.

"Please forgive me, I beg you," Pons continued. "I now know that I wanted what happened between us as much as you did. We were both so young, so naïve. We are both human, after all. Only human. We both have human desires, human frailties, and human weaknesses" He turned to her with real tears in his eyes.

Thinking quickly, and indeed recognizing that after so many years of refusing to talk to her, refusing to even acknowledge her, and actually turning his back on her, he was now talking to her about human desires and weaknesses, Beatrice misread his intentions. Her mind leaped to the worst possible interpretations.

"Who does he think he is?" she asked herself. "What is he trying to get this time? Is he looking to fornicate? Is he hoping to use me again?"

She jumped to her feet, highly indignant. Yet at the same time, she was also just a bit relieved, and the tiniest little flicker of hope was rekindled—hope at the possibility that her life might finally yet change. Her life had been so hard, so very hard, so unbearably hard. Her situation had been so very difficult for the past two decades, certainly since their first encounter. If only he knew. But how could he? How could he—this well-fed priest who had everything taken care of for him in his comfortable church buildings—know?

For his part, when Beatrice jumped to her feet, Pons feared he had offended her by admitting overtly that he had blamed her. He, too, jumped up and quickly but almost involuntarily caught her to stop her from running away offended before he could make amends, and then, again involuntarily, took her into his arms to console her. She could not help but respond and put her arms around him.

They clung together in silence, innocently hugging, each starved for so long for the loving embrace of another human being, each so hungry at their core for the warm touch of another person. Both were deeply comforted by this simple act of acceptance, by the warm touch of another person, by this genuine human warmth they had both craved for so long but had each either denied themselves or been denied. Deep within, each of them desperately needed this warmth, this emotional support, this bonding with another caring person. Both needed to be touched. Both needed to be held. Both were, after all, only human.

As they clung together, the little spark of hope within Beatrice began flaring up uncontrollably, involuntarily, against her wishes. Was he proposing to take her, to take care of her? To somehow make her his own? Had he finally given up that celibacy foolishness? Was her life at last to change, even a little bit, for the better?

Still clinging together in silence, after some time Pons recognized that his member's response to this physical touch was betraying him, and he had to pull away from her. Now facing her directly but standing a bit away from her, he composed himself before beginning to speak.

"If God had not spoken so clearly to me, if . . . Well, things might have worked out so very differently for us," he continued at last, again throatily. "I truly believe I loved you that night. I think I even wanted to marry you that night, and I thought about you for so long afterwards. You are still so very beautiful, and so very desirable, as desirable as ever. I still love you. I do still love you."

Listening intently, and looking directly into Pons's eyes, Beatrice found her resolve beginning to melt. "Yes, yes!" she thought. "Maybe at last . . . Oh, please, please, merciful God."

"But God did speak to me," Pons continued unthinkingly after a moment, "and He clearly laid out for me the path my life is to take. That path cannot include you or any woman. God has told me to build a cloistered chapter, to bring the *vita apostolica*, the celibate communal life, to our chapter." He explained this patiently, honestly trying to make amends with the woman he had wronged. "I do so hope you can see God's plan for me and understand . . . and give me your blessing," he concluded, naïvely taking Beatrice by the shoulders and expecting her to smile and nod, to endorse what he had said.

Beatrice gasped, pierced to the heart by his words and embarrassed to her core at her own foolishness in letting even a small flicker of hope flare up.

Yellow bile now welled up and coursed through her body, choking her and blinding her in a choleric rage.

"You stupid ass! You foolish pig!" she now shrieked, pushing him away violently. "You turd! You turd! Who do you think you are? You men take your pleasure with us women and then run away. You run away from life, hiding behind your priestly robes. First you run away to take refuge in your chapter, and now you're going to hide out in a cloister!

"You and your damned, warm, safe, communal life! That's fine for men like you. I'd counsel any young man to escape into your safe, comfortable, communal life! Does God ever talk to you about us women? You have no idea what it's like to be used and thrown away! You don't know what it's like to be deserted, to be alone, all alone, to have to fight to stay alive. To be hungry, to be cold, to have no one to take care of you, to not know whether or not you're safe, to not know whether you're going to live or die," she screamed as he, in confusion, tried to touch her arm again, to calm her.

"You can go to hell in your damned cloister! Blessing? You'll not get any blessing from me. You and your cloister be damned!" she spat, scratching him as she violently pulled away before running off as quickly as she could, mingling with the crowd to disappear as she neared the Roman arena.

Shocked at the vehemence of her response, Pons was dumbstruck. He had truly been trying to put things right by asking for her forgiveness, by explaining to her about God's mission for him. So he thought. Yet it had all gone awry. She apparently had been angry all along and was even angrier, very bitter, and more unforgiving now.

He was so puzzled, so completely flummoxed at what had happened that he almost could not believe it. What had he done wrong? Why couldn't she understand what he was trying so earnestly to tell her? How could she not respond to what God wanted, to what God had told him to do? Confused and rather dazed, Pons held his head in his hands for several moments before finally slowly turning around to begin walking away.

He would throw himself back into his work to finish his project, to finish preparations for the solemn translation of the relics that was to take place next week. Work would help. Work always helped. God's work always helped. He would lose himself in his work. With a furrowed brow and a heavy heart, Pons descended the hill to return to the cathedral compound.

When the bells rang to mark the end of day at sunset and to call everyone to leave work and come for *Vespers*, Pons was so relieved to be able to join in celebrating the office. As always, the service began with the *lucernare,* the ritual lighting of the lamps, recalling the office of the lights at the Church of the Holy Sepulchre. Pons always found the *lucernare* comforting somehow, because he, like everyone else, associated it with the risen Christ. At *Vespers* at the end of the day, the *lucernare* promised the rising of the sun the next morning, the rising sun that recalled the risen Christ and that was marked with bells at the beginning of the day.[300] Both hours suggested the risen Christ, and the echo, the implied promise, the repeated association at both the beginning and end of day was somehow very comforting. Comforting not only in its imagery, but in its repetitive rhythm, its predictability.

This solemn office continued with a hymn of light and an opening prayer. Then came the singing of a series of psalms called the *Lucernales*, the first and principal of which was Psalm 140, the *Psalmus lucernalis*, which was usually accompanied by another important ritual: the offering of incense, which could recall the evening sacrifices once offered in Jerusalem's temple.[301]

"Domine clamavi ad te exaudi me intende voci meae cum clamavero ad te

Dirigatur oratio mea sicut incensum in conspectu tuo elevatio manuum mearum sacrificium vespertinum"

(*Psalmus* 140:1-2)

"I have cried to thee, O Lord; hear me: hearken to my voice, when I cry to thee

Let my prayer be directed as incense in thy sight; the lifting up of my hands, as evening sacrifice"

(Psalm 140:1-2)

After the singing of the psalms, the recitation of supplication, commemorations or litanies, some intercessions, and the collect, there was, as always, concluding prayers and the blessing.

After *Vespers*, Pons returned to the cloister and stood at the west end of the north gallery. There she was on the capital, the siren, whom he recognized as Beatrice, with her lovely face needing to be held, her full mouth begging to be

---

300   On this association, and for the structure of the *Vespers* service, see Powell, "Introduction."

301   On this association, see Powell, "Introduction."

kissed, her rounded breasts wanting to be caressed, her beautiful torso begging to . . . Turning quickly away, he focused intently on *luxuria*, lust, whom he now recognized as Isabel, with her demonized body luring men into damnation, drawing them into the fires of hell. But now he could turn around the northwest corner pier and see Ste. Mary Magdalene, the woman, one of the three Holy Women who were buying spices, preparing to cleanse and anoint Jesus's body. Mary Magdalene, the woman, the whore, the reformed whore, the reformed sinner, forgiven by Christ, beloved by Jesus, who would anoint Jesus's body.

"Why? Why couldn't I make Beatrice understand?" he sighed.

The following week, the day for the solemn event arrived and was another of those glorious, absolutely perfect Provençal days. The sky was a clear azure blue, and the sun emblazoned the world in brightness, with clear light, making all the colors of the earth more luminous, the yellows warmer, the oranges more vibrant, the reds more on fire, the blues clearer, the greens fresher, and the browns richer and more alive. Surely, thought Pons, God was bestowing His blessing on this solemn occasion.

Many of the faithful had gathered outside the small church of Saint-Honorat at Les Alyscamps to witness the solemn ceremony there with the procession and translation of the relics. Les Alyscamps, sitting on the Roman *Via Aurelia* and originally a Roman necropolis, had early become a renowned Christian cemetery, where the martyr St. Genest and the first bishops of Arles were buried. After the priory of Saint-Honorat was established there in 1040, Les Alyscamps had become a required stop on the pilgrimage route to Santiago de Compostela.

With much ceremony, the service began, with chanting, incense, and Archbishop Raymond de Monte Rotundo officiating. At length the service culminated with the archbishop blessing the reliquary containing the holy relics of the venerated St. Trophîme. Then, after raising the reliquary up and placing it on a large vestment-covered tray with handles, he covered the reliquary lightly with another vestment before again blessing both the covered reliquary and its carrier tray. Hughes Amelius as dean; Pons de Baux as *precentor*; and two other canons, William Garnerius as *capiscol*, or chancellor, and Peter de Armazaniels as sacristan,[302] now each stepped up to take one handle, to gently lift the well-protected precious load. They then followed immediately

---

302   Albanes and Chevalier, *Arles,* includes lists of those holding chapter positions, but the lists are incomplete.

behind the archbishop, who began to lead the entire chapter of canons in a procession out of the church of Saint-Honorat.

They walked slowly, solemnly, quietly, with all the faithful in attendance now joining the end of what became a very long procession. From the church of Saint-Honorat they walked down *l'Allée des Sarcophages*, with its rows and rows of Roman and early Christian carved stone sarcophagi. Continuing to walk in procession, they left Les Alyscamps, finally crossing over to the old Roman city walls of Arles.

The Provençal sun beating incessantly on the procession made the archbishop and canons uncomfortably warm in their heavy clerical garments, formal garb that was more suited to the cooler interior of a stone church. Pons now began to feel a bit lightheaded, even a bit nauseous. The leaders of the procession followed along the ancient city walls, disregarding the heat, before eventually passing through the canons' portal and entering the cathedral grounds. They slowly crossed to the northeast corner, always followed by their train, the long procession. At the northeast corner of the cloister, the five leading the procession, the archbishop and the four canons carrying the precious relics, stopped for a few minutes at the statue of St. Stephen. Here Pons, as *precentor*, was to lead the beginning of a Gregorian chant, but just as he was about to raise his voice in song, he stopped abruptly.

Arles. Cloister, north gallery, looking west from northeast corner.

Pons looked directly at the figure of St. Stephen, one of the first deacons in the early church, and the first Christian martyr. The saint appeared perhaps not unlike Pons himself, except that Pons was a bit leaner, somewhat taller, and of course much older. For just a fleeting moment Pons thought that the figure of Stephen was staring directly down at him, with a slightly quizzical look of sad resignation. Was Stephen distressed at being bumped from his place of honor as namesake of the church which after today would no longer be dedicated to him? Was Stephen trying to tell him of his disappointment?

Arles. Cloister, northeast corner. Pier relief, Martyrdom of St. Stephen.   *Arles. Cloister, northeast corner. Pier figure, St. Stephen.*

"No, no," thought Pons to himself in answer to the saint. "We are honoring you by beginning the chant here in front of you, but, more importantly, we have commemorated you and your martyrdom with a relief sculpture depicting your stoning. No other figure—other than our Lord Jesus Christ, of course—is so honored here." Pons could not help but turn to look at the depiction of martyrdom, with two men hurling stones as Stephen knelt, praying, while Christ, enframed above as a vision, is blessing the martyr.

Pons now confidently raised his voice and began the chant, singing masterfully, in a loud, clear voice, and the practiced voices of the other first few canons joined his in perfect unison to rise up clearly and strongly and ring through the stone tunnel vault. The voices of the other canons following in the procession tried to join in, but being out in the open air, their chant was softer and more diffuse, with no resonance at all as their vocal notes dissipated into the air.

Still singing, still in the northeast corner, the lightheaded Pons was just about to begin walking again to lead the procession when his eyes fell on the pier figure of St. Paul. The figure was bald, older, bearded, slim yet strongly built, and this life-sized Paul seemed to be shifting his body and turning his head to speak to Pons. Had Pons ever noticed that before? He had always been so busy getting the north gallery finished that he now realized he had never really looked closely, intimately, at these figures before!

 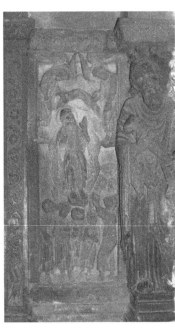

Arles. Cloister, northeast corner pier figure. St. Paul.

Arles. Cloister, northeast corner pier relief. Ascension of Christ. (Pier figure of St. Paul to the right.)

Paul was trying to direct him to look at what was immediately next to him: the relief depicting Christ, within a crowd of his disciples, ascending to heaven in a mandorla and being received by two angels. But for Paul directing his attention, Pons would have missed the image showing this most important event!

The leaders of the procession now began walking again, but slowly, in cadence with the chant, and the choral music began slowly building under the stone vault as more of the procession entered the north gallery. Pons's eyes now fell on the large pier figures of Jesus Christ with Doubting Thomas. Here was Christ, who with such sadness and deep humility had removed His upper tunic to expose most of His beautifully smooth chest. Christ was pointing with quiet resignation to the wound in His side, openly inviting Thomas to place his finger there. And Thomas, fully dressed, arrogant, and so impudent, was boldly extending his hand to disrespectfully probe Christ's wound with his own finger.

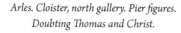

Arles. Cloister, north gallery. Pier figures. Doubting Thomas and Christ.

Arles. Cloister, north gallery. Pier figures. Doubting Thomas and Christ; detail.

The sound of the choral chant was growing steadily and beginning to swell. Pons's gaze now fell on the three large figures: Christ and the two Pilgrims on the road to Emmaus, dressed as travelers with caps, capes, walking sticks, and satchels. But Pons now noted these pilgrims were clearly en route to Emmaus because their satchels were decorated with little flowers rather than the scallop shell of St. James, always shown on satchels of pilgrims to Santiago de Compostela.

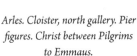

Arles. Cloister, north gallery. Pier figures. Christ between Pilgrims to Emmaus.   *Arles. Cloister, north gallery. Pier figures. Christ and Pilgrim to Emmaus; detail.*

The choral chant now began swelling up through the entire length of stone tunnel vault, where its pure tones resounded, reverberating slightly, in a resonance that created overtones. But the strong, well-practiced chant of the canons singing in perfect unison under the stone vault was now counterbalanced by the choral sound of the clerics and laypeople in the long procession, who were in a different medium: open air under an open sky. They were trying to join in the chant outside, but their less practiced voices were following, imitating, and were therefore delayed ever so slightly, creating echoes, transient and sometimes punctuating echoes, complementary and ephemeral.

Pons was transfixed, surrounded by the sound. As Pons had been exalted by the beauty and purity of the Gregorian chant sung in perfect unison, he was now equally carried away—overcome, even—by the magnificent added complexity of this echoing chant song. His soul soared, lifted by the cadence. His soul was stirred as it had not been since visiting Cluny. God was here. He knew God was here. God was coming to him. God was going to speak to him.

He closed his eyes for a moment, filled with hope, then opened them again to glance to the right as his gaze fell for a brief moment on the north wall.

Arles. Cloister, north wall of north gallery.

| *Arles. Cloister, capital on north wall of north gallery. Siren. (near middle on photo of wall.)* | *Arles. Cloister, capital on north wall of north gallery. Luxuria (lust). (to left on photo of wall.)* |

For a brief moment his gaze fell on the capital with the small, seductive figure of the siren, the temptress, the female, the half-woman with the soft, voluptuous torso. But he immediately stepped forward and instinctively looked two arches further ahead to the capital of lust, where those voluptuous breasts were being eaten by the serpents of hell, the chastisement for such carnal desire, which had no place here today, no place at all.

Momentarily startled, he immediately turned his head again to his left and was relieved when his gaze met St. Peter. Pons was being commanded by the life-size figure of St. Peter, bearded, with a head of loose curls, who

Arles. Cloister, northwest corner pier. Pier figure of St. Peter; Relief of Christ's Empty Tomb.

Arles. Cloister, northwest corner pier figure. St. Trophîme. (Flanked by relief of Empty Tomb and pier figure of St. Peter, to the left; and by relief of Holy Women Buying Spices and pier figure of St. John, to the right.)

was shifting his body slightly and turning his face away from the canon. Pons now understood. Yes, Pons understood. Peter was commanding him, directing him, instructing him, and he obediently looked beyond Peter to the relief showing the empty tomb of Christ's Resurrection, with angels and sleeping soldiers.

Pons was now totally transfixed and transported by the music, and he thought he finally understood. Yes! He now fully understood. He now knew his steps were retracing, but backward in time, the miraculous appearances of Christ after His Crucifixion—the Crucifixion that was the core of his belief. And leading him along this path were the apostles St. Peter and St. Paul.

Just as he was turning, along with the other three bearers of the precious relics, to enter the portal to the stairs west of the chapter house, Pons's gaze now fell on the figure of St. Trophîme. He suddenly stopped walking, abruptly halting the progress of the procession because again he understood. Pons recognized that the thin, ascetic bishop, whose relics he was carrying, had raised his hand . . . to bless him. To bless him! The bishop was now blessing him. St. Trophîme, to whom the church and cloister would be dedicated, was blessing him, Pons.

St. Trophîme was giving him God's blessing! God was blessing him!

And next to St. Trophîme were the three Holy Women buying Spices—one of them

Mary Magdalene, the reformed sinner, beloved by Jesus, forgiven by Jesus. God had forgiven them both, Mary Magdalene and him, Pons, the sinner.

Still stopped, motionless, he now saw, as if for the first time, next to the Holy Women, the pier figure of St. John, the beloved apostle. The apostle Christ had loved most.

Pons's voice now faltered as he swooned and gasped for breath. The music had transmuted all of this, all of the cloister gallery, everything around him. He knew God was speaking to him through these sculptures, speaking directly to him. God had forgiven him! God loved him! God was blessing him! God was instructing him to complete his mission of living in emulation of the apostles. God was giving His approval to what Pons was trying so hard to do. God was saying to him, "Yes, this is good!"

Pons was overwhelmed. His direct communion with God now overcame him, and he began shaking visibly and started to collapse. The keen young Pons Rebolli, immediately recognizing that something was amiss, stepped forward unexpectedly, momentarily breaking the lineup of the procession, to take Pons by the elbow and waist to help support him.

Arles. Cloister, northwest corner pier. Relief of Holy Women Buying Spices; Pier Figure of St. John.

After taking a few slow, deep breaths, Pons was able to straighten up again and continue walking unsupported, but as if in a trance. He continued singing and carrying the sacred relics, but he was no longer aware of where he was or what he was doing. He was elsewhere; he was communing with God. He was no longer aware that he was now again leading the procession through the portal and down the stairs into the south transept of the newly reconstructed cathedral with its newly raised choir above the crypt where the relics would eventually be placed.[303] He was no longer aware that he passed his nephew

----

303   On the newly raised choir with apse, main altar, and transept raised four meters above the crypt that would receive the relics of St. Trophime in 1152, see Rouquette, *Provence,* 271–274.

Hugh, the new Lord of Baux who would now honor a renewed pledge to support and defend the church and cloister at Arles.

Approaching near the altar, the bearers set down the reliquary. Pons continued to remain so absorbed in his own private dialogue with God that he was still unaware of what he was doing, but nevertheless he continued assisting with the ceremony, reacting appropriately, apparently by rote. When the new vestments were sanctified with incense and holy water, the experienced canon performed his duties well in assisting the archbishop in receiving the venerated relics and then finally carrying them again down into the newly refurbished crypt, completing their translation to the church, which would now be dedicated solely to St. Trophîme.

The several years ahead would prove to be extremely difficult for Pons, and he would dearly need again and again to recall that God had indeed spoken to him, that God had given him His approval and His blessing during the translation ceremony.

*　　*　　*

Two years earlier, in 1150, Pons had already mourned the personal loss of his older brother, Raymond, Lord of Baux, who had treated him benevolently as a child and whose political and territorial ambitions had failed. After Raymond of Baux was forced to submit to the Count of Barcelona, all four of his sons had relinquished their hereditary claim, signing a peace treaty at Arles in 1150.

But the peace would not last. In 1155 Raymond's widow, Stephanie, and her four sons mounted a second brief war against the Catalans to claim the lands, again with the support of the house of Toulouse, but this time without the support of the Consulate of Arles that had hosted the signing of the now broken peace treaty. Once again, the House of Baux received official sanction and confirmation of their claims, this time from the new Holy Roman Emperor, Frederick Barbarossa, but again it was to no avail. By 1156 the Baux lost not only the war, but much of their land holdings and castles as well and retained only the castles at Baux and Trinquetaille, along with their defenses in and near Arles.

The proud House of Baux was thoroughly humiliated. Dispossessed of its land holdings, it had lost much of its power and influence, as well its income from those lands. The Baux had not yet completely given up their hope of claiming the territory, but Canon Pons could no longer be certain the support he had previously enjoyed from his family would continue from his new benefactor, his nephew Hugh II. After the defeat in 1156, the Baux neither could, nor would so enthusiastically have defended the church and claustrum *at Arles. And Pons could no longer count on their unfailing, continuing financial support for his project.*

The situation within the city of Arles was becoming ever more unstable. In 1150 Archbishop Raymond de Monte Rotundo had drafted a charter strengthening the consulate of Arles, but the archbishop's relationship with the town of Arles had deteriorated and was deeply strained.

Archbishop Raymond de Monte Rotundo moved his principal residence from Arles to Salon, to the Château de l'Empéri,[304] built in the ninth century on the rock of Puech, the biggest castle fortress in Provence in the twelfth century. The town of Arles revolted against the archbishop. By the 1160s the first statutes of the consulate were drafted.[305]

In addition, and perhaps even more importantly, in mid-century the entire Christian world was to suffer the loss of three great men, influential leaders who had left their mark on Christianity forever. If one man can affect the course of history and change the world for better or worse, these three Christian leaders certainly did, and all of Christendom, including Canon Pons, would mourn their loss. All three had directly influenced Pons's path, and Pons now mourned the loss of two who had been his spiritual mentors.

One was Bernard of Clairvaux, whose life was a model for renouncing personal wealth and property to live the truly communal celibate life, which for Pons as a canon, rather than a monk, meant adopting the Rule of St. Augustine and the vita apostolica. *Bernard of Clairvaux was a well-respected leader, who helped make successful the monastic Order of Cîteaux, which promoted embracing hard physical labor, poverty, communal life, and celibacy, all values of austerity. Yet after dedicating his life to selflessly serving the church, toward the end of his life Bernard found himself in what he called a "season of calamities." The heresies he had fought so hard continued to flourish. The Second Crusade he was called on to promote had failed so disastrously that he proclaimed "divine judgments" were the cause of the failure. The celebrated monk became an object of abuse.*

Although still strong in spirit, his body began to fail him as he continued the severe fasting and hard labor of his austere life. As his health failed, he begged "to

---

304   See "Histoire d'Arles à l'Époque Médiévale: Déplacement du Lieu de Résidence des Archévêques," *Wikipedia.*

305   See "Histoire d'Arles à l'Époque Médiévale: La Création du Consulat," *Wikipedia.*

depart and be with Christ," and when his fellow monks prayed for his recovery, he asked them, "Why do you thus detain a miserable man? Spare me. Spare me and let me depart." He died on August 20, 1153.[306]

Pons's other mentor was Peter the Venerable, whose attitude toward art had influenced Pons's decision to build a beautifully decorated cloister with vaulted galleries richly decorated with magnificent sculpture as the heart of the cloister complex. As head of the Order of Cluny, Peter the Venerable presided over the wealthiest and most influential monastic order in Europe. He refused to have anything to do with the Second Crusade, believing that Muslims should be met not with armies and swords, but with scholars and dialogue. He is often credited with designing the theological program for the portal at Vézelay depicting the Mission of the Apostles. As abbot of Cluny for thirty-four years, he had guided the order at the apex of its golden age. This golden age of Cluny had nurtured art and music in the church, had encouraged and nurtured the elaborate decoration of churches with both figural and decorative sculpture and painting, and had culminated in the construction of Cluny III, the largest, grandest, and most beautiful church ever built at that time. He died at the pinnacle of glory and success on December 25, 1156.[307]

The third leader the Christian world now lost was Abbot Suger. Early in 1151, a year before the marriage of Eleanor of Aquitaine and King Louis VII was severed, Abbot Suger passed from the world never having realized his great hope of seeing the Holy Land made securely safe once again. A humble, wise counselor and mentor to King Louis, who called him "Father of his Country," Abbot Suger died with fame and honor, having served two generations of French monarchs. He acted as regent during King Louis's crusade and subsequently built a cloister embellished with large, physically substantive column figures. Most importantly, however, Abbot Suger envisioned and created a new style of art. His new vision of light and space created a new style of architecture, starting in the ambulatory and radiating chapels of the choir at the abbey church of Saint-Denis. He envisioned and created a new style of sculptural church decoration with rows of statues of Old Testament kings, queens and prophets addorsed to columns on the "royal portal" of the west

....

306   This well-known quote is frequently found. See for instance "St. Bernard of Clairvaux," *Medieval Sourcebook*, https://sourcebooks.fordham.edu/source/eb9-bernard.asp. See also James Morison, *The Life and Times of Saint Bernard Abbot of Clairvaux AD 1091–1153*, (Cambridge, UK: Cambridge University Press, 1863; digital version, 2012), 497.

307   "Blessed Peter of Montboissier," *The Catholic Encyclopedia*.

façade at Saint-Denis. The new style of art would be called "Gothic," and it would put France forever at the forefront of culture. The new Gothic style would come to reign supreme in architecture, sculpture, and painting.

Though it was the new Gothic style that would triumph, during that decade in mid-century the sculptural façade of the abbey church of Saint-Gilles gained renown. The abbey church became an important pilgrimage site, bringing many pilgrims flocking into the region. In a papal bull, Pope Adrian IV (1154–1159) granted an indulgence of forty days to those faithful who made the pilgrimage to visit the church of Saint-Gilles,[308] and written reports from possibly as early as 1157 describe the large crowds of people trying to get next to the saint's tomb there.[309]

Both the themes and the style from the façade sculpture at Saint-Gilles soon traveled up the Rhône River Valley as sculptors visiting the church returned home to carve their own copies. Within Provence and not too far away at Beaucaire, within a decade or so, ten scenes of the Passion of Christ were copied from ones on the superstructure of Saint-Gilles, but in a crude, inferior, rustic style, for a long sculptural frieze on the façade at Notre-Dame-des-Pommiers, where they were reused when the church was reconstructed.[310]

Further up the Rhône, the theme of the Last Supper from the lintel of the central portal at Saint-Gilles was copied in Burgundy on the lintel of the church of Saint-Julien-de-Jonzy by the middle or third quarter of the century.[311] At Condrieu, a tympanum and lintel, probably carved in the 1150s and later reused there, shows the Holy Women at the Sepulchre, the Crucifixion, and Christ Carrying the Cross, as well as the Last Supper, all themes taken directly from Saint-Gilles.[312]

But sculptors also came to the region from much farther afield, from the Italian states. The ancient Via Francigena *was an important trade and pilgrimage route connecting Rome and France in the twelfth century, when it was also used to link with the pilgrimage route to Santiago de Compostela. The* Via Francigena *was not a single paved Roman road, but a general route, so it offered various alternative pathways. It began in Rome, went northward through western Tuscany,*

---

308   Stoddard, *Façade*, 158 cites Goiffon, *Bullaire*, 78 on the papal bull.

309   Stoddard, *Façade*, 158.

310   See Stoddard, *Façade*, 179–197 for the dependence of the frieze at Beaucaire on Saint-Gilles. Remains of the frieze were later reused there when the church was reconstructed.

311   See Beckwith, *Early*, fig. 205.

312   Stoddard, *Façade*, 150–151. Stoddard notes that it was A. K. Porter who dated this tympanum to the 1150s after identifying the architectural structures depicted in the scenes as monuments in Jerusalem, one of which was not completed until 1154.

through Lucca, to Piacenza and Pavia. From that area, one could either continue northward, crossing the Alps to Lausanne and Switzerland into France, Besancon, Chalons-sur-Marne, Rheims, Arras, to Sombre and the English Channel, which could then be crossed to Canterbury. Or, from the Piacenza and Pavia area, one could instead head west to join the route to Santiago de Compostela, crossing the mountains through Torino, Sagra di San Michele and Susa, and on to Arles, Saint-Gilles, Toulouse, and eventually Compostela.

One sculptor who must have taken that route and who most probably saw both the cloister at Arles and the façade at Saint-Gilles was a Guglielmo,[313] *who is known by an inscription to have carved an altar in 1158–1161 for the Cathedral of Pisa, although the altar was later dismantled and moved to the Cathedral at Cagliari. On the front face of both long pieces is a salient group of three figures in very high relief, all standing on a plinth, one facing forward, flanked by two facing obliquely, and the salient figures have little relationship to what is either above or below them. This configuration of three grouped figures in high relief standing on a salient plinth first appeared as a structural component in the north gallery of the Arles cloister, where the supporting pier figures were a solution to supporting a heavy vault, but on Guglielmo's altar, it is purely decorative, and probably was copied from the pier figures on the piers at Arles.*

Two of the reliefs on this altar show the three Holy Women at the empty tomb with soldiers beneath and recall the pier reliefs at Arles and the friezes at Saint-Gilles. Six other altar reliefs show themes that also appear on capitals in the east gallery at Arles, including the Annunciation, Visitation, and Nativity with the washing of the babe, and an extended Magi cycle, including the Magi before Herod, the Massacre of the Innocents, the Adoration of the Magi, and the Return of the Magi.

---

313   This is probably not the Guillelmo who worked earlier at Arles, because their styles are quite different.

A possible relationship between Guglielmo's altar and both the frieze sculptures at Saint-Gilles and the sculptures in the cloister at Arles has long been discussed and argued as central to the debate about whether there was an influence by the Provencal monuments on Pisan and Tuscan sculpture, or vice versa. Most scholars argue that the new proto-Renaissance style developed independently from antique influences in the two sites. See Stoddard, *Façade*, 269–271, for a brief summary.

However, Guglielmo most likely had seen the north gallery of the cloister at Arles, because the inexplicable plastic sculptural configuration of three salient grouped pier figures in high relief standing on a salient plinth can be directly traced to the Arles cloister, where it had reason to appear.

Another sculptor who took that route certainly visited Saint-Gilles, and may also have seen Beaucaire, before returning to the Cathedral of Modena, where he carved, probably not until about 1170, a pontile, or choir screen. In his own elegantly refined style, this sculptor not only copied the Passion cycle scenes from the superstructure at Saint-Gilles, but he copied them in a sequence, left to right, identical to what appears on the central portal lintel at Saint-Gilles, with Christ washing the Feet, followed by the Last Supper, Betrayal, Christ before Pilate shown with the Flagellation, and Simon carrying the Cross. He also placed separately in the spandrels of the pontile two additional scenes, Christ's prophecy of Peter's denial and the payment to Judas, that were to the left of the central portal at Saint-Gilles but had also appeared at Beaucaire.[314]

During the second half of the twelfth century, several church portals in Lucca, on the Via Francigena *in western Tuscany, were adorned with lintels depicting the Entry into Jerusalem, a theme derived from that on the façade at Saint-Gilles. One was at Sant'Angelo in Campo (now in the Palazzo Mazzarosa in Lucca) and one was at San Cassiano a Settimo, where it appears with a scene of the raising of Lazarus. A third was originally on the portal from San Leonardo al Frigido at Lucca (but is now preserved in the Cloisters Collection of the Metropolitan Museum in New York), and it was carved around 1175 by a Master Biduino and his workshop, who worked in the Pisa-Lucca area.*[315]

In Pistoia in western Tuscany, again during the second half of the twelfth century, three more churches were adorned with narrative lintels showing themes also found on the portals at Saint-Gilles and in the cloister at Arles. The Magi before Herod and the Adoration of the Magi appear on the lintel at Sant'Andrea; the Last Supper appears on the lintel at San Giovanni Fuorcivitas; and the Doubting Thomas appears with the Mission to the Apostles on the lintel at San Bartolomeo in Pantano.[316]

The Via Francigena *route to Provence was well traveled through the third quarter of the century. In fact, Lucca and Pistoia, both on that route in western Tuscany, also became important destination travel sites in their own right at that time. Lucca was an important textile center, and by the second half of the twelfth century it had acquired*

....

314   Many scholars have discussed the relationship between Saint-Gilles and the sculpture of Northern Italy. For an overview, see Stoddard, *Façade*, 151–153 and 180–196. For a photo of the Modena pontile, see Stoddard, *Façade*, plate 192.

315   See Dorothy F. Glass, *Portals, Pilgrimage, and Crusade in Western Tuscany* (Princeton, NJ: Princeton University Press, 1997), 29–36.

316   See Glass, *Portals,* 15–28.

an important relic known as the Volto Santo, the wooden crucifix believed to have been carved by Nicodemus, one of Christ's followers. Pistoia also held an important relic, a piece of the head of St. James, from Santiago de Compostela.[317]

So it is not at all surprising that in the later part of the third quarter of the century, possibly around 1170,[318] Benedetto Antelami, a young sculptor from Lombardy, would travel the Via Francigena to see Saint-Gilles and pass through Arles, seeking to further his training.

Arles. Cloister, east gallery. Capital sometimes attributed to Antelami. Joseph leading donkey in Flight into Egypt.

Work had begun again at Arles, and it has been suggested that he joined sculptors working on capitals in the east gallery at Arles, where he probably carved the capital showing the Flight into Egypt and Dream of the Magi.[319]

This historiated capital is one of four in the south two bays of the east gallery that expand the Magi story that was only suggested by the Adoration of the Magi tympanum on the north portal at Saint-Gilles. Immediately next to the four Magi capitals at Arles is another depicting the Entry into Jerusalem, reflecting the celebrated lintel at Saint-Gilles, and next to the Entry capital is one showing the Mission of the Apostles, recalling the pier figures of the

....

317   See Glass, *Portals*, 4–6.

318   The date of Antelami's arrival at Saint-Trophîme at Arles can be deduced as sometime in the later part of the third quarter of the century, possibly around 1170. Antelami's subsequent known work continues through the end of the twelfth century, so he could have been a young man in his early to mid-20s if he arrived at Arles in the late 1160s or early 1170s.

319   De Francovich, *Benedetto*, 136–137, first suggested that Antelami worked or apprenticed at the cloister of Saint Trophîme at Arles, where he may have carved the capital of the Dream of the Magi and Flight into Egypt in the east gallery, but not all scholars have accepted this direct connection, and none have directly linked the other sculptures in the Arles cloister to north Italy. Other scholars do accept a general connection between Provence and north Italy, however, a connection resulting from sculptors having visited Provence. See Stoddard, *Façade*, 270–271 and 296-297 where he suggests a general "Provence-North Italy axis of influence."

apostles at the portal of Saint-Gilles. The juxtaposition of themes suggests that the north portal of Saint-Gilles inspired the capitals.

Unfortunately, however, Pons de Baucio would not live to see those later east gallery capitals.

* * *

That time period just after mid-century, when the portal at Saint-Gilles began to gain renown, proved both very difficult and frustrating for Pons. Throughout that first decade after the translation of the relics, work on the claustral buildings had continued, but ever so painfully slowly. Work on the church took priority, but even there, progress was slow. Financing, direction, energy, and enthusiasm had to be split between the two projects, and additional financing was desperately needed.

Although Pons had competent masons to complete the church renovation, and eventually to begin erecting a dormitory with its adjacent east gallery of the cloister, there was no longer a master sculptor to direct and oversee a workshop to carve sculptures for those structures. Work on the sculptural façade of the church had not yet been begun. Nor had work progressed on sculptures for the east gallery of the cloister, where only a couple of capitals were carved by sculptors passing through the region.

Moreover, additional new funding would be necessary to complete the cloister, and Pons had to appeal to his now beleaguered Baux clan for further generosity and support. Pons had already insisted that any new capitals for the east gallery expand the Nativity cycle that had already been begun, but with additional focus on the Magi. He wanted an expansion of what was only hinted at on the Adoration of the Magi tympanum at Saint-Gilles because he understood the value and special significance of the Magi for his benefactors, his family, the Baux, who bore the star of Bethlehem as their emblem on their coat of arms. Pons needed their support to complete the sculptural decoration of the east gallery; he needed their continuing support to be able to complete the cloister.

But the stars were not aligned. Events then intervened. In 1162 Hugh II of Baux started war again, still obsessed with reclaiming his family's rights. In the previous year Ramon Berenguer II, the young Count of Provence, accompanied by his uncle, Ramon Berenguer IV, Count of Barcelona, had traveled to Italy to petition

Frederick Barbarossa, the Holy Roman Emperor, for formal confirmation of the young count's position and holdings in Provence. After their return, the powerful uncle died and Hugh of Baux saw this as his opportunity. Still hoping to press his mother's hereditary territorial claim to Provence, and now further enraged at his recent defeat, Hugh of Baux now tried to change the outcome of the last war.

Open warfare broke out in 1162 for a third time, marking the third, short, final Baux war. Hugh II sought the support of Frederick Barbarossa, citing the two earlier imperial official confirmations given to the Baux territorial claims, first by Conrad and then by Frederick himself, but the Holy Roman Emperor refused to acknowledge the earlier confirmations of approval and ignored Hugh's plea for support. In less than a year, the House of Barcelona totally crushed the Baux forces, demolishing their fortress at Trinquetaille, leveling the House of Baux, and emerging absolutely victorious.

This was the end. The stars that had long nurtured the Baux were badly misaligned, ending forever their territorial claims, ending—for a time, at least—their tremendous wealth and power, and ending—for a time, at least—the special relationship the canons and the church at Arles had long enjoyed with the Baux as their great protectors and benefactors.

Compline
Night Prayers—bells on retiring

Anno Domini MCLXV
VIII Idus Octobris[320]

I t was early October 1165. The dormitory had finally recently been completed.[321] The east gallery of the cloister had been erected and vaulted but was far from completed. Only a couple of historiated capitals and one pier figure had been carved and installed, all in the northernmost bay of the gallery. These had been carved by two sculptors passing through Arles whom Pons had convinced to work for a short time on the sculptures. A few ornamental

....

320 As clarified earlier, the Roman Julian calendar was used in the medieval era, and the days of each month were identified by how many days they preceded Kalends, Nones, and Ides, with the first day counted being the named day, so VIII Ides would be the eighth day before Ides on the middle, or fifteenth of October, which would be October 8 in our calendar. See footnote 206 on the medieval calendar in chapter 5, *Sext,* p. 213.

321 On this dating of the dormitory to 1165, instead of the erroneously late date of 1180 that had been previously cited by almost all scholars, see Schneider, "Sculptures," 42–43, fig. 4, and 18–23. Documentary evidence shows that the dormitory had been constructed by the end of 1165, because a document of 1166 carefully recorded that a resolution had been reached over an earlier controversy involving the vineyard of Marie Nevaira, and that the resolution was reached *"in canonica in dormitorio"* on the day of Epiphany (January 6).

An edited version of the document is included in Albanes and Chevalier, *Arles,* no. 2531, but for the entire text, see *Authentique,* Arles MS 1242, fol. 122.

capitals had also been attempted by the assistant. Except for the northeast corner, the piers were devoid of figure sculpture and instead showed blocks of unfinished stone, which hopefully someday, and someday soon, would be replaced by others transformed by a sculptor's chisel into figure sculpture. At best, the east gallery could be described as a work still in progress.

Nevertheless, the canons were now able to use the dormitory and had moved into it only weeks earlier. The chapter of canons, having adopted the Rule of St. Augustine, were now fully embracing the *vita apostolica*, living, eating, and sleeping communally. It was not yet commonly known, however, even among all the townspeople in Arles that the canons were now able to sleep in a common dormitory and live communally behind their cloistered walls.

Very late in the night there was a loud, rude pounding on the canons' portal just outside the communal complex. The forceful pounding continued unabated, accompanied by loud, drunken curses.

"Young Peter," Pons finally cried to one of the young postulants. In addition to being *precentor*, Pons was also now *capud scole*, so he oversaw the cathedral school and knew all the young candidates. "Go see what the problem is. It's probably some beggar seeking food or shelter who doesn't know we cannot let him into our communal complex and doesn't have the sense to know we cannot help him this late at night. Tell him to come back in the morning, and we will try to help him then."

The youth roused himself from sleep, slowly scratched below his belly before quickly throwing on a short tunic, and then walked slowly to the portal. After a short commotion, punctuated with an audible, bone-chilling laugh and some shrieked vile curses, the youth returned to report.

"It was a gruff-looking and very drunken man I'd never seen before," said Peter. "He said his name was Gilbert. He wanted a place to sleep for the night for himself and his friend who was with him. They smelled really bad, reeking of vomit and excrement. They had certainly not washed or even had access to a fire to smoke themselves or their clothes to cover the odor for quite some time.

"He said he was a canon in Paris but had visited here many years ago. He said he would never have returned here but that he is passing through the town and cannot find any place to sleep. Everything is full, and nobody will take him and his friend in for the night. I certainly can understand why not!

Anyway, he said he finally decided to risk coming here and asking you, Canon Pons—whatever that means!

"I told him that he cannot stay here. I explained that the chapter has adopted the Rule and is now living and sleeping communally, but he only gave out a frightening laugh and shouted some really terrible profanities about . . . well, about vile sinful things, so I quickly shut and locked the door. I think they've finally left."

"You were correct to do so. Now, go back to bed and try to get some sleep," Pons offered kindly, although he seemed a bit rattled.

Pons was indeed rattled. He was unnerved. Recognizing that the intruder probably was Gilbert, the canon he had called "Satan" when they were at Vézelay, Pons was filled with a vague and unsettling foreboding. Why on earth had he returned here? What would make him come here, of all places? Pons tossed and turned for quite some time, unable to get back to sleep.

It was early evening, two days later, *VI Idus Octobris*. The chapter would soon celebrate *Compline*, the canonical hour that indicated the completion of the day and signaled the time to retire. A small group of canons had gathered momentarily in the chapter house where they were huddled in admiration around a beautifully embroidered new set of church vestments that had been delivered earlier that day, just after *Sext*.

"Aren't they exquisite?" remarked Canon William Bernardus, *sacristan*, who had requested this new set of vestments. "The fabric is luxurious, the brocade is just magnificent, and the needlework is absolutely exquisite! I wanted to show both of you how beautiful they are, and I do want to thank both of you for helping me steer my request for these new vestments success-fully through the chapter."

"They are beautiful," responded William Boso, who as *prepositus*, or provost, was now ultimately responsible for all church property and posses-sions. "And they were needed. Quite frankly, we took to heart your plea that last spring you were somewhat embarrassed by the faded appearance of the church vestments for the Lenten season celebrations."

"And so many wanted to participate in the Lenten and Paschal celebrations last spring," added Pons, who as *precentor* was still responsible for the musical part of the services. "The Passion plays we authorized for Easter were so well received. And so many of the faithful asked permission to walk through the cloister afterward, through our completed north gallery, at least, to see the relief sculptures of the three Holy Women buying spices and the empty tomb."

"Your nephew Hugh asked to see those sculptures too, but I suspect he just wanted to see the whole communal complex," added William Boso. "We were able to lead a small procession from the canons' portal across the green and up the vaulted east gallery, past the not quite yet completed dormitory, across the north gallery, and past the chapter house to end at the sculptures of the Three Women and the empty tomb before descending into the church."

"But now that we have decided to focus our efforts on the church façade sculpture, I am not sure when we will be able to complete the east gallery . . . or even start the other two galleries," added Pons with a sigh of resignation.

"Oh! Oh! I'm sorry! Hurry!" interjected William Bernard with embarrassment. "I have kept you too long! They have already started to celebrate *Compline*." The three clerics dashed quickly down the stairs into the church to join their brethren and quickly made the sign of the cross before joining in singing the prescribed Invitatory from Psalm 50.

"Domine labia mea aperies et os meum adnuntiabit laudem tuam." (*Psalmus* 50:17)	"O Lord, thou wilt open my lips: and my mouth shall declare thy praise." (Psalm 50:17)

The chapter proceeded to celebrate the divine office of *Compline*. In preparing them for sleep, it also daily prepared each canon's soul for its passage to eternal life, and it began with an examination of conscience.

The office began with Psalm 4.

"Cum invocarem exaudivit me Deus iustitiae meae in tribulatione dilatasti mihi miserere mei et exaudi orationem meam . . . Irascimini et nolite peccare quae dicitis in cordibus vestris in cubilibus vestris conpungimini diapsalma . . .	"When I called upon him, the God of my justice heard me: when I was in distress, thou hast enlarged me. Have mercy on me: and hear my prayer . . . Be ye angry, and sin not: the things you say in your hearts, be sorry for them upon your beds . . .

In pace in id ipsum dormiam et requiescam	In peace in the self same I will sleep, and I will rest.
quoniam tu Domine singulariter in spe constituisti me."	For thou, O Lord, singularly hast settled me in hope."
(*Psalmus* 4:2, 5, 9, 10)	(Psalm 4:2, 5, 9, 10)

And continued with Psalms 90 and 133, as long traditional for *Compline*.[322]

"Qui habitat in adiutorio Altissimi in protectione Dei caeli commorabitur . . ."	"He that dwelleth in the aid of the most High, shall abide under the protection of the God of Jacob . . ."
(*Psalmus* 90: 1)	(Psalm 90:1)
". . . in noctibus extollite manus vestras in sancta et benedicite Domino . . ."	". . . In the nights lift up your hands to the holy places, and bless ye the Lord . . ." (Psalm 133:2)
(*Psalmus* 133: 2)	

And continuing as usual, the canons then raised their voices to sing that most beautiful evening hymn, *Te lucis*.[323]

"Te lucis ante terminum, rerum Creator, poscimus ut solita clementia sis praesul ad custodiam.	"To Thee, before the close of day Creator of the world, we pray That with Thy wonted favor, Thou Wouldst be our Guard and Keeper now.

. . . .

322   There was a great variety in liturgical celebrations in medieval churches, but St. Benedict of Nursia early established that for monasteries, three specific psalms would be used to celebrate *Compline*. See Powell, "Introduction."

Note that a modern copy of the *Rule of St. Benedict*, Chapter 18, still lists these three psalms for *Compline*. See https://www.solesmes.com/sites/default/files/upload/pdf/rule_of_st_benedict.pdf

323   This is the earliest version of the evening hymn *Te lucis ante terminum*, which may have been composed by St. Ambrose in the fourth century. English translation by J.M. Neale (1818–1866). Both texts are from Wikipedia, "Te lucis ante terminum" https://en.wikipedia.org/wiki/Te_lucis_ante_terminum.

Procul recedant somnia
et noctium phantasmata;
hostemque nostrum comprime,
ne polluantur corpora.

Praesta, Pater omnipotens, per
Iesum Christum Dominum,
qui tecum in perpetuum
regnat cum Sancto Spiritu.
Amen."

From all ill dreams defend
our sight,
From fears and terrors of the night;
Withhold from us our ghostly foe,
That spot of sin we may not know.

O Father, that we ask be done
Through Jesus Christ Thine
only Son,
Who, with the Holy Ghost
and Thee,
Doth live and reign eternally.
Amen."

The canons continued the celebration of this hour as usual with a short reading from scripture, the lesson, the *Nunc Dimittis*, the concluding prayer, and the benediction.

Having celebrated *Compline* and with their souls now prepared to go to sleep, the group broke up as each man either wandered into the dormitory or ambled southward toward the well or the privy. Pons headed straight into the dormitory and was settling in for the night when a loud banging at the canons' portal broke the peaceful spell. Although at first everyone tried to ignore the noise, the banging only became more insistent.

"Young Peter," Pons finally called to the young postulant. "Go see what the problem is. Once again, it's probably a beggar seeking food or shelter who doesn't understand we cannot let him into our dormitory or help him this late in the day. Tell him to come back in the morning.

"But if it's that same gruff-looking man, Gilbert, who disturbed us the other night," Pons added, now overcome once again with vague foreboding, "tell him to wait, but close the door quickly and come get me. I'll deal with him."

The young postulant rose, threw on his short tunic again, and obeyed his superior by sauntering across the cloister to approach and peek through the portal, where he spoke with the intruder for a short time.

"It's an old woman," he exclaimed in exasperation upon returning to report to Pons in the dormitory. "It's an old woman, and she will not go away. She insists on speaking with Canon Pons Rebolli."

Pons could see that the young Canon Rebolli had finally completed his nightly ablutions and was just entering the dormitory. As if to force Pons into his decision, the banging began again, more vigorously than ever.

"Okay, Canon Rebolli, you are still dressed," said Pons. "Go see what her problem is. But really, do please get rid of her tonight. The townspeople must learn that we are now living communally. Tell her to return tomorrow if she needs help."

Now filled with curiosity, young Pons Rebolli left quickly to deal with the intruder. When he did not return for quite some time, Pons, who was already filled with foreboding, became truly apprehensive. As *capud scole* he was responsible for the young canon, and he had sent him alone to deal with the problem—and after that unnerving reappearance of Gilbert the other night! Pons now dressed quickly by throwing on a tunic and hurried to the portal.

There at the portal he saw Pons Rebolli and . . . Beatrice! The woman was sobbing openly on the young canon's shoulder, clinging desperately to his arms. Pons gasped at the sight of her. Still very handsome and attractive despite her age—in fact still quite beautiful, but now with wide silver streaks in her hair—Beatrice was terribly disheveled but dressed as for travel, in a heavy cape with a hood falling back on her shoulders.

"Sir," young Rebolli began, "I don't believe you have ever met my mother. You were off on your travels to Cluny and Vézelay when I was admitted into the chapter. This is Beatrice, my mother, who raised me after my father died just before my birth. She is also the talented seamstress who has made several of the beautiful vestments that were commissioned for the church."

"Oh, eh . . . We . . . *have* met," Pons stuttered almost incomprehensibly. Then, recovering himself, he continued. "We met over a decade ago . . . when she delivered the vestments for the ceremony to translate the relics of St. Trophîme from Les Alyscamps to the cathedral."

"She delivered another set of vestments to us earlier today," Rebolli responded. "And she is in quite some difficulty for having done so," he added. Then he politely instructed the woman, "Tell Canon Pons what you just told me, why you are in such trouble and need a place to stay tonight."

Her head bowed, eyes cast downward, her entire body awash with melancholic black bile, Beatrice began speaking softly, almost in a whisper, beginning in a flat voice with little or no affect and without ever once looking up.

"I thought it would be safe for me to deliver the vestments today. Your chapter insisted they wanted them now, and I really thought it would be safe, so I brought them. I had to. Your chapter wanted them. We know the Genoese are gone. I know there are still some Pisan galleys here now, she continued, her voice now beginning to rise, "but we helped the Pisans. Our town sided with them." She now cried softly.

"I had no trouble at all walking here this morning," she continued, her voice now breaking up, "but I had to return home the same day. I had no place to stay here in Arles. I cannot pay with coin for a bed for the night, and my son was too busy with your chapter work to see me," she added, raising her head to look coldly at the elder Pons as she took a deep breath before continuing.

"But this afternoon when I tried to return home, a group of Pisan sailors blocked the path. They had left their galleys and were skulking about in the Camargue. At first they just taunted me, calling me an 'old hag,'" she continued, as she began to shake and sob. "They wouldn't let me pass." She now began choking on her words as she tried to continue, muttering almost incomprehensibly.

"Then they . . . grabbed me. They ripped open my clothing. They were yelling, 'Hey, she's not such a bad hag.' They started trying to . . . force . . . me. I slashed at them with my knife, as hard as I could. I'm not stupid, you know. I had carried a knife, just in case! They just laughed! They took the knife from me and stuck it into the ground just beyond my reach. They . . . They . . . Oh, there were so many of them! It was terrible! So . . ." And she stopped as her deep, guttural sob pierced the silence. "When they were through with me, they got bored and left me. When I was able to get up, I finally got away, but I couldn't continue on toward home. I had to turn back, but I had nowhere else to go. So . . . I came here."

"She may have known there are still some Pisan galleys hanging about in the lower Rhône now," young Pons added, earnestly beginning to defend his mother, "but she also knew she had to deliver the vestments. And she did try to arm herself with a knife for defense!"

"But you started out alone, even though you must have known the war is still going on?" the elder Pons blurted out incredulously, in horror, not sure what to say or how to proceed.

He simply could not believe what he had heard, what had happened, or what she had allowed to happen by starting out alone. And what was even more distressing was that he could not do anything about it, anything at all. His heart pounded violently. Yellow bile coursed through his body as his spleen churned out its choleric fluid. Overcome with anger, he wanted to chase down, to catch and to beat her attackers, but he could not—because by now it would be impossible. He would kill them if he could. Yes, he would kill them, if he could. But he could not, because his religious vows forbade it. He desperately longed to comfort Beatrice, to hold her innocently in his arms to comfort her, but he knew he could not do even this, at least not here in front of the young canon. He was helpless. He was powerless. He was impotent. Impotent! He could do nothing! Nothing! Nothing at all!

Enraged at what had happened, embarrassed at his powerlessness, furious at himself for his own impotence, he could only withdraw from Beatrice and her pain into himself, where he now began a clumsy but desperate attempt to manage and control this horror by examining surrounding events with some detachment. Refusing to look at her, after a few moments he began speaking again, but impersonally, with a stone face, as if speaking to the wall.

"Everyone knows about the war between Pisa and Genoa that broke out again this summer after the truce between them was broken,"[324] the elder Pons began in a patronizing tone, as if lecturing to a subordinate. He then set about methodically reciting the recent local events of the war in a desperate attempt to manage what he had just learned, to distance himself from it enough to be able to get in control, to be rational and calm in the face of this unthinkable horror. "Since July the war's been waged right in front of the town of Saint-Gilles. The town was pulled into the thick of it," he continued in this superior tone, trying to keep his balance and composure as he spoke. "We all know what happened. A Pisan fleet first went up the Rhône to Saint-Gilles, but they were followed by the Genoese and only narrowly escaped capture. In anger the Genoese then torched some merchant vessels at the town's wharves, so when they then tried to land to take on supplies, the citizens of your town refused them in revenge, and they had to return to Genoa."

He paused briefly, thinking to himself, "How could this have happened to her?" before continuing his lecture, to try to gain control. In that same brief pause Beatrice lowered her tearful face in dismay and disbelief. "Why is he

---

324   This account of the Pisa-Genoa war and the involvement of the town of Saint-Gilles is taken from William Heywood, *A History of Pisa, Eleventh and Twelfth Centuries* (1921; repr. Cambridge, UK: Cambridge University Press, 2010), 171–174.

now lecturing me on events I lived through myself?" she asked herself. "Why is he doing this to me?"

"By August," he continued aloud in his condescending tone, desperately working to be controlled, "the Genoese must have thought that Pisan ships were still at Saint-Gilles, because they sent another fifty galleys up the Rhône for a night attack. But just before they reached the town, some of their ships went aground in the dark, and the others that were following crashed into them. They were all stuck there in a huge pileup and could go no further. Your town's magistrates then warned them that if they violated the neutrality of Saint-Gilles, the town would side with the Pisans," the elder Pons continued pedantically, desperately working to appear balanced, desperately trying to be composed.

"Get control," he thought. "Get yourself under control."

And as he continued droning on and on, so impersonally, so condescendingly, and seemingly with full composure and complete balance, Beatrice slowly released her grip on her son and turned to face this composed monster, who had once been her lover in her youth. She had stopped sobbing. With an icy expression, she now stared coldly, defiantly, directly into his eyes.

"Everyone knows the Genoese then tried another tactic: bribes!" the elder Pons continued in his patronizing tone, desperately clinging to his pedantic lecture, blind to her gaze. "That is, to bribe Raymond, Count of Toulouse, for his support, not realizing the sly fox would simply take their bribe and then switch sides when the Pisans offered him more. So the Genoese were counting on the count's support when they landed near Saint-Gilles again several weeks ago to launch their attack, and they were easily defeated before nightfall. They left almost immediately for home, because they now fear the Pisans are now preparing to raid Genoa."

His humors now somewhat under control, Pons had managed to regain some balance. He could now truly face her. He could now look directly at her.

"So everyone knows there are gangs of Pisan sailors about!" Pons proclaimed now with a bit more distress and real emotion in his voice. "Everyone knows about them. You must have known about them! Marauding gangs of sailors. Victorious warriors who take what they want as booty, as the spoils of war. There are still some thirty Pisan galleys in the lower Rhône now!" Pons added. "And the sailors are elated and full of themselves after their recent victories. This is the site of an ongoing war!"

Beatrice now choked with choleric rage at what she was hearing. This inhuman beast, this arrogant monster, this horrid pig was lecturing her, blaming her for venturing out of her town. His chapter had insisted on having the vestments delivered. And he was chiding her for trying to deliver them, for trying to make the delivery on time—for trying to deliver his damned vestments to his God-forsaken chapter!

To be forsaken by her lover in her youth had been devastating, more destructive than he could possibly have known, but though humiliated and desperate at the time, she knew she had come to terms with it. She had learned how to deal with it. She had done what she had to do. She had done whatever she had to do to survive.

But this! She could not believe what she was hearing. She had been forcibly raped, again and again and again, by a gang of sailors! And he was telling her she was responsible for it? He was telling her and her son—telling her son!—that *she* had brought this unspeakable indignity on herself! That she had brought it on herself by doing what she had learned to do to survive. That she had brought it on herself by doing whatever she had to do to support herself and her son. She was horrified. Disgusted at his insolence. Furious at his arrogance. Aghast at his impudence.

"But what can we do to help her now?" the younger Pons asked the elder one, looking compassionately at his mother and recognizing the extent of her horror and excruciating pain—recognizing that she desperately needed comfort and understanding, not a lecture, recognizing that she needed a safe haven where she could calm down, a place to rest and recover.

"It is nighttime, and she has no place to go," he continued reasonably. "We all know the pilgrims' hostel is full to overflowing with travelers stranded here because of the war hostilities. Those already there are taking such advantage of the hospitality, the hostel will not let others in. And they certainly will not accept an unknown lone woman. Everyone and anyone with an extra bed has let it out to someone. I know she cannot stay here. I've told her she cannot stay here. But where can she go?"

"Go knock on old Lucius's door," Pons answered slowly after thinking for a few moments. "He's the tanner up the path just past the old arena. He should have some room, certainly at least a bed for a lone woman, because his place always smells so bad that no one asks to stay there. He has long known me and should be willing to take her in. Tell him she is your mother and that it is

I who sent you, I who is asking him to take her in and let her sleep there for the night—with his own children on their pallet, if that's the only space there is. He is indebted to me. He will not refuse. Leave her here with me for now while you wake him up to ask him."

The younger canon left quickly, turning left and sprinting up the hill. Pons turned to Beatrice, took her hand, and, without thinking about the propriety of it, began to quickly lead her past the refectory, directly along the west edge of the cloister, as far as possible from the dormitory, until they arrived at the western end of the north gallery outside the chapter house. She followed, stunned, as in a daze, momentarily unable to resist. Although he knew he had to keep her away from the dormitory, he also needed to sit down with her so he could speak quietly with her, in private. He offered her a seat on the stone plinth.

At first he did not know how to begin, and neither of them spoke for a short time. They sat in silence. Pons, so relieved at being able to do anything to help her, anything at all, even such a small thing as finding her a place to sleep, now began becoming more sanguine as his liver began flooding his body with blood. He could now recall how protective he had once felt toward the young Beatrice after the heretic's execution. He now felt close to this woman again, so protective of her once again. He wondered if this could really be only the fifth time in his life that he had spoken with this beautiful woman, who had been at the core of his struggles with celibacy for such a long time. Beatrice—long in his heart and at the heart of his struggles.

As they sat in silence, Pons suddenly realized how appropriate it was to sit with Beatrice here in the corner near both the siren and *luxuria* figures and the three Holy Women buying Spices, one of them the blessed and beloved Mary Magdalene. After all, these were the female figures that had guided him in his struggles with his love for her. As this recognition slowly dawned on him, he finally found his voice.

"I'm truly sorry we cannot take you in here," Pons began, now speaking very softly and gently. "And although the tanner is very gruff and his place smells terrible, he is a good Christian with a good and kind heart, and I know you will be safe there. I am sure you will *feel* safe there, too. He is so kind and gentle with his children. I know him well. I just want you to feel safe and secure. I am so very, very sorry for what you have just gone through."

"You? Sorry? Sorry for what I have gone through?" Beatrice choked and hissed, now emerging from her daze. She leaped to her feet and jerked herself away from him when he tried to touch her arm as he, too, stood up. "You have the nerve to tell my son it was my fault . . . my fault, because I was trying to get those God-forsaken vestments to you on time!"

"But if I had known," Pons cried, "I would have sent someone to pick them up from you. I really didn't know."

"You monster! You damned ass! You . . . ! You!" she spat with hatred, flailing her arms at him. "You're trying to turn my son against me! I came here tonight to get help from my son. From my own son! I couldn't ask *you* for help. But he is my son, and he denied me help. My own son denied me a bed! He told me I can't stay here because of you and your damned Rule. Because your chapter has adopted your God-forsaken Rule. Because you are all now living communally. Living in chastity. No one owns anything. Like living in poverty. So no one owns a pallet, and my son can't even give me a place to sleep!"

"Beatrice, Beatrice, please, please calm down and listen to me," he responded as he tried to grab hold of her arms, to restrain her physically.

"You God-damned hypocrite!" she hissed maliciously. "Living in poverty. You! What do you know about poverty? You eat very well, indeed. You pay in coin for beautiful vestments. You pay in coin for beautiful sculptures, for new stone buildings. What do you know about poverty?

"You? Living in chastity? Hah! That's the real joke!" she spat venomously as she fought to free herself. "You fornicator! You had your way with me all right. You knew me and you loved it. You loved every moment of it, and you know it. And you walked away. You walked away! You deserted me. You turned your back on me! Who did you go to next? Wasn't I good enough for you? Who else did you go to?" she spat as she began pummeling him with her fists.

"Beatrice, I did love you . . . I think. But as a young lad, as a boy, as a child. I love you now. I do love you now, but in a better, purer way," he continued quietly. Thinking it would help calm her, the naïve and incredibly stupid but well-intentioned fool started quoting scripture. "As St. Paul taught us, 'cum essem parvulus loquebar ut parvulus sapiebam ut parvulus cogitabam ut parvulus quando factus sum vir evacuavi quae erant parvuli'

(1 ad Corinthios 13:11)

'When I was a child, I spoke as a child, I understood as a child, I thought as a child. But, when I became a man, I put away the things of a child.'

(I Corinthians 13:11)

"I am now living the celibate communal life, as God has ordered me to do as a canon, but that does not mean I don't love you . . . deeply, but purely . . ." he continued, as he again tried to take her in his arms, wanting innocently to hold her, to calm her, to reassure her.

"What do you know about love?" she spat, now more enraged than ever. "What do you know about *anything*?" she choked, as she began beating him with her arms. "You ass! You hypocrite! You religious fool!

"You're all fools! I only let my son join you here as a cleric so he would never go hungry, so he would never have to scrounge for food and shelter," she screamed, "and so maybe I would no longer have to scrounge, so I would not go hungry. I lied and stole so we would not go hungry! I lied to get him accepted here. I lied and I stole to get him accepted into your chapter so he would not go hungry, not know cold. And now you are taking him from me, too!

"You left me. You left your son. Your own son! Pons is your son! Your son! And he never knew. The son you denied! And now you are taking him away from me—taking him too!" she screamed almost incomprehensibly as she arched away from the man.

Stunned by her words, knocked insensible by what she had said, Pons let his arms fall to his side, and his mouth fell open, gaping in confusion, as she broke one arm free and thrust it beneath her cloak where she found her knife—the knife she had been unable to defend herself with earlier but could use now. She pulled it out. Pons stood there motionless. He was simply unable to accept that she could mean to do him physical harm.

"I hate you! He will never know. My son will never know! I hate you! I hate you! I hate you!" she shrieked uncontrollably as she plunged the knife into his neck.

"But Beatrice, I do love you," he wheezed as he grabbed his neck. The gallery began to spin as he slid down to the stone walk. And as he fell, what he saw was the female figure of lust, *luxuria*, being devoured by serpents.

The loud commotion of the last few moments had raised the canons from the dormitory, and they came running. William Boso grabbed Beatrice's wrists, forced the knife from her hand, and led her away to the refectory, where she could be restrained to be dealt with later.

Christianus and Guilelmo Bernardi straightened out Pons's body and bunched up a garment to put under his head. Having just returned and now bursting through the canons' portal into the cloister, Pons Rebolli now came running up, knelt down, and held the elder Pons's head.

"What happened? Oh, dear God! What did she do?" he cried meekly, in horror.

"Forgive me . . . forgive me . . ." whispered the older canon, struggling for breath, as blood pulsed rhythmically from his neck, pooling on the stone walk. "I . . . did not . . . know . . ."

"You must unburden your conscience and quickly make your last confession," gasped the horrified but quick-thinking young canon, who recognized the severity of the wound. The victim would die. His soul was imperiled. Last confession, absolution, and the *viaticum* were imperative![325] Without them, his soul would be damned to all eternity.

"Last rites! Get me what I need. Now! Quickly!" he commanded the others.

Kneeling on the slick red surface that was already spreading out in a pool beside the wounded man's head and shoulders, the young canon took the older man's hand as he bent his ear to the man's lips.

"The Rule . . . canons . . . cloister . . ." the older canon whispered almost inaudibly as his eyes overflowed with tears.

"Please, Canon Pons," began the young canon, not understanding the full import of what the wounded man was trying to say. "Don't worry. I promise to carry on your work, to complete the cloister and the renovation of church for you. Now, quickly, make your last confession," the young canon urged.

....

325   On Extreme Unction and the Last Rites in the medieval period, see Paul F. Bradshaw, ed., "Funerals. Medieval and Roman Catholic," *New SCM Dictionary of Liturgy and Worship* (2013), 217–218. See James Ginther, "Extreme Unction" in *The Westminster Handbook to Medieval Theology* (Louisville, KY: Westminster John Knox Press, 2009).

"No . . . *vita apostolica* . . . never . . . Son . . ." Pons gurgled almost incomprehensibly as his eyes started dimming and becoming fixed.

"*Te absolvo*. I absolve you of all your sins," the young canon proclaimed, as he took from Christianus a small box and opened it.

"Say the words along with me," implored the young canon, as he began quickly. "I believe in God, the Father Almighty, Maker of heaven and earth, and in Jesus Christ, His only begotten Son–. . ." The young canon swiftly murmured the Apostles' Creed as the injured man's lips did not move.

Taking from the box a wafer, the young canon quickly blessed it, broke off a bit, forcibly opened the older canon's lips, and inserted the crumb, saying "The Body of Christ." This was the final communion, the *viaticum*, food for the journey into death, provision for the dying man's journey from this world to eternal life.

"You must swallow it! Try!" he cried, and with eyes filled with tears, he thrust his finger directly into the mouth, physically pushing the wafer into the back of the motionless mouth. "Say it with me," he repeated. "Amen. May the Lord Jesus Christ protect you and lead you to eternal life," the young canon proclaimed, his eyes now streaming with tears.

Gently closing the eyes of the elder canon, the young canon then opened the small vial, and, with a bit of the oil, he made the sign of the cross on the deceased's brow to begin extreme unction, the last anointing. The young canon completed the rite and gave a final prayer and blessing.

The bewildered canons surrounding the pair were at a loss. They immediately began solemnly chanting the *Requiem aeternam,* the Introit to the liturgy of the requiem Mass,[326] then the *Kyrie* and the Gradual. This was the only thing they could think of to do. Bewildered, awash with black bile, this was their spontaneous response to this loss, to this event they could not comprehend. They looked to their God for solace and help, both for the deceased and for themselves.

....

326   The Latin and English translations here are both taken from *The Requiem Survey,* http://www.requiemsurvey.org/latintext.php.

"Requiem aeternam dona
eis, Domine,
et lux perpetua luceat eis.
Te decet hymnus, Deus, in Sion;
et tibi reddetur votum
in Jerusalem.
Exaudi orationem meam
Ad te omnis caro veniet.

Kyrie, eleison!
Christe, eleison!
Kyrie, eleison!

Requiem aeternam dona
eis, Domine:
et lux perpetua luceat eis.
In memoria aeterna erit iustus,
ab auditione mala non timebit . . . "

"Eternal rest give unto them, O Lord
And let perpetual light shine
upon them
A hymn, O God, becometh
Thee in Zion
And a vow shall be paid to thee in
Jerusalem.
Hear my prayer;
All flesh shall come before Thee.

Lord, have mercy on us.
Christ, have mercy on us.
Lord, have mercy on us.

Eternal rest grant unto them, O Lord
and let perpetual light shine
upon them.
He shall be justified in
everlasting memory,
And shall not fear evil reports . . ."

When they had finished, William Boso and Jordan asked young Pons to help them carry their beloved friend's dead body into the chapter house, where it could remain overnight, to be tended to the next morning. Still distressed, still confused, all the other canons slowly returned to the dormitory, one by one. When the hour of *Matins* arrived, few had yet found any sleep, but they arose and descended to the church for the office.

When the cock finally crowed at daybreak, and the bells rang to mark *Lauds*, the hour of sunrise, the young Canon Pons still had not found sleep. He was too troubled by what had taken place and was struggling to resolve it. He readily and willingly rose to join the others in celebrating the office.

Young Pons would strive to find solace and resolution in the music, as had his elder namesake just over thirty years ago the morning following his own fateful encounter, but the young Pons was to find his own answers.

After quickly making the sign of the cross on his chest, he began celebrating *Lauds*, beginning, as usual, with the singing of Psalm 92.

"... Dominus regnavit decore indutus est ..."	"The Lord reigneth, he is clothed with majesty ..."
(*Psalmus* 92:1f)	(Psalm 92:1f)

The office continued with the singing of Psalm 97.

"Cantate Domino canticum novum quoniam mirabilia fecit salvavit sibi dextera eius et brachium sanctum eius ..."	"Sing ye to the Lord a new canticle: because he hath done wonderful things. His right hand had wrought for him salvation, and his arm is holy ..." (Psalm 97:1f)
(*Psalmus* 97:1f)	

As he began singing Psalm 62, the beautiful "morning psalm," young Pons stopped struggling with his confusion and resolutely surrendered himself wholeheartedly to the words and music of the psalm.

And the young canon began to hear God speaking directly to him through the chant.

"Deus Deus meus ad te de luce vigilo sitivit in te anima mea quam multipliciter tibi caro mea	"O God, my God, to thee do I watch at break of day. For thee my soul hath thirsted; for thee my flesh, O how many ways!
In terra deserta et invia et inaquosa sic in sancto apparui tibi ut viderem virtutem tuam et gloriam tuam ..."	In a desert land, and where there is no way, and no water: so in the sanctuary have I come before thee, to see thy power and thy glory ..."
(*Psalmus* 62:2–3f)	(Psalm 62:2–3ff)

The office continued with the canticle of praise from Daniel 3 in the Old Testament,[327] which is the song of the three youths, Sedrac, Misac, and

---

327   The Canticle of Praise in Daniel 3 was often used for *Matins* or *Lauds*. See Powell, "Introduction."

The Canticle of Praise in Daniel 3:57–88 appears in the Greek *Septuagint* version of the Bible but is not found in the Hebrew or Aramaic text of the Book of Daniel. It appears in Roman Catholic and Eastern Orthodox Bibles but is considered apocryphal by Protestants. (So it is not included in the King James Version.) See "The Prayer of Azariah and Song of the Three Holy Children," *Wikipedia*.

Abdenago, who were thrown by King Nabuchodonosor into the fiery furnace, where they praised God and were met by an angel of the Lord, who delivered them unharmed from the fire.

"Benedicite omnia opera Domini Domino: laudate et superexaltate eum in saecula.

"All ye works of the Lord, bless the Lord: praise and exalt him above all for ever.

Benedicite Angeli Domini Domino: laudate et superexaltate eum in saecula.

O ye angels of the Lord, bless the Lord: praise and exalt him above all for ever.

Benedicite caeli Domino: laudate et superexaltate eum in saecula. . .

O ye heavens, bless the Lord: praise and exalt him above all for ever. . .

Benedicite sancti et humiles corde Domino: laudate et superexaltate eum in saecula.

O ye holy and humble of heart, bless the Lord: praise and exalt him above all for ever.

Benedicite Anania, Azaria, Misael Domino: laudate et superexaltate eum in saecula. Quia eruit nos de inferno, et salvos fecit de manu mortis, et liberavit nos de medio ardentis flammae, et de medio ignis eruit nos."

O Ananias, Azarias, Misael, bless ye the Lord: praise and exalt him above all for ever. For he hath delivered us from hell, and saved us out of the hand of death, and delivered us out of the midst of the burning flame, and saved us out of the midst of the fire."

(*Daniel* 3:57ff, 87ff)

(Daniel 3:57ff, 87ff)

As the office continued, young Pons continued to hear God speaking to him, speaking directly to him through the psalms, through the canticle. Slowly, ever so slowly, God led him toward an understanding of what had happened, of what he had to do.

The canons lifted their voices in the three glorious *laudate* Psalms. First, Psalm 148.

"Laudate Dominum de caelis
laudate eum in excelsis . . .

Laudent nomen Domini quia ipse
dixit et facta sunt ipse mandavit et
creata sunt."

(*Psalmus* 148: 1, 5)

"Praise ye the Lord from the
heavens: praise ye him in the high
places . . .

Praise the name of the Lord. For
he spoke, and they were made:
he commanded, and they were
created." (Psalm 148: 1, 5)

The office continued with Psalm 149. God was speaking, and the young canon was listening.

"Cantate Domino canticum
novum laus eius in ecclesia
sanctorum . . ."

(*Psalmus* 149:1ff)

"Sing ye to the Lord a new
canticle: let his praise be in the
church of the saints . . ."

(Psalm 149:1ff)

Finally, with Psalm 150, everything was revealed. God showed him his mission and the way forward. It all became clear to young Pons.

"Laudate Dominum in sanctis
eius laudate eum in firmamento
virtutis eius

Laudate eum in virtutibus
eius laudate eum secundum
multitudinem magnitudinis eius

Laudate eum in sono tubae laudate
eum in psalterio et cithara

Laudate eum in tympano et choro
laudate eum in cordis et organo

Laudate eum in cymbalis bene
sonantibus laudate eum in
cymbalis iubilationis.

Omnis spiritus laudet Dominum."

(*Psalmus* 150)

"Praise ye the Lord in his Holy
places; praise ye him in the
firmament of his power.

Praise ye him for his mighty acts:
praise ye him according to the
multitude of his greatness.

Praise him with the sound of
trumpet; praise him with psaltery
and harp.

Praise him with timbrel and choir:
praise him with strings and organs.

Praise him on high sounding
cymbals: praise him on cymbals
of joy:

Let every spirit praise the Lord.
Alleluia." (Psalm 150)

The chapter then began singing the hymn *Te deum laudamus*.[328] Only a few of the canons knew that this hymn had been written in part by St. Augustine, whose Rule the deceased canon had brought to the chapter, but for young Pons, it was a clear confirmation of what God had just revealed to him.

"Te deum laudamus te dominum confitemur Te aeternum patrem omnis terra venerator Tibi omnes angeli Tibi caeli et universae potestates Tibi cherubim et seraphim incessabili voce proclamant Sanctus sanctus sanctus dominus deus sabaoth Pleni sunt celi et terra maiestatis gloriae tua . . ."	"You are God: we praise you; You are the Lord: we acclaim you; You are the eternal Father: All creation worships you. To you all angels, all the powers of heaven Cheubim and Seraphim, sing in endless praise; Holy, holy, holy, Lord God of power and might, heaven and earth are full of your Glory . . ."

After *Lauds*, the chapter met to discuss how to proceed. Young Pons was bursting with emotion as yellow bile coursed through him, energizing him. He was overwhelmed, so overcome with everything that had transpired that he could barely restrain himself. He was also somewhat relieved and wanted to share with his brethren his new understanding.

"I do not fully understand why my mother did what she did, or at least why she believes she did this," he began. "She used a weapon against a canon. She killed him," he began haltingly, choking on his words. "And, in keeping with *privilegium canonis*, such use of physical violence is punishable by excommunication, or possibly even by anathema, in accord with the recent decrees.[329]

---

328   On this hymn, see "*Te Deum laudamus* (hymn)," *Britannica Online Encyclopedia*, https://www.britannica.com/topic/Te-Deum-laudamus, from which both the Latin and the English translations have been taken.

329   Earlier, according to canon law, the punishment for physical violence against a cleric or monk was severe penance or sometimes excommunication (i.e., exclusion from the sacraments), but after the Second Lateran Council (1139) and by the mid-twelfth century, canon law made the punishment stricter: *ipso facto* anathema, which is not only exclusion from the sacraments, but exclusion from the Church, from the body of the faithful, and this punishment could be lifted only by the pope. See "Ecclesiastical

She must be bound over for punishment. May God have mercy on her soul. May God have mercy on her soul. May the most benevolent God have mercy on my beloved mother's soul!

"Canon Jordan, may I ask you to take charge of her, to minister to her, to visit her, to care for her, and, most importantly, to take her confession, and to work most diligently to save her soul? She is my mother; I cannot be her confessor. I beg you to try to save her soul." As Jordan nodded his head in solemn agreement, the young canon pleaded, "I beg you all to pray for her soul!

"Just before our beloved *precentor* and *capud scole* received last rites," young Pons now continued, "he spoke to me, and I promised him I would complete the cloister and the renovation of the church.

"But God then spoke directly to me during *Lauds*. I now see that this was all part of God's plan. I now understand this must be why my mother and I were involved in this tragedy," the young Pons declared with absolute certainty. "God acts in His own mysterious ways. He may put us in the desert, but He delivers us. He may let us be thrown into the fiery furnace, but He delivers us. He tries us, punishes us with His left hand, but delivers us with His right hand.

"He delivers us so we can praise Him, so we can sing His praises in our church, in His Church, so we can work to His greater glory. God wants our church finished—so we can praise Him and work to His greater glory. But God also wants our vaulted cloister finished. God spoke directly to me through our deceased brother, so that our brother could pass on His mission to me. God wants me to continue His mission."

"Amen," William Boso called out.

"God has now given this mission to me. My mission now is first to complete the church which still needs a decorated portal, and then to complete the cloister," Pons concluded. "With your approval and agreement, may I now take on this mission?"

"Yes. Yes."

After a long pause, William Boso spoke up and took charge. "We must now begin preparations for burial, and that brings up a real question," he began. "Our usual, common practice, as well as tradition, would be to bury our dearly departed brother in the hallowed ground at Les Alyscamps. Our chapter still

Privileges: *Privilegium canonis*," in *The Catholic Encyclopedia*, https://www.newadvent. org/cathen/12437a.htm holds burial rights there, of course, and it would certainly be appropriate to bury him in that Christian burial place of such renown.

"But I propose that we bury him right here instead, on our own hallowed claustral grounds, in the beautiful cloister he dedicated his life to erecting. We all know God directed him to do this, so that we could adopt the Rule of St. Augustine and live the communal life, the *vita apostolica*, in the claustral complex built around the cloister. Canon Pons shall be the first of us to be given the right of burial here, as would indeed be appropriate for the canon who took on this mission."

And so it was agreed.

*   *   *

Poncius de Baucio was buried in the garden of the cloister he had built. His epitaph was carved with some flourish and placed in the cloister, where sometime later it was embedded in one of the blind arcades on the north wall of the north gallery, where it remained until the renovations of the late twentieth century.[330]

· · · · · · · · · · · · · · · · · · · ·

330   The epitaph was removed during a restoration of the cloister, chapter house, and dormitory that was carried out in the 1980s. Following its removal, the epitaph was displayed for a while inside the former chapter house. It now seems to be missing. See Albanes and Chevalier, *Arles,* no. 2572, where the year was first erroneously interpreted as 1201 by Albanes and Chevalier, who suggested that although the date had earlier been described as MCI, that date could not be correct because "regular life" did not exist that early. Stoddard later accepted and repeated the erroneous 1201 year. See Stoddard, *Façade,* 259–260 and fig. 369.

It was Robert de Lasteyrie who first correctly deciphered the date as 10 October 1165. Other scholars, such as Léon-Honoré Labande and Léon Pressouyre, interpreted the year correctly as 1165, considering the epitaph as evidence that the chapter had adopted the Rule of St. Augustine by 1165 at the latest. For a comprehensive discussion of the various interpretations posed for this epitaph, see Schneider, "Sculptures," 67–79. For a shorter discussion, see "Arles, Cathedral of Saint-Trophîme, Cloister and Church Portal" in the Afterword.

VI IDVS OCT

OBIITT PONCIVS DE

BAUCIO CAPVT SCOLE ET

CANONICUS REGVLARIS

SCI TROPHIMI ANNO

DNI M⁰C⁰ ~L⁰ ✳ QV'NTO

VI Ides of October (Oct 10th),[331]

died Poncius de

Baucio Chancellor and

Canon Regular Church of

St.Trophîme, in the Year of Our

Lord, $M^0C^0L^0X$ Fifth (Quinto)

Arles. Epitaph of Poncius de Baucio, + 1165, as seen before its removal from the cloister, north gallery, north wall, blind arcade.

For the year, 1165, the carver used Roman numerals for the millennium (M), century (C), and decade (LX), with a written out ordinal (Quinto, fifth) to indicate the year within the decade, all of which was standard practice. Both Jordan and William Boso were close friends with Pons, and Pons had shared his fascination with Arabic numerals with them, teaching them everything he had learned about Arabic numbers and proudly sharing with them the bit of vellum with the copy made for him of several Arabic numerals. So they ensured the carver referenced the Arabic number system in their friend's epitaph by placing a small O above each of the three Roman numerals to indicate it would have its own position in the Arabic place-value system. They also asked him to include a small Arabic numeral 6, which was copied directly from the scrap of vellum Pons had brought from Barcelona, and which ended up looking like a scrolled ligature, or letter S lying on its side.

. . . .

331   For reckoning the calendar day of VI Ides as October 10, recall that in the Roman Julian calendar, VI Ides would be the sixth day before Ides, in the middle or on the fifteenth of the month, and counting Ides as the first day, the sixth day would be October 10 in the Gregorian calendar we now use. See footnote 206 on page 213 above.

And finally, certainly no one was surprised that the all-important Christian symbol of the cross was superimposed on top of the X in the LX. Pons's closest friends recognized, however, that the resulting figure also suggested the Star of Bethlehem, which was appropriate for the epitaph of their beloved friend of the House of Baux.

So on the epitaph, the year 1165 is carved:

M°, or millesimo; C°, or centesimo; the Arabic numeral 6 that looks like a sideways S;

L°X, or sexaginta, here with the X superimposed with a cross, the common notation for Christian death, suggesting a star; and Quinto, fifth year (of the decade).[332]

There is no epitaph for Beatrice. Few women in that era would have been so honored and commemorated in death, unless they were noblewomen of great stature, such as Eleanor of Aquitaine, or perhaps a wellborn nun. Beatrice was only a woman. She was only a woman, a member of what was then considered, especially by the church, a lower order of human beings. Moreover, because she had struck, stabbed, and taken the life of a canon, Beatrice would have been bound over to ecclesiastical authorities for punishment, which would have included execution and, more terrifyingly, excommunication and anathema, in keeping with the privilegium canonis. Excluded from the sacraments and from the church, she would have been denied Christian burial.

Immediately following Pons de Baucio's death in 1165, Bertrand Geraldi assumed the duties of precentor,[333] and William Boso assumed the duties of capud scole.[334] Pons Rebolli also began helping with the sculptural program, but only as an operarius, or workman. His training limited to what he could learn from sculptors who came to work at Arles, Canon Poncius Rebolli was still deemed only a workman, a sculptor of limited abilities.

The sculpture on the portal of the church was completed, probably within the next decade, in the late 1160s or early 1170s, possibly by another master from

....

332   For the author's original analysis and early flawed interpretation of the epigraphy of this epitaph, see Schneider, "Sculptures," 80–87.

333   Bertrandus Gerardi is named as *precentor* in documents after 1165. See Schneider, "Sculptures," 78–79. See also Albanes and Chevalier, *Arles*, nos. 610, 611, 615.

334   Willelmus Boso is named as *caput scole* or *capud scole* in documents after 1165. See Schneider, "Sculptures," 78–79. See also *Authentique*, Arles, MS 1242, fol. 138 no. 113 and fol. 143 no. 129.

north Italy.[335] The church portal would most certainly have been completed by 1178, when the Holy Roman Emperor Frederick Barbarossa was formally crowned King of Burgundy by the Archbishop of Arles in a ceremony at the cathedral.[336]

The sculpture in the east gallery of the cloister had still not yet been completed when Poncius Rebolli died in 1183.

VII:KaL':JANUARII	26 December
ANNO:DNI:M:C:LXXXIII:O	In the year of Our Lord
BIIT:PONCIUS REBOLLI:SA	MCLXXXIII (1183) died Poncius
CERDOS:ET:CANONICUS :	Rebolli, Cleric and Canon
REGULARIS:ET:OPERARI'	Regular and Workman Church St.
ECCLESIE:SANCTI:TROP	Trophime. Pray for Him.
HIMI:ORATE:PRO:EO	

Arles. Epitaph of Poncius Rebolli, + 1183,
as now seen following its recent removal from the cloister.[337]

....

335   For the dating of the portal sculpture and its possible connections with North Italy, see Stoddard, *Façade*, 287–297 and 269–271.

336   Rouquette, *Provence*, 273, 286.

337   This epitaph is at Ville d'Arles. The photograph was provided for use here courtesy of Jean-Marie Dumas, Service du Patrimoine, Ville d'Arles.
See Albanes and Chevalier, *Arles*, no. 2546. See Stoddard, *Façade*, fig. 367 for a photo of the epitaph before it was damaged. The calendar day, VII Kal' JANUARII, was possibly engraved later in the frame.
The epitaph of Poncius Rebolli was removed during the recent restoration of the cloister (2007–2014) and was unfortunately severely damaged. Only a void now remains in the east wall of the east gallery where the epitaph was long installed.

He, too, was buried in the hallowed grounds of the cloister where he had worked as an operarius, and a stone plaque with his epitaph was set into the wall at the northern end of the east wall of the east gallery of the cloister. The elder Pons had never discussed Arabic numerals with this much younger novice, so he had not asked for little Os on the date on his epitaph.

As William Boso and Jordan approached their own deaths within that same decade, they, too, asked to be buried in the cloister that their beloved friend had struggled so hard to create, but they did ask to have the years carved on their epitaphs with the little Os, whose meaning their learned dear friend had shown them.

William Boso died in 1181, and his epitaph was set into the east wall of the east gallery.[338]

III·ID'S·SEPTEMBRIS·OBIIT·VI	On 11 September died
LeLM' BOSO·SACERDOS·CA	William Boso, Cleric,
NONICVS·REGVLARIS·ET	Canon Regular and
PREPOSITVS·SCI TROPHIMI	Provost of St. Trophîme
ANNO·DNI·M⁰C⁰ LX⁰XX·PRIMO	In the year of Our Lord
	MCLXXX First (1181)

Arles. Cloister, east gallery. Epitaph of Wilelmus Boso, + 1181.

When Jordan, Pons's closest friend, then died in 1188, he, too, was laid to rest in the cloister. His epitaph was carved, albeit with some obvious difficulty, directly onto the socle of the northwest corner pier, on the west face, beneath the pier figure

....

338   See Albanes and Chevalier, *Arles,* no. 2544 and Stoddard, *Façade,* fig. 271 for the epitaph.

of St. Trophîme, who had been standing there for over three decades near the pas-sageway into the church where his relics now resided.

Canon Jordan's epitaph reads[339]:

*II⁰ KaL·OC§:OBIIt·IOR	On 30 September died Jor-
dAN'· DECAN'·SCI·TROPhIMI:	dan Dean St. Trophîme
ANNO DNI' M⁰·C⁰ LXX⁰X·VI⁰II+	In the year of our
	Lord MCLXXXVIII
	(1188) +

Arles. Cloister, northwest corner pier. Socle. Epitaph of Jordanus, + 1188.

Not too long thereafter, the remaining large pier figures and relief carvings would be carved in the cloister's east gallery, which would finally be completed by the early thirteenth century.[340] However, Arles had already reached its apogee during the twelfth century, and by the thirteenth century the fortunes of the city of Arles and of its cathedral were beginning to wane.[341] Further "construction" on the cloister ceased. The cloister was incomplete, still lacking its south and west galleries.

....

339   See Albanes and Chevalier, *Arles,* no. 2551 and Stoddard, *Façade,* fig. 368 for the epitaph.

340   See Stoddard, *Façade,* 237–255 for a chronology and analysis of the styles of the east gallery sculptures.

341   Rouquette, *Provence,* 300–301. See also Jean-Maurice Rouquette, Claude Sintès, Louis Stouff, and Andreas Hartmann-Vimich, Service du Patrimoine, Ville d'Arles, *Saint Trophime Cloister,* Mini Guide, 2000, "The crisis of the Late Middle Ages (unpaginated)."

Nunc dimittis

Concluding prayer of *Compline*, Night Prayer

QUARTUSDECIMUS SAECULUM

FOURTEENTH CENTURY

Nunc dimittis servum tuum, Domine, secundum verbum
tuum in pace
Quia viderunt oculi mei salutare tuum
Quod parasti ante faciem omnium populorum:
Lumen ad revelationem gentium, et gloriam plebis
tuae Israhel.

(*Secundum Lucam* 2: 29–32)

Now thou dost dismiss thy servant, O Lord, according to
thy word in peace:
Because my eyes have seen thy salvation,
Which thou hast prepared before the face of all peoples;
A light to the revelation of the Gentiles, and the glory of
thy people Israel.

(Luke 2: 29–32)

By the late fourteenth century the cloister was finally completed, with both the southern and western galleries erected in the Gothic style.[342] Pons de Baucio's mission to build the communal architectural complex around a beautiful cloister was finally realized.

Only a short while earlier, however, in 1355, the chapter had once again become secularized, formally renouncing the vita apostolica, formally rejecting the Rule of St. Augustine that Pons had struggled so single-mindedly to bring to the chapter. The canons gave up communal life, choosing instead each to hold private property and to live in private houses erected within the cathedral enclosure.[343] Pons de Baucio's mission to regularize the chapter had come to naught.

When the chapter decided to renounce the vita apostolica in the mid-fourteenth century, Arles was in a decline.[344] The city had begun losing its stature much earlier, possibly beginning in 1180, when the Catalans moved their residence and the capital of the County of Provence to Aix, and during the political, territorial and religious tumult of the following century, Provence and Arles came under the control of the Angevin dynasty, forecasting their future inclusion in the French domain.[345] By the fourteenth century the archdiocese of Arles was declining in importance, especially after the papacy was installed at Avignon in 1309, overshadowing Arles. Moreover, by the mid-fourteenth century there was widespread famine in the area.

There had been a brief rich flowering of intellectual life at Arles in the thirteenth and early fourteenth centuries among the Jewish scholars in Trinquetaille, who had been received there by the lords of Baux,[346] but by the mid-fourteenth century that intellectual flowering, too, was in decline.

....

342 Rouquette, *Provence*, 346–347. See Actes Sud and Ville d'Arles, eds., *Le Cloître Saint-Trophime d'Arles*, 2017, 109–112, but note this recent study unfortunately still holds to the mistaken late dating for the north gallery of the cloister.

343 Rouquette, Sintès, Stouff, and Hartmann-Vimich, *Saint Trophime*, "The crisis of the Late Middle Ages."

344 For the complicated history of Arles from the late twelfth through the thirteenth and early fourteenth centuries, see the detailed "Histoire d'Arles: Histoire d'Arles à l'époque médiévale," *Wikipedia*.

345 Provence eventually became part of France, part of the French royal domain, in 1486 after Louis XI inherited title from Charles du Maine in 1481.

346 In the thirteenth and fourteenth centuries, Jewish scholars living in Trinquetaille included Meir ben Isaac, author of *Sefer ha-Ezer*; Nathan ben Meir, author of a commentary on the Pentateuch and of *Sha'are Tefisah*; Todros ben Meshullam ben David; and Joseph ibn Caspi, also known as Sen Bonfos or Don Bonafoux de L'Argentiere, who, after being chased out of Languedoc, arrived in Arles to join Kalonymos ben

What immediately preceded and really prompted the canons' renouncing the vita apostolica, however, was the "Great Plague," also called the "Great Pestilence" and later named the Black Death, that swept through Europe by the middle of the century. Originating in the east, it had spread via the Silk Road and by ship, reaching Sicily by the end of 1347, and the maritime republics of Genoa and Venice, and then Pisa, in early 1348. Reaching Marseilles, the "Great Plague" then swept northwest through France to Spain, Portugal, and England, and then spread further through Germany and Scandinavia within two years. It first appeared in Arles and Avignon in January 1348.

A contemporary fourteenth-century chronicler, Jean de Venette, who was a Carmelite friar, reported that as the devastation of the Great Plague was approaching Paris in August 1348, there appeared in the skies a large, bright "star in the west," a portentous ball of fire, that scattered rays over all of Paris before disappearing. Although he left it to astronomers to explain the nature of the bursting star, Venette recognized and interpreted the appearance of this "star in the west" as a warning sign, as a portent of the terrible pestilence and devastation that soon followed.[347]

The Great Plague was devastating. Overall, it killed seventy-five million people in Europe, or almost half the population. The death rate varied by region, however, and some were much more severely hit than others. It was particularly vengeful in Mediterranean Europe, in the south of France, in Italy, and in Spain, where it killed an estimated 78– 80% of the population. In Arles, an estimated 15,000 succumbed, or at least half the population.

Hardest hit were those in crowded cities. Few of those administering to the sick could escape death themselves, including the priests and clerics who heard the crucial, obligatory last confessions and administered the all-important holy viaticum.[348]

....

Kalonymos, producing *Tirat Kessef*, an introduction to the Pentateuque. See both "Histoire d'Arles à l'époque médiévale tardive," *Wikipedia* and Isidore Singer and S. Khan, "Trinquetaille," in *Jewish Encyclopedia*, http://www.jewishencyclopedia.com/articles/14520-trinquetaille.

347   Jean de Venette. *The Chronicle of Jean de Venette*, Richard A. Newhall, ed., Jean Birdsall, trans. New York, Columbia University Press, 1953, 48-51. See Perry M. Rogers, *Aspects of Western Civilization* (London, UK: Pearson, 2000), 353–365.

348   On the effects of the Black Death, see Venette, *Chronicle*, 353–365.

The canons at Arles would have been hit particularly hard, living closely together, living communally within a crowded city, and doing service to the general public on behalf of the cathedral. Many canons, if not most of them, would have died.

The chapter would also have become quite wealthy, however. The plague took people of all ages, and from all classes. Many of its victims died without heirs, leaving their entire estates and all their worldly goods to the churches and monasteries that had cared for their souls, especially at the end of their lives, and these certainly included the cathedral church and claustrum at Arles. During the second half of the fourteenth century, the chapter's communal fortunes would have improved substantially—improved enough to enable them finally to complete the cloister.

Such widespread pestilence, such devastation demanded explanation, demanded something to blame—demanded someone to blame. With no other explanation for the horrible pestilence, many believed the plague was caused by "infection of the air and waters." Many blamed the Jews, whom they believed had poisoned the wells and corrupted the air.[349] At Saint-Rémy-de-Provence the synagogue was burned down. In Barcelona the Jewish quarter was pillaged. There began widespread, indiscriminate slaughtering of Jews by Christians. Entire Jewish communities, both large and small, were destroyed. At Arles the city formally separated itself from Trinquetaille, home of the Jews, the town with which it had become incorporated only decades earlier.[350]

Who could explain the origin of the Great Plague? Who could explain such horrors? When called upon to explain the plague, the medical faculty at the University of Paris in 1348 gave their scientific report that the primary and universal cause was a malign conjunction of three planets in Aquarius that had occurred at 1 p.m. on 20 March 1345. They explained that a conjunction of Saturn and Jupiter caused mortality of races and population loss, while a conjunction of Mars and Jupiter caused pestilence in the air. So the stars had badly misaligned.

The faculty finally concluded, however, that any pestilence is the result of divine will.[351]

Yes, most people acknowledged that any pestilence has to be the result of divine will. Most people recognized that the Great Pestilence was so horrible that it could

349   Taken from Rosemary Horrox, trans. and ed., *The Black Death* (Manchester, UK, and New York, N.Y. Manchester University Press, 1994), https://web.stanford.edu/class/history13/Readings/Horrox.htm

350   See Singer and Khan, "Trinquetaille."

351   Horrox, "The Black Death."

only have been a vengeful act of God. Most understood and recognized it as a punishment from God, the result of God's anger and wrath.[352]

    God had spoken.

. . . .

352   See Venette, *Chronicle,* 353–365.

$\mathcal{A}$fterword
Some Bits of Art History
Relevant to this Tale

$\mathcal{S}$ ome readers may want to know just a little bit about some of the beautiful art and architecture mentioned in the tale; some may want to know a lot more about little bits of art history alluded to here. The evolution of sculpture during the life of Poncius de Baucio is truly astounding and can hold one's interest captive for decades. The art itself is even more captivating, still enigmatically complex after over 100 years of intense scholarship, and still mesmerizingly beautiful after almost 900 years of wear, tear, and abuse. Just go to see it. Visit Arles. Visit Saint-Gilles.[353] And then . . .

Saint-Gilles, Abbey Church, West Façade

The dating of the pier figures and carved lintels and tympana on the façade of Saint-Gilles has long been fiercely debated among medieval art historians.[354] The beginning of construction of the church is documented by a carved inscription on its base as begun by Abbot Hugh in 1116, but aside from this fact, there has long been little agreement. For over a century there has been a deep divide, with most French art historians dating the façade sometime in the

353 The town of Saint-Gilles is now also called Saint-Gilles-du-Gard. After the French Revolution, Gard was a department created out of the province of Languedoc.

354 For an excellent summary of the prolonged debate and intimidatingly extensive literature, see Stoddard, *Façade*, 127–159, esp. 153–156.

second half of the twelfth to early thirteenth century, but most German and American art historians dating it to the middle or earlier in the twelfth century.

It was Vöge,[355] an eminent German art historian, who probably started the schism in 1894 when he mistakenly proposed that the sculptures at Arles were seminal monuments of French Romanesque sculpture and that based on stylistic analysis, Saint-Gilles should be dated around 1150, after both the cloister and portal at Arles, which he saw as influencing the *Portail Royal* of Chartres. The sculptures at Arles were soon accepted as dependent, subordinate to the façade at Saint-Gilles. But the burning, underlying question then became which came first? Provence or Île-de-France? Saint-Gilles or Chartres?

Subsequently, innumerable scholars have tried to establish a firm dating for the façade sculptures at Saint-Gilles. They have used detailed architectural analyses, sought for and found indirectly related historical documents, done superbly refined stylistic comparisons and analyses, and closely examined the iconography. Some focused on the crypt, on the chronology of construction, which most now agree proceeded in general from west to east.[356] Many, many eminent scholars took on the challenge of trying to date the façade at Saint-Gilles, resulting in dates ranging from 1120 to the 1180s and later, because the evidence is not firm or clear-cut and often seems contradictory. There is still no firm scholarly consensus on the dating of the façade.

Many scholars, however, now accept, albeit rather uneasily, a compromise dating of mid-twelfth century. Stoddard's exhaustive study and analysis placed it in the 1140s to early 1150s, and he sees 1178—the firm date of Benedetto Antelami's deposition relief in the Cathedral of Parma, which was copied from the façade of Saint-Gilles—as a *terminus ante quem*, or the date before which the façade at Saint-Gilles was completed.[357]

Arles, Cathedral of Saint-Trophîme, Cloister and Church Portal

At the Cathedral of Saint Trophîme at Arles, the twelfth-century Romanesque sculpture falls into three different main groups: the north gallery of the

....

355   Wilhelm Vöge, *Die Anfänge des Monumentalen Stiles im Mittelalter* (Strassburg, Germany: Heitz, 1894), 47ff, 101 ff.

356   See Stoddard, *Façade*, 131–134 for a summary of the views and for a discussion of the chronology and vaulting of the crypt.

357   See Stoddard, *Façade*, 153 for this conclusion.

cloister, the east gallery of the cloister, and the church portal sculpture. The sculpture of the west and south galleries of the cloister is much later and is Gothic in style.

The dating of the Romanesque sculpture at Arles early became mired in controversy when Vöge proposed that the portal sculpture should be dated 1135, before Saint-Gilles, and that the north gallery sculpture was early and influenced Chartres. Drawn into the fiery debate, Arles, like Saint-Gilles, became a focus of art historians.[358] They used stylistic and iconographic analyses and architectural analysis of the cloister, but at Arles they were able to incorporate and focus on what seemed to be more concrete evidence: several dated epitaphs inserted into the cloister walls and a dated ceremony, the translation of the relics of St. Trophîme back into the church in 1152.

It was Léon-Honoré Labande,[359] a French art historian, who long focused intensively on Arles. Using historical records to try to find when the canons reformed and decided to live communally, which would require the construction of communal buildings around a cloister, he then tried to consolidate with this the evidence from the epitaphs and stylistic analyses. However, the first citation he found of a communal building was a dormitory in 1180,[360] which did not support an early date for the cloister. Although he first proposed 1150–1180 for the beginning of the cloister, and the end of the twelfth to early thirteenth century for the portal, he eventually concluded with a dating of 1165–1180 for the north gallery of the cloister and 1180 for the portal.

Following Labande, it became generally accepted that the north gallery sculpture preceded most of the east gallery sculpture. It also became firmly accepted that the style of this Romanesque sculpture at Arles was dependent on that of Saint-Gilles.

Most significantly, it was long assumed that Labande's extensive studies of Arles were thorough and that his examination of the historical records had been exhaustive. Consequently, his citation of 1180 as the first mention of a communal cloister building was subsequently universally accepted and often

358   For a summary of the debated dating and literature, see Stoddard, *Façade*, 255–271, especially 255–259.

359   Léon-Honoré Labande, "Étude Historique et Archéologique sur Saint-Trophime d'Arles du IVᵉ au XIIIᵉ siècle," *Bulletin monumental* LXVII (1904) 22–38; Léon-Honoré Labande, "Eglise Métropolitaine de Saint-Trophime," *Congrès archéologique de France* II (1909), 218–223; and Labande, *L'église*, 218–223.

360   Labande, "Étude," 36–37.

repeated[361] as evidence for a late dating of the Romanesque sculpture in the cloister at Arles.

However close examination of the original manuscript records finally revealed that Labande had read only the published transcriptions of the documents in Albanes and Chevalier's *Gallia christiana novissima, Arles,* where the editors had condensed or sometimes deleted seemingly inconsequential bits.[362] We now know that the concept of building a canons' cloister at Arles appeared by 1142, because the first references to a twelfth-century *claustrum* at Arles are in 1142/43, when it is mentioned at least four times in contemporary documents:[363]

- Record of pledge by Petrus de Lambisco and his family, of 1142.[364]

- Pledge by Alphonse Jourdain, (Ildefonsus), Count of Toulouse, of 1143. See Chapter 4, *Terce,* with photos; see the *Authentique du Chapitre,* Arles, Bibliothèque Municipale, MS 1242, fol. 146–146v.[365]

- Another record of pledge by Alphonse Jourdain, (Ildefonsus), Count of Toulouse, of 1143.[366]

- Record of pledge by Raymond of Baux, the dating of which has been corrected to as early as 1142/1143.[367]

We also now know that by 1165/66 there was a dormitory, because a document of 1166 reports that the resolution of a controversy was reached

....

361   See for example Jacques Lacoste, "La Galerie Nord du Cloître de Saint-Trophime d'Arles," *Les Cahiers de Saint-Michel de Cuxa* 7 (June 1976), 133–134 and Jacques Thirion, "Saint-Trophime d'Arles," *Congrès Archéologique de France* 134 (1976), 440–442.

362   See Schneider, "Sculptures," 18 ff. The published transcriptions are in Albanes and Chevalier, *Arles.*

363   See Schneider, "Sculptures," 23–33.

364   See Albanes and Chevalier, *Arles,* no. 543, discussed in chapter 4, *Terce.*

365   See Albanes and Chevalier, *Arles,* no. 548, where the references to the *claustrum* were omitted in the abbreviated transcription.

366   See Albanes and Chevalier, *Arles,* no. 549.

367   See Albanes and Chevalier, *Arles,* no. 563. For the correction of the dating, see Schneider, "Sculptures," 30–33.

"*in canonica in dormitorio*" on the day of Epiphany, or January 6.[368] In 1178 another act was passed "*in dormitorio*" at St. Trophîme.[369]

We also now know that by or before 1144 there may have been a refectory, because a document of that date mentions "*unum ex clericis de domo et mensa Sancti Trofimi,*"and "*mensa*" could possibly be interpreted as "a common table."[370] By 1153 there certainly was a refectory,[371] because a document of that date identifies what was owed annually to the *refectorio*.[372] The *refectorium* is mentioned again in 1158 in a list of what the monks of Saint-Gilles were obliged to pay to the refectory at Arles.[373]

As Labande first clarified, it was the canons' decision to reform and to live communally, to adopt the strict Rule of St. Augustine, that would have been the impetus for them to build communal buildings around a cloister, and he saw the epitaph of Poncius de Baucio, embedded into the north façade wall of the cloister, as the first reference to a "canon regular" at Arles. It was Robert de Lasteyrie who had first deciphered the date as 10 October 1165.[374] Labande accepted this interpretation of the date in his many studies of the Arles sculptures, noting that a papal bull of 1153 did not mention regular life at Arles while one of 1186 termed the reform as "nuper," and concluding that the canons adopted the Rule sometime between 1153 and 1165.[375]

The date on the epitaph had been variously interpreted as 1151, 1155, 1165, and 1201. Wilhelm Vöge had early interpreted it as 1155 and considered it a *terminus ante quem,* or "date before which" for the north gallery.[376] Albanes and Chevalier then first erroneously read the date as 1201; they suggested that although the date had earlier been interpreted as MCI, that date could not be correct because "regular life" did not exist that early, and they listed a "Pons de Bars (?) (Barcia) 10 Oct. 1201" in their list of "capiscoles" solely on

....

368   Albanes and Chevalier, *Arles,* no. 2531, but the entire text is found only in *Authentique,* Arles, MS 1242, fol. 122.
369   Albanes and Chevalier, *Arles,* no. 2540, see *Authentique,* Arles, MS 1242, fol. 123
370   Albanes and Chevalier, *Arles,* no. 552. See Schneider, "Sculptures," 40–42.
371   Schneider, "Sculptures," 41–42.
372   See Albanes and Chevalier, *Arles,* no. 2525.
373   Albanes and Chevalier, *Arles,* no. 594.
374   Robert de Lasteyrie, "Études sur la Sculpture Francaise au Moyen-Age," L'Académie des Inscriptions et Belles-Lettres, Fondation Pict, *Monuments et Memoires,* VIII, 50.
375   Labande, "Étude," 33–39.
376   Vöge, *Die Anfänge, 132.*

the basis of their reading of this epitaph.[377] A. K. Porter then interpreted the date as MCLI and concluded the north gallery existed by 1151.[378]

Stoddard disagreed with most of this, having accepted Albanes and Chevalier's erroneous dating of 1201 along with the spurious "Pons de Bars (?)" in their list of "capiscoles;" he also proposed that the canons had adopted the Rule by 1060, a proposal based solely on a comment Albanes and Chevalier had appended as a title to their transcription of a document.[379] Léon Pressouyre immediately countered Stoddard's dating of the epitaph, correcting the identification of the deceased to the canon whose career could be documented from 1131 to 1165/66, and after providing additional new evidence from papal bulls, Pressouyre concluded that the Rule was adopted at Arles between 1155 and 1165.[380]

Other scholars have since shied away from using the epitaph as evidence to date the cloister. Rouquette had earlier adopted Labande's analysis but noted that the epitaph was embedded in a wall and was no longer in its original position.[381] It was Rouquette who then led the restoration that opened the blind arcade and removed the epitaph. Jacques Lacoste dismissed the epitaph as being too insecurely identified and dated to be useful, and concluded that all the evidence suggested the north gallery was begun around 1180.[382] Jacques Thirion agreed with Labande and Pressouyre about the dating and identification of the epitaph, but after finding papal bulls suggesting the reform was not realized without difficulty, he insisted the first evidence of a communal building at Arles was the document of 1180 citing a dormitory, and he concluded the north gallery should be dated 1180–1190.[383] For a comprehensive

....

377   Albanes and Chevalier, *Arles,* no. 2572, and Chronological Tables at col 1413..

378   Arthur Kingsley Porter, *Romanesque Sculpture of the Pilgrimage Roads* (Boston, MA: Marshall Jones Company, 1923), I, 298.

379   Stoddard, *Façade,* 259–263. See Albanes and Chevalier, *Arles,* no. 407 with its title added by the transcribers.

380   Léon Pressouyre, Review of Whitney S. Stoddard, *The Façade of Saint-Gilles-du-Gard. Its Influence on French Sculpture.* Middleton, 1973, in *Zeitschrift für Kunstgeschichte* 39, no. 1 (1976): 79–80.

381   Rouquette, *Provence,* 299–300, 302.

382   Jacques Lacoste, "La Galerie Nord du Cloitre de Saint-Trophime d'Arles," *Les Cahiers de Saint-Michel de Cuxa* 7 (June 1976) : 133–134.

383   Jacques Thirion, "Saint-Trophime d'Arles," *Congrès archéologique de France* 134 (1976), 440–442.

discussion of the various interpretations posed for this epitaph, see Schneider, "Sculptures," 67–79.

We now know, however, after carefully reading the original church documents, that Poncius de Baucio's epitaph records his death in 1165, and that this is the first mention of a "canon regular" at Arles. We also now know that a *claustrum*, which would certainly imply if not directly indicate a canons' cloister, was conceived of by 1142/43; that by or before 1153 there was a common refectory; and that by or before late 1165 there was a dormitory. So the canons probably were living communally by 1165.

We also now know from architectural and stylistic analyses that the earliest work on the cloister was at the west end of the north gallery and began with carved capitals for columns that would support a wooden-roofed porch for the chapter house, a porch that would later be expanded eastward and vaulted to become the north gallery of the cloister.[384]

Saint-Denis, Abbey Church, West Façade

Abbot Suger, who was abbot from 1122 to 1151, began the twelfth-century reconstruction of the Abbey Church at Saint-Denis. He began with the west front of the church, commissioning three large portals decorated with figural sculpture, including large figure statues on columns, and with a rose window above, all of which was completed by 9 June 1140, when oratory chapels in the upper story there were dedicated. The dedication dates provides a *terminus ante quem*, or "date before which" for the completion of the sculptures, so it is assumed the portals were begun by 1130, and the jamb figures at Saint-Denis are now dated before 1140.[385]

All twenty column figures were removed from the three doorways on the west front in 1771 and destroyed, and little remains. Fortunately, however, drawings of them were made by Antoine Benoit and included by Dom Bernard de Montfauçon in his *Les Monumens de la Monarchie Françoise*, 1729, vol I., plates XVI, XVII, and XVIII.[386]

....

384 See Schneider, "Sculptures," 99–100, 186–189, 101–115, and 133–146.
385 For an excellent overview, including a succinct summary of the history, state of preservation, program, style, and dating of the figures, as well as for reproductions of Montfaucon's drawings, see Sauerländer, *Gothic*, 379–381 and illustrations 1, 2, 3.
386 Montfaucon, *Les Monumens*, vol. I.

After completing the façade at the west end of the church, Abbot Suger then began reconstruction of the east end, designing a new choir with an ambulatory with radiating chapels, which was completed by 11 June 1144.

To be able to raise the vault up high, to free the walls from having to support the weight and thrust of the vault, to be able to pierce the walls with magnificent large stained glass windows, Suger's builders used and combined in a new manner several new or evolving known architectural features and building practices, including the pointed arch; the ribbed vault; the clustering of columns, each of which supports a separately springing rib; and the flying buttress.

Suger realized his extraordinary vision of space and light, creating a breathtakingly beautiful new architectural style that would eventually become known as Gothic architecture.

Saint-Denis, Abbey Cloister

Abbot Suger also built a cloister with column figures, presumably before his death in 1151. Curiously, although Suger provided detailed written descriptions of the new work on the west façade and in the choir, he did not mention the cloister, suggesting, perhaps, that it was a very late undertaking.

The cloister and all the sculpture were presumed to have been destroyed. Fortunately, however, Antoine Benoit had made drawings of three column figures from the cloister at Saint-Denis before their destruction, and these were also included by Dom Bernard de Montfauçon in his *Les Monumens de la Monarchie Françoise* (vol. I, pl. X), published in 1729. Montfauçon's engravings were long believed to be the only visual record of the column figures from Abbot Suger's cloister.[387]

However, Vera K. Ostoia[388] has identified a four-foot-tall statue of a king, now at the Metropolitan Museum in New York, as one of the "two statues of Merovingian Kings with nimbi, sculptured on two columns supporting the cloister... in the oldest part of the cloister of the Monastery of Saint-Denis,"[389] which was illustrated by Montfauçon in his *Monumens de la Monarchie Françoise*. Note, however, that Ostoia rejects Montfauçon's identification of

387 For a short overview, see Sauerlander, *Gothic*, 381–382 and illustration 4.
388 Vera K. Ostoia, "Statue," 298–304.
389 See Crosby et al., *Royal*, esp. Little, "Monumental," 25–60, esp. 29–33 and 44–49.

the figure as a Merovingian king and proposes it must be an Old Testament figure, probably Solomon, who was a wise and just king.

Ostoia notes that although some scholars have doubted the accuracy of details of the king's costume, notably the center neck opening and the decorative long ends of the belt, there are very similar neck openings on the male apostle figures on the façade of Saint-Gilles and on the pillars in the cloister of Saint Trophîme at Arles.[390] Such similarities of costume lend some support to our hypothesis that a Provençal sculptor, whom we call Master Guillelmo, who worked at Arles and Saint-Gilles, also worked on the column figures in Suger's cloister.

Ostoia also notes that Montfauçon's engravings reveal a variety of styles in the sculpture, undoubtedly resulting from Abbot Suger's having employed diverse workshops.[391] Certainly both of the other two figures illustrated by Montfauçon show an even closer affinity to the sturdy, substantive Provençal style of Master Guillelmo. And other capitals now identified as also coming from the old cloister at Saint-Denis[392] certainly also show affinities with the Provençal style.

Chartres, Cathedral of Notre Dame, West Façade

The sculptures of the "Royal Portal," the west doorways at Chartres, are now dated 1145–1155. This dating is derived from what is known about the architectural history of the church. A fire in 1134 spared the Romanesque nave but became the impetus for building work on the west end, starting with the north tower. A report of 1145 mentions the cathedral's towers being built, so by or before 1145 what was envisioned was a twin-towered façade with a triple portal at the west end of the Romanesque nave. So the west doorways were presumably begun by 1145, and because of the overall coherence of the style of the sculptures of the "Royal Portal," they are dated 1145–1155.[393]

....

390   Ostoia, "Statue," 300, but on page 301 she rejects Montfaucon's identification of the figure as a Merovingian king and proposes it must be an Old Testament figure, probably Solomon, who was a wise and just king.

391   Ostoia, "Statue," 303.

392   See Little, "Monumental," 47–49 for photos.

393   For this history, for the dating, and for the sculptures, see Sauerlander, *Gothic*, 383–386.

Cluny, Abbey Church

The monastery at Cluny was established in 910. The second church on the site, erected in the tenth century, was reconstructed beginning in 1088. The third church was stone vaulted and completed in 1121, but unfortunately the vaulting of the central nave collapsed soon after its completion. However, the vault was successfully rebuilt for the consecration of the church in 1130.

When finally completed in the twelfth century, this third church, called Cluny III, was enormous for that time, the largest church in Christendom. Tunnel vaulted throughout, the nave arcade used pointed arches, one of the first such uses in the west, and above the arcade ran a small triforium passage, above which was the clerestory through which light entered. It was also magnificently decorated with sculpture and wall frescoes.

The entire monastic complex is now destroyed, and only a little remains. The reconstruction of the original complex became the life work of K. J. Conant, and the original structure and decoration are known through his thorough excavations and studies.[394]

Toulouse, Cathedral of Saint-Étienne, Chapter House and Cloister

The pier figures and capitals associated with Master Gilabertus from Saint-Étienne, Toulouse, are now usually dated between 1120 and 1140. The dating has never been firmly established. These sculptures have been placed as early as 1120 and as late as the 1150s purely on the basis of stylistic analyses and comparisons with other sculpture, mostly with capitals from another cloister, La Daurade at Toulouse, with the relief sculptures of the porch at Moissac, and with the façade sculptures of Saint-Denis and Chartres.[395] Stoddard places them in the late 1130s or 1140s.

The pier figures from Saint-Étienne, Toulouse were long in the Musée des Augustins and were mistakenly thought to have decorated the portal of the church. They were identified as having originally been placed in the chapter house, where they supported the transverse arches of the barrel vault, by Linda Seidel, who dated them about 1125.[396]

....

394   See for example Conant, *Cluny*.
395   For a succinct review of the dating, see Stoddard, *Façade*, 149–150
396   See Seidel, "Romantic," 33–42.

Autun

The Cathedral of Saint-Lazare, Autun was begun around 1120 and mostly finished by 1146. An inscription, "*Gislebertus hoc fecit,*" appears on the Last Judgment tympanum, which is usually dated 1130-1135 or before 1135. It has long been assumed that the inscription identifies the sculptor, Master Gislebertus, who worked there from 1120–1135,[397]but this identification has been challenged.[398] Many of Master Gislebertus's carved capitals show the elongated distortion of the figures on the tympanum, but some, including the Magi capitals, which are now on display at the Musée Rolin near the Cathedral, show a gentle charm comparable to that of the Cluny capitals.

The portal sculptures at Autun suffered much in the eighteenth century, when the changing tastes of the church clergy led to the Last Judgment tympanum being plastered over. Sculptures of the patriarchs and prophets originally above that tympanum were completely removed.

The lintel showing the nude Eve has also been attributed to Gislebertus[399] and originally appeared on the north portal but is now displayed in the Musée Rolin at Autun. Only this relief sculpture of Eve survives from the north portal, having long been hidden after being confiscated in the eighteenth century for use as building material. The sculptures of the raising of Lazarus, of Adam, and of the devil are gone. However, an ivory replica of the Eve figure, with an accompanying ivory depicting Adam, now appearing in the collection of the Yuko Nii Foundation, are believed to be replicas showing the original configuration at Autun, and they reveal how extraordinary the original stone carvings must have been.

Vézelay

Sainte-Madeleine at Vézelay[400] was a Benedictine abbey of the Order of Cluny. Perched high on a hill, the abbey church held the relics of Ste. Madeleine, brought by the mid-eleventh century from the Holy Land. The new abbey church was begun in 1104 but was constructed 1120–1150. Vézelay marked

397　See Beckwith, *Early*, 212–215 and fig. 202.

398　See Seidel, *Legends,* 6 ff. See above in the *Preface*, xiv and footnote 18.

399　See Grivot and Zarnecki, *Gislebertus.*

400　On Vézelay, see Francis Salet, *La Madeleine de Vézelay* (Melun: Librairie d'Argences, 1948).

the beginning of one of the four main pilgrimage routes to Santiago de Compostela, and the abbey church soon became so popular a site for pilgrims that a large narthex, or enclosed porch, was built to accommodate them, and the narthex was dedicated by Pope Innocent in 1132.

Therefore, the tympanum on the inner west doorway showing the Mission to the Apostles and the Ascension is firmly dated 1125–1135.

Bernard of Clairvaux called for the Second Crusade at Vézelay on Easter 1146.

Sagra di San Michele, Zodiac Portal

The Zodiac Portal is an installation of individual carvings, now forming a portal, at the ancient Sagra di San Michele abbey,[401] which sits perched on Mount Pirchiriano, near Turin, Italy. Situated on the *Via Francigena*, the antique chapel was modified and expanded, beginning as early as the tenth century with major construction in the eleventh and twelfth centuries.

Master Niccolo is credited with the major construction of the twelfth century. The *Porta dello Zodiaco* sits at the top of a long stairway of 243 steps, called the *Scalone dei Morti* (Stairway of the Dead), which leads to the separate church.[402]

The Zodiac Portal is the first sculptural program signed by Niccolo, and it is usually dated 1120. Niccolo's inscription begins on the edge of the pilaster along the left side of the portal,

VOS LEGITE VERSUS QUOS ESCRIPSIT NICHOLAUS

(You are reading the verses that Niccolo wrote and carved)

and continues on the opposite edge of the portal:

VOS QUI TRANSITIR SURSUM VEL FORTE REDITUS

(You who are going upwards, or maybe returning)

On the upper part of the right door post is the inscription that will be seen again at the Cathedral of Piacenza:

....

401   This beautiful abbey was the inspiration for Umberto Eco's novel *The Name of the Rose*.

402   See photos in Antonio Salvatori, *Paying a Visit to the "Sacra di San Michele"* (2002), 24, 25, 30.

HOC OPUS INTENDAT QUISQUIS BONVS EXIT
[ET] INTRAT

(May any good person who exits and enters view this work)

Piacenza, Church of Sant'Eufemia

In the Emilia Romagna region of Italy, the Church of Sant'Eufemia at Piacenza was consecrated by Bishop Aldo in 1107, after which a porch with columns and capitals was added.

The porch capitals have been attributed to Niccolo and his workshop by Christine Verzár Bornstein.[403] Bornstein found stylistic parallels with the earliest work of Niccolo at the Zodiac Portal of the Sagra di San Michele of 1120 and with the earliest capitals in the interior of the Cathedral of Piacenza, but she suggested that the capitals at Sant'Eufemia lacked the refinement of Niccolo's work on the south portal of the Cathedral of Piacenza, which she dated 1122–1130.

Bornstein identified the style of another sculptor there, who she suggested worked on some foliate capitals and human and animal figures that are not attributable to Niccolo. She called him the "master of Sant'Eufemia," suggested that he was unfamiliar both with the work of Wiligelmo (earlier Master who worked at Modena Cathedral) and of Niccolo. She contended that he subsequently worked on some of the capitals in the interior of the Cathedral of Piacenza and influenced the head style of the figures on the north portal there.[404] Could this sculptor be the young Pietro just beginning his training with Master Niccolo?

Piacenza, Cathedral

The dating of the sculpture at the Cathedral at Piacenza is problematic. The cathedral has three double-storied porch portals, which were quite innovative in Emilia/Romagna, because the single version first appeared

---

403   See Bornstein, "Capitals," 15–26.
404   See Bornstein, "Capitals," 22–24.

in Emilia/Romagna earlier in the century at the Porta dei Principi at Modena Cathedral.[405]

The lower portion of the façade of Piacenza Cathedral is usually dated after 1122 because of a reference to this date inscribed on the south porch façade, but the validity of this inscription has been challenged. Difficulties in unraveling the complicated building history of the cathedral are further complicated by its extensive renovations. Nevertheless, it is usually now accepted that the earliest sculptural work at Piacenza Cathedral includes the north and south portal lintels, along with their immediately adjoining sculpture, but that the lateral porches are later additions.

The central portal and porch are even more problematic and have been called, quite correctly, a "veritable nightmare of guesswork attribution" because well-intended restoration has blended in or removed all clues about what was originally there.[406] It can be argued that for the central portal, only parts of the porch and portal—notably, the telamons of the architrave and lintel, the signs of the zodiac and their cosmic symbols on the extrados of the porch arch, and finally, the four figures around the apse window—are original.

On the lower edge of the lintel of the south portal is a moralizing inscription, and although it does not name Niccolo and the end of it has been partly chipped away, it closely recalls Niccolo's moralizing inscription on the Zodiac Portal, supporting the attribution of the work at Piacenza to Niccolo and his workshop. This inscription reads:

> HOC OPUS INTENDAT QUISQUIS BONUS EXIT
> ET INTRAT.

> (May any good person who exits and enters view
> this work.)

The early sculpture at Piacenza Cathedral is now attributed to Niccolo and his workshop. The south portal and south portal lintel are attributed to Niccolo himself, and the north portal lintel is now usually attributed to another sculptor in his workshop.[407] This sculpture on the north and south portal can be dated between 1122–1130 (i.e., after the Zodiac Portal at the

---

405   See Dorothy F. Glass, *The Sculpture of Reform in North Italy, ca 1095-1130* (Farnham, UK, and Burlington, VT: Ashgate, 2010), 220–221.

406   Kain, *Sculpture*, 27.

407   See for example Bornstein, "Capitals," 22.

Sagra di San Michele, and immediately following the 1122 date suggested by the inscription for the beginning of work).

But there is dissent. How much of this work is by Niccolo himself or by his workshop? And was it created early in Niccolo's career (i.e., before his work at the Sagra di San Michele) or later (i.e., after Ferrara or around the time of Ferrara and the San Zeno porches)?[408] How and when the earliest sculpture at Piacenza Cathedral fits within the chronology of Niccolo's workshop is somewhat uncertain.

Ferrara, Cathedral

Ferrara Cathedral is now traditionally considered to have been begun in 1135, based on several inscriptions and documentary references, but it is unknown whether that date refers to the actual beginning of work or to the consecration of the cathedral. It is only the lower west façade with a central portal and two side portals that are associated with the Niccolo workshop.[409]

Around the rim of the tympanum is the inscription:

> *ARTIFICE(M) GNARV(M) Q(UI) SCULPSERIT HEC*
> *NICOLAV(M) HV(N)C CONCVRRENTES LAVDENT*
> *PER S(AE)CVLA GENTES.*

(May people coming to visit this place forever praise
Niccolo, the skilled craftsman who sculpted this.)

Although it has long been postulated that Master Niccolo traveled to France and must have seen not only the apostle figures from the Chapter House of Saint-Étienne, Toulouse, but also the many church tympana filled with carved figural sculpture in Burgundy and Aquitaine, some doubt the connection. It is argued that Niccolo's incorporating sculpture into a tympanum can be the result of a general French influence.[410]

The fact remains that it is at Ferrara Cathedral that the first church tympanum filled with figural sculpture carved in high relief is to be found anywhere

---

408   For a full discussion, see Kain, *Sculpture*, 11–49, esp. 33ff.

409   For a full discussion, see Kain, *Sculpture*, 75–126. Kain notes (p. 98) a stylistic difference in the Ezekiel figure, which she proposes was carved by someone other than Niccolo.

410   See Kain, *Sculpture*, 107–114.

in Italy. It is also the first church with pier figures carved into the salient angles of piers to be found anywhere in Italy.

Verona, Church of San Zeno

After being damaged by the earthquake of 1117, the church of San Zeno at Verona was restored and enlarged in 1138, according to an inscription dated 1178 on the south flank of the church that reports the restoration of forty years earlier.

Most scholars recognize most of the sculpture on the lower central section of the façade of San Zeno (i.e., the porch, portal, and façade) as work of Niccolo and his workshop that can be dated around 1138 because of the inscriptions: the one of 1178 reporting the restoration of forty years earlier; the inscription on the Creation of Adam panel in the Genesis reliefs, which names Nicolai; and the inscription above the central portal naming Nicholaus.

There are many inscriptions on the façade sculptures, most identifying the scene depicted. Three inscriptions refer to the sculptors.[411]

Above the central portal (i.e., on the outer molding of the lush vine surrounding the lunette) one inscription naming Niccolo begins:

> ARTIFICEM GNARVM/ QVI SCVLPSERIT
> HEC NICHOLAVM

(This learned artist who sculpted this, Nicholaus)

and then continues in a somewhat different vein:

> OMNES LAVDEMVS CRISTVM D(O)M(INU)M Q(UI)
> ROGEMVS CELORV(M)REGNVM SIBI DONET VT
> IPSE SVP(ERN)V(M)

(Let us all praise Christ the Lord, whom we ask to admit him into the kingdom of Heaven so that [he may be] with him)

Within the Creation reliefs (i.e., on the stone of the frame above Adam of the Creation and carrying across onto the stone with God the Creator) is another inscription naming Niccolo:

....

411   For the inscriptions, see Kain, *Sculpture*, 173, 174, 178.

HIC EXE(M)PLA TRAHI POSSV(N)T LA(V)D(I)S
NICOLAI

(These examples can bring praises to Niccolo)

Above the Life of Christ reliefs (i.e., on the separate stone of the cornice above the two possibly later triangular pediment sculptures) is an inscription naming Guillelmus as sculptor:

QVI LEGIS ISTA PIE NATVM PLACATO MARIE
SALVET I(N) ETERNV(M) QUI SCVLPSERIT ISTA
GVILLELMVM INTRANTES CONTI SUCVRRANT
HUIC PEREVNTI

(You, who read this, pray to the one born of Mary that he
save in eternity this Guillelmus who sculpted this
Let all who enter help this mortal.)

There is now some disagreement, however, about what the earlier restorations included and how much was later rearranged and/or restored again.[412] Kain, for example, argues that the original porch and portal of Niccolo's workshop was much reduced in scale from what now appears there.[413] She proposes that the original portal of 1138 included a reduced tympanum and lintel, with the foliate strip of animated vines surrounding the tympanum; the vertical foliate pilaster now placed in the middle of the New Testament reliefs; and the two vertical foliate pilasters now placed in the middle and at the right (southernmost) edge of the Old Testament reliefs. She also proposes that the figure of San Zeno in the tympanum is a later insertion, but this argument about the tympanum is neither entirely convincing nor necessarily correct.

Kain proposes[414] that the Old Testament Genesis reliefs, the New Testament Life of Christ reliefs, as well as the secular reliefs of Theodoric and battle scenes were carved by members of Niccolo's workshop sometime mid-century, mostly because of stylistic differences with the other "core" Niccolo work. She proposes that the Old and New Testament reliefs may originally have been carved for a piece of church furniture, such as a choir screen.

....

412   For an excellent full summary, see Kain, *Sculpture*, 169–205.
413   See Kain, *Sculpture*, 190ff.
414   See Kain, *Sculpture*, 185, 194ff.

Kain further proposes[415] that the Old and New Testament reliefs were installed on the façade when it was rearranged, possibly around 1200, by Adamino di Sa Giorgio, who is documented as having done work then on the crypt entrance at San Zeno. She also dates the pedimental forms and the top of the New Testament reliefs to that later date. Because the signature "Guillelmus" is inscribed on the cornice above the pedimental sculpture, she suggests Guillelmus was not a member of the Niccolo workshop, but rather a sculptor of around 1200 when the reliefs were re-installed on the façade.

However, if the relief sculptures were moved and then re-installed, the stones bearing Niccolo's signature, "*HIC EXE(M)PLA TRAHI POSSV(N)T LA(V)D(I)S NICOLAI,*" would now identify Niccolo's workshop as the creator(s) of the Creation reliefs. If another sculptor, Guillelmus, had created the scenes from the Life of Christ reliefs and had signed his name on the cornice, would those re-using the reliefs probably not also have re-installed the signature-bearing stone possibly now as a cornice?

Verona, Cathedral

Documents report the construction of the Cathedral of Verona in 1139, and although there is no mention of the sculpture, it is usually assumed to follow closely on the beginning of construction (i.e., 1139–1145). The original two-story porch is preserved.

Niccolo's work at the Cathedral of Verona is now usually recognized as being later than that at the Cathedral of Ferrara. What is sometimes debated is whether his work at the Cathedral of Verona preceded or followed that at San Zeno, Verona.[416]

....

415   See Kain, *Sculpture,* 185ff, 194ff, 196.
416   For a review, see Kain, *Sculpture,* 127–144.

Quotation Credits

Scripture quotations in Latin from *Psalmi, Daniel, Evangelium secundum Matthaeum, Evangelium secundum Marcum, Evangelium secundum Lucam, Actus, Epistula ad Corinthios,* and *Epistula ad Timotheum* are taken from the *Biblia Sacra Vulgata,* public domain.

Scripture quotations translated into English from *Psalms, Daniel, Matthew, Mark, Luke, Acts, Corinthians,* and *Timothy* are taken from the 1899 *Douai-Rheims Bible,* public domain.

Quo corda adhuc torpentia, hymn. Both Latin and English texts are from Abbot Charles Egger (trans. Fr. Lawrence Byrne), "The Liturgy of the Hours according to the Tradition of the Spiritual Authors of the Canonical Order," *The Liturgy of the Hours,* Canons Regular of Saint Augustine, http://newsite. augustiniancanons.org/ Retrieved April 25, 2011. See web archive: https:// web.archive.org/web/20111220222621/http://newsite.augustiniancanons. org/liturgy/liturgy-of-the-hours/

Te lucis ante terminum, hymn. English translation by J.M. Neale (1818-1866). Both Latin and English texts are from Wikipedia, "Te lucis ante terminum"

Requiem aeternam. Both Latin and English texts are from *The Requiem Survey,* http:www.requiemsurvey.org/latintext.php

Te deum laudamus, hymn. Both Latin and English texts are from The Editors of Encyclopaedia Britannica, Encyclopaedia Britannica, April 28, 2020, https://www.britannica.com/topic/Te-Deum-laudamus,

Excerpts from *Disciplina monasterii*, Rule of St. Augustine, are from Pierre Mandonnet, O.P. (trans. Sister Mary Benedicta Larkin, O.P.), "The Role of St. Augustine, Teacher of the Apostolic Life" in *St. Dominic and His Work* (St. Louis: Herder, 1945), chap. 21.

Excerpts from the *Praeceptum* or Supplement are from Robert P. Russell, O.S.A., trans., *The Rule of our Holy Father St. Augustine* (1976), which is based on the critical text of Luc Verheijen, O.S.A., *La règle de saint Augustin, Etudes Augustiniennes* (Paris, 1967).

Quote about Bernard of Clairvaux's eloquence, "mothers hid their sons, wives their husbands, companions their friends," is taken from "Saint Bernard of Clairvaux," *Medieval Sourcebook*, http://www.fordham.edu/halsall/source/eb9-bernard.html

Bernard of Clairvaux quote, "Why do you thus detain a miserable man? . . ." taken from "St. Bernard of Clairvaux," *Medieval Sourcebook*, http://www.fordham.edu/halsall/source/eb9-bernard.html

Bernard of Clairvaux quote, taken from Sancti Bernardi, *Epistola*, 106, "Ad Magistrum Henricum Murdach," in Jacques-Paul Migne, ed., *Patrologia Cursus Completus, Series Latina*, Paris, 1859, vol 182, col 241-242. Also quoted and translated in "Saint Bernard of Claivaux," *Medieval Sourcebook*, http://www.fordham.edu/halsall/source/eb9-bernard.html

Bernard of Clairvaux quote, taken from Sancti Bernardi, *Epistolae* 247, in Migne, *Patrologia Latina*, vol 182, col. 447.

Bernard of Clairvaux quote, taken from Sancti Bernardi, *Epistolae*, 363, in Migne, *Patrologia Latina*, vol 182, col. 566.

Bernard of Clairvaux quote, taken from Sancti Bernardi, *De Consideratione*, II, ch. 1, in Migne, *Patrologia Latina*, vol 182, cols 741-743. The translation is from James Brundage, *The Crusades: A Documentary History*, (Milwaukee: Marquette University Press, 1962), 115-121.

Bernard of Clairvaux quote, taken from Sancti Bernardi, *Operum Tomus III, Sermo II,* in Jacques-Paul Migne, ed., *Patrologia Cursus Completus, Series Latina,* Paris, 1859, vol. 183, col 43.

Peter Damian quote, taken from S. Petri Damiani, *Contra clericos regulares proprietarios,* in Jacques-Paul Migne, ed., *Patrologia Cursus Completus, Series Latina,* Paris, 1853, vol. 145, col 485-486. Translation is taken from Pierre Mandonnet, O.P. (trans. Sister Mary Benedicta Larkin, O.P.), "The Role of St. Augustine, Teacher of the Apostolic Life" in *St. Dominic and His Work* (St. Louis: Herder, 1945.)

Peter the Venerable quote, taken from Petri Venerabilis, *Contra Petrobrusianos hereticos,* in Jacques-Paul Migne, ed., *Patrologia Cursus Completus, Series Latina,* Paris, 1854, vol 189, cols. 805-6. Translation is from James Fearns, ed., *Petri Venerabilis. Contra Petrobrusianos hereticos* (Corpus Christianorum, Continuatio Mediaevalis, X), Turnhout Belgium, 1968, 109-10 (c. 184)

King Louis VII's letter from Saint-Gilles. Francois M. Guizot, The *history of France from the earliest times to the year 1789,* London, 1882, vol I, p 429.

Illustration Credits

All photos and images by author unless otherwise credited.

Vincent Van Gogh. A Wheat Field with Cypresses. Metropolitan Museum of Art, New York, N.Y. Public domain.

Vincent Van Gogh. Field with Irises near Arles. Van Gogh Museum, Amsterdam (Vincent van Gogh Foundation). Used with permission of Van Gogh Museum.

Excerpt from page of *Codex Vigilanus*, a manuscript preserved in the library of the Monasterio del Escorial in Madrid, Spain (Escorialensis d 1 2.). Public domain.

Winchester Psalter, British Library. Cotton MS Nero C. IV, f.39, Hellmouth locked by an Angel. Public domain.

Saint-Denis. Drawings of the now destroyed Column Figures from the west portal, from Dom Bernard de Montfaucon, *Les Monumens de la Monarchie Françoise* (1729), vol. I, plate XVII. Used with permission of BnF or Bibliothèque nationale de France.

Saint-Denis, Cloister. Drawings of the destroyed column figures, from Dom Bernard de Montfaucon, *Les Monumens de la Monarchie Françoise*, vol. I (1729), pl. X. Used with permission of BnF or Bibliothèque nationale de France.

Metropolitan Museum of Art, New York. Column Statue of a King, identified as one of the Column Figures from Cloister of Saint-Denis. Public domain.

Pier figure of St. Andrew. Toulouse, Musée des Augustins. Photo Daniel Martin. Used with permission of Musée des Augustins.

Capital depicting the Death of Saint John the Baptist. Toulouse, Musée des Augustins. Photo Daniel Martin. Used with permission of Musée des Augustins.

Capital from destroyed church choir at Cluny. First Gregorian Tone. Musée Ochier, now Musée d'Art et d'Archéologie. Photo used with permission of its author and owner, © Ricardo Muñoz Nieva - RicardMN Photography.

Epitaph of Poncius Rebolli. This epitaph is @Ville d'Arles. Photo used with permission of its author, Jean-Marie Dumas, Service du Patrimoine, Ville d'Arles.

Cover photo. Arles, Cloister of Saint-Trophîme, north gallery. Adobe stock image.

About the Author

Marilyn Schneider first encountered Pons de Baucio in twelfth-century documents while conducting research for her PhD dissertation, "The Sculptures of the North Gallery of the Cloister of St.-Trophîme at Arles." As she endeavored to connect the dots of his life and read between the lines of what she discovered in the historical records, inspiration for an historical novel emerged. *A Canon's Tale*, her debut, is the result.

She was awarded a PhD in Art History by Columbia University in 1983 and has since enjoyed a varied and rewarding career teaching medieval art at Queen's University, working in research administration, and serving as executive director of the Canadian Breast Cancer Research Alliance. She and her husband, a professor emeritus at the University of Toronto, live in downtown Toronto near their two grown sons and their families. She still loves to follow in Pons's footsteps by visiting Arles and its related magnificent landmarks as often as possible.

CPSIA information can be obtained
at www.ICGtesting.com
Printed in the USA
LVHW071429120722
723336LV00027B/291

9 781525 582486